Supporting Individuals Who Use

Augmentative and Alternative Communication

BREAKING DOWN OPPORTUNITY BARRIERS

Supporting Individuals Who Use

Augmentative and Alternative Communication

BREAKING DOWN OPPORTUNITY BARRIERS

Susan S. Johnston, PhD, SLP
Cindy Gevarter, PhD, BCBA-D
Samuel Sennott, PhD
Lateef McLeod, MFA
Eric J. Sanders, PhD, CCC-SLP

PLURAL
PUBLISHING
INC.

5521 Ruffin Road
San Diego, CA 92123

e-mail: information@pluralpublishing.com
Website: https://www.pluralpublishing.com

Typeset in 11/14 Minion Pro by Flanagan's Publishing Services, Inc.
Printed in the United States of America by Integrated Books International

Library of Congress Cataloging-in-Publication Data:

Names: Johnston, Susan S. (Susan Stowe), editor. | Gevarter, Cindy, editor. | Sennott, Samuel, editor. | McLeod, Lateef, editor. | Sanders, Eric J., editor.
Title: Supporting individuals who use augmentative and alternative communication : breaking down opportunity barriers / Susan S. Johnston, Cindy Gevarter, Sam Sennott, Lateef McLeod, Eric J. Sanders.
Description: San Diego, CA : Plural Publishing, Inc., [2023] | Includes bibliographical references and index.
Identifiers: LCCN 2022037467 (print) | LCCN 2022037468 (ebook) | ISBN 9781635503913 (paperback) | ISBN 9781635503920 (ebook)
Subjects: MESH: Communication Aids for Disabled | Communication Disorders--rehabilitation | Health Knowledge, Attitudes, Practice | Organizational Policy | Communication Barriers
Classification: LCC RC428.8 (print) | LCC RC428.8 (ebook) | NLM WL 340.2 | DDC 616.85/503--dc23/eng/20221108
LC record available at https://lccn.loc.gov/2022037467
LC ebook record available at https://lccn.loc.gov/2022037468

Contents

Preface

It is well established that a wide variety of individuals with complex communication needs can increase their ability to communicate efficiently and effectively using Augmentative and Alternative Communication (AAC). AAC includes unaided and aided modes of communication. Unaided modes do not involve the use of additional equipment or materials (e.g., facial expressions, body language, gestures, sign languages, and sign systems). Aided modes do use additional equipment/materials and include systems that do not use technology (e.g., photographs, line drawings, written words), systems that utilize technology that is relatively simple in form (e.g., simple battery-operated devices, single message voice output devices), and systems that use technology that is more complex such as speech generating devices and laptops/tablets with software that allows them to operate as AAC systems.

Although AAC can increase communicative efficiency and effectiveness, many individuals who use AAC experience barriers in their development of communication skills. The Participation Model (initially conceptualized by Rosenberg and Beukelman in 1987 and then revised by Beukelman and Mirenda in 2013) provides a comprehensive and systematic framework for AAC assessment and intervention, including an evaluation of barriers related to access (limitations in the current capabilities of the individual or in the communication systems that they use) and opportunity (limitations based upon policy, practices, knowledge/skills of professionals or communication partners, and attitudes; Beukelman & Light, 2020). It is essential to consider both access and opportunity barriers when designing systems and supports for individuals who use AAC. However, Light and McNaughton (2015) note that, too often, the focus of research and practice has been on issues related to access barriers with far less attention to opportunity barriers.

The Purpose of This Book

This book is designed to support those who find themselves frustrated by the opportunity barriers experienced by individuals who use AAC and are searching for ways to break down those barriers. Individuals who may be in a position to break down opportunity barriers include people who rely on AAC, speech-language pathologists, occupational therapists, physical therapists, special education teachers, family members, and other professionals in school, health care, and community settings.

Section and Chapter Format

The text is divided into four sections, with each section devoted to a frequently encountered opportunity barrier (knowledge/skill, practice, attitude, policy). Within each section, readers will (a) develop a deeper understanding of the impact of the barrier through the eyes of individuals who use AAC or their families, (b) acquire knowledge based on current research and recommended practices related to addressing the barrier, and (c) learn how professionals have successfully addressed the barrier via case examples from the field.

Readers will note that both identity-first and person-first language is used in this book. This is intentional. The language used in different parts of this text (e.g., interviews, case studies) honors the preferences of the individual (or group of individuals) and reflects the language that the individual used to describe themselves (American Psychological Association, 2020; University of Kansas, Research and Training Center on Independent Living, 2020).

Section I: Knowledge/Skill Barriers and Supports

Chapters 1 to 3 are devoted to understanding and addressing knowledge and skill barriers. Knowledge barriers refer to deficits in understanding how to best address the communication needs of AAC users. In contrast, skill barriers occur when professionals do not have the skills needed to serve these individuals, despite having adequate knowledge. *Chapter 1* includes interviews with two parents of children who use AAC. Both interviews highlight how knowledge/skill barriers and supports have impacted their child's communicative success and provide the reader with a personal perspective that underscores the need to attend to knowledge/skill barriers when supporting individuals who use AAC.

Research suggests that the experiences of the individuals interviewed in *Chapter 1* are not unique, and many professionals and communication partners report experiencing knowledge/skill barriers that prevent them from fully supporting individuals who use AAC (e.g., Assistive Technology Industry Association, 2012; Cameron et al., 2018 Norburn et al., 2016; Sanders et al., 2021). As a result, *Chapter 2* provides strategies and user-friendly tools for addressing knowledge/skill barriers, including (a) identifying AAC knowledge/skill needs, (b) accessing resources to address knowledge/skill needs, (c) using principles of instructional design, (d) engaging in instructional coaching, and (e) supporting professionals and communication partners via virtual instruction and telepractice.

Chapter 3 illustrates the successful use of the strategies presented in *Chapter 2* through three case examples from the field. The first case demonstrates the use of instructional coaching to tackle the knowledge/skill barriers experienced by a school team. The second case shares how the knowledge/skill barriers of preservice and inservice professionals were addressed through online training. The third case illustrates the use of telepractice to attend to the knowledge/skill barriers experienced by the parents of a toddler with complex communication needs.

Section II: Practice Barriers and Supports

Chapters 4 to 6 are devoted to understanding and addressing practice barriers. Practice barriers involve common practices of organizations, schools, businesses, or communities that, although not formally written as policy, are accepted in that context (Beukelman & Light, 2020). *Chapter 4* includes interviews with an adult with cerebral palsy who relies on AAC, and a parent whose child with autism spectrum disorder relies on AAC. Together, the two interviews demonstrate how practices can serve as either barriers or facilitators to AAC implementation. The interviews also highlight the importance of individualizing AAC decisions, the benefits of interprofessional collaboration, and the need to seek family input.

Although the two interviews in Chapter 4 largely focus on barriers and facilitators experienced in school contexts, practice barriers related to time, resources, and personnel constraints exist across a variety of settings (Andzik et al., 2019; Chung & Stoner, 2016; Gormley & Light, 2019; Uthoff et al., 2021). These barriers can limit an AAC team's ability to (a) individualize AAC systems, (b) collaborate with other professionals, and (c) meet cultural and/or familial needs. *Chapter 5* describes how common practice barriers identified in research create limitations to AAC assessment and implementation. In addition, this chapter provides freely available resources that teams can use to advocate for and support changes to practice and includes examples of evidence-based practices that can be adopted under less-than-ideal practice conditions.

Finally, *Chapter 6* provides case examples from three speech-language pathologists who work with children or adults across school, home, and medical settings. The case studies highlight common practice limitations as well as demonstrate how context and individual client and family characteristics can lead to unique barriers. Each of the cases provides concrete examples of how strategies discussed in *Chapter 5* can be applied in real-world contexts.

Section III: Attitude Barriers and Supports

Chapters 7 to 9 focus on understanding and addressing attitude barriers. Negative attitudes held by family members, professionals, and peers can present obstacles to realizing the full benefit of AAC. In *Chapter 7*, three men who use AAC recount their experiences related to negative attitude barriers and discuss potential pathways for addressing attitude barriers based on their experiences. From their respective points of view, it becomes clear how attitudinal barriers such as low expectations, misunderstandings about how individuals learn AAC, and ableism, affect these individuals.

Chapter 8 focuses on the research related to attitude barriers and strategies to address these barriers. Literature examining negative attitudes toward individuals with disabilities, including those who use AAC, is reviewed. This includes a focus on attitudes toward both children and adults who use AAC as well as tools for assessing attitudes. Further, strategies and pathways for overcoming attitude barriers such as increasing visibility of individuals who use AAC, and increasing communication partner understanding of AAC are presented.

The final chapter of this section, *Chapter 9*, provides three case studies that further our understanding of attitudinal barriers. Specifically, we learn from an adult who uses AAC who details her experiences with attitudinal barriers and the strategies she has used to overcome them. Further, we hear from two speech-language pathologists who discuss attitudinal barriers and "real world" solutions to those barriers based on experiences in their clinical practice.

Section IV: Policy Barriers and Supports

Chapters 10 to 12 focus on understanding and addressing policy barriers. We often first think of policies as legislation or formal laws. However, policy is also enacted at the level of organizations (e.g., a school system's policies around inclusion and AAC, a vocational rehabilitation organization's policy on job coaching and personal care). Policy is also present in an individual's written home "rules." Collectively, policies can serve as powerful facilitators for access, supports, and services for individuals who use AAC.

Chapter 10 provides interviews with two people who use AAC and who are experts in the policy field. These interviewees share insights and examples of how policies effect the AAC community. Further, the interviewees discuss how law and policy need to change in order for people who use AAC to experience more equity in society.

Chapter 11 focuses on (a) major types of AAC policies, (b) policy consideration frameworks, (c) AAC policy barriers and pathways, and (d) future directions. Here, literature is reviewed that identifies the role of policy in relation to AAC service provision. In particular, barriers are identified and ways to address these barriers are detailed.

Chapter 12 offers three case examples that illustrate how people who use AAC experience barriers in policy and the strategies that they have used to address those barriers. The first case describes how a team worked through special education policy challenges to end a lack of access to AAC in the classroom for a child with an intellectual disability. The second case provides a more personal account of how policy impacts the life of a person who uses AAC in ways the general public takes for granted, such as an expectation of adequate writing instruction at school. The final case provides an international perspective on the impact of policy on AAC service provision and shares a vivid exemplar of how hard families work to navigate the complex policy environments they may encounter.

Conclusion

Chapter 13 provides readers with information on how to go "beyond the book" by actively addressing the unique opportunity barriers that they encounter in home, school, and community settings. Recognizing that barriers are uniquely influenced by the contexts in which they occur, Chapter 13 discusses the importance of considering variables related to contextual fit and provides a framework (as well as several tools and examples) that incorporates the use of group problem-solving processes to develop strategies to address opportunity barriers.

References

Andzik, N. R., Chung, Y. C., Doneski-Nicol, J., & Dollarhide, C. T. (2019). AAC services in schools: A special educator's perspective. *International Journal of Developmental Disabilities, 65*(2), 89–97.

American Psychological Association. (2020). *Publication manual of the American Psychological Association* (7th ed.).

Assistive Technology Industry Association. (2012). *The critical need for knowledge and usage of AT and AAC among speech-language pathologists* [Survey white paper]. https://www.atia.org/wp-content/uploads/2018/12/ATIA-SLP-Survey-2011.pdf

Beukelman, D., & Light, J. (2020). *Augmentative and alternative communication: Supporting children and adults with complex communication needs* (5th ed.). Paul H. Brookes.

Beukelman, D., & Mirenda, P. (2013). *Augmentative and alternative communication: Supporting children and adults with complex communication needs* (4th ed.). Paul H. Brookes.

Cameron, A., McPhail, S., Hudson, K., Fleming, J., Lethlean, J., Ju Tan, N., & Finch, E. (2018). The confidence and knowledge of health practitioners when interacting with people with aphasia in a hospital setting. *Disability and Rehabilitation, 40*(11), 1288–1293.

Chung, Y. C., & Stoner, J. B. (2016). A meta-synthesis of team members' voices: What we need and what we do to support students who use AAC. *Augmentative and Alternative Communication, 32*(3), 175–186.

Gormley, J., & Light, J. (2019). Providing services to individuals with complex communication needs in the inpatient rehabilitation setting: The experiences and perspectives of speech-language pathologists. *American Journal of Speech-Language Pathology, 28*(2), 456–468.

Light, J., & McNaughton, D. (2015). Designing AAC research and intervention to improve outcomes for individuals with complex communication needs. *Augmentative and Alternative Communication, 31*(2), 85–96.

Norburn, K., Morgan, S., Levin, A., & Harding, C. (2016). A survey of augmentative and alternative communication used in an inner-city special school. *British Journal of Special Education, 43*(3), 289–306.

Rosenberg, S., & Beukelman, D. (1987). The participation model. In C. A. Coston (Ed.), *Proceedings of the National Planners Conference on Assistive Device Service Delivery* (pp. 159–161). Washington, DC: RESNA, The Association for the Advancement of Rehabilitation Technology.

Sanders, E. J., Page, T. A., & Lesher, D. (2021). School-based speech-language pathologists: Confidence in augmentative and alternative communication. *Language, Speech, and Hearing Services in Schools. 52*(2), 512–528.

University of Kansas, Research and Training Center on Independent Living. (2020). *Guidelines: How to write about people with disabilities* (9th ed.). https://rtcil.org/guidelines

Uthoff, S. A., Zinkevich, A., Boenisch, J., Sachse, S. K., Bernasconi, T., & Ansmann, L. (2021). Collaboration between stakeholders involved in augmentative and alternative communication (AAC) care of people without natural speech. *Journal of Interprofessional Care, 35*(6), 821–831.

Acknowledgments

We wish to acknowledge David R. Beukelman (1943–2022). Dave had an incredible impact on each of us individually and on the entire AAC community. His legacy lives on in our work.

—Susan S. Johnston, Cindy Gevarter, Samuel Sennott, Lateef McLeod, and Eric J. Sanders

I am indebted to the individuals with disabilities and their families who have allowed me to be a part of their journey. Further, I am grateful to my husband, Jim Coletta, and my son, Ben, who are extremely generous with their patience and support. I also acknowledge my university students who have influenced my work through their enthusiasm, experiences, and unique perspectives. Finally, I thank my mentor, Dr. Joe Reichle, who has tirelessly served over the past 34 years as a mentor, role model, and colleague.

—Susan S. Johnston

First, I want thank the children and families who continue to drive my desire to improve AAC outcomes. A special thanks to the Medrano family for inspiring and supporting me. I am grateful to my clinical supervisors, academic mentors, and colleagues for their guidance. I also want to acknowledge my university students whose curiosity and questions have informed the barriers I address in this book. Finally, I want to thank my siblings and parents for their support. An extra thank you to my mother, Sherry, who helped me find my passion, and has supported it at every turn. I write in memory of my father, Jeffery, who showed such pride in his children.

—Cindy Gevarter

Little did I know that the Michael Carter Lisnow Respite Center would play such a pivotal role in my life. I acknowledge the directors, Sharon Lisnow and Mary McQueeney, plus the community members that both inspired and supported me like a second family. It took this project to realize that the "social model of disability" was written deeply into my heart and mind through that special time physically spent at Respite. In sixth grade, Stanley Wexler taught us about principles that fascinated me, such as "nature vs. nurture." Again, not until this project did I realize that the "community" that he created was the real magic ingredient in his teaching. I also acknowledge Familia Superaço and Associação aBRAÇO a Microcefalia, and the terrific Brazilian AAC community. Special thanks to the amazing Angelman community and to all of the communities I am privileged to serve. To these "neighbors," I am forever grateful for being in community with you. To my parents and siblings, thank you for supporting me with such love and patience. To my Aunt Jan, thank you for being such an incredible role model and introducing me to the mountains. To my grandmothers, both named Ginny, thank you for always believing in me. To my wife and children, you are my world.

—Samuel Sennott

I would like to acknowledge my parents, Beverly and Phillip, who taught me the value of advocating for justice from a young age. I also want to thank both my sisters, Stephanie and Jennifer, for all their love and support over the years. Also, thanks to my girlfriend, Brittanie, who showed tremendous love, encouragement, and care as I worked on this project. Finally, this book is dedicated in memory of my grandmother whose love and care from a young age made me the person I am today.

—Lateef McLeod

There are many people I would like to thank for their support. First, I would like to thank the children and families I have had the privilege to serve throughout my time as a speech-language pathologist. They serve as an inspiration for this work and my continued work in this field. I would also like to thank my wife, Emily Dings, for her tireless support, love, and companionship. Additionally, I would like to acknowledge my parents, Bill and Iris Sanders, and my sister, Robin Sanders, for their unwavering encouragement.

—Eric J. Sanders

About the Authors

Susan S. Johnston, PhD, SLP is a professor in the Department of Special Education at the University of Utah and is the program area coordinator for Early Childhood Special Education. She has been with the University of Utah since 1997. She received her MA and Ph.D. in Speech-Language Pathology from the University of Minnesota in Minneapolis, MN. As a speech-language pathologist, she worked in early intervention, preschool special education, and elementary school settings. Prior to coming to Utah, Dr. Johnston was an Assistant Professor in the Department of Special Education at Eastern Michigan University in Ypsilanti, MI. Dr. Johnston's research and teaching focuses on evidence-based strategies and supports for individuals with complex communication needs, and she is first author on a book titled, *AAC Strategies for Individuals With Moderate to Severe Disabilities.*

Cindy Gevarter, PhD, BCBA-D is an associate professor in the Department of Speech and Hearing Sciences at the University of New Mexico. She received a B.A. in psychology from the University of Virginia (UVa), an M.T. in special education from UVa, and a Ph.D. in early childhood special education from the University of Texas at Austin. As a special education teacher and early interventionist, she primarily worked with children with autism spectrum disorder (ASD) and developmental disabilities who had complex communication needs. Her research and teaching interests include ASD, augmentative and alternative communication (AAC), naturalistic early communication interventions, interdisciplinary collaboration, and communication partner training.

Samuel Sennott, PhD is an associate professor of special education and leads the Universal Design Lab in the College of Education at Portland State University. Dr. Sennott is a research scientist focused on fundamental mechanisms to communication and language acquisition, community based participatory research approaches and AAC, single-case design research practices and tools, and assistive technologies. As a hands-on teacher and practitioner, Dr. Sennott envisioned and co-created the original Proloquo2Go application. He holds a Ph.D. in Special Education and AAC from The Pennsylvania State University.

Lateef McLeod, MFA earned a BA in English from UC Berkeley, an MFA in Creative Writing from Mills College, and is currently in his sixth year of study at the Anthropology and Social Change Doctoral program at California Institute of Integral Studies in San Francisco. His dissertation will explore how young people who use AAC gain leadership and advocacy skills through peer mentoring. Lateef was a consumer consultant for Dynavox from 2007 to 2011. He also served on the executive board for the International Society for Augmentative and Alternative Communication from 2016 to 2020. He published his first poetry book entitled, *A Declaration of A Body Of Love* in 2010 and published his second poetry book entitled *Whispers of Krip Love, Shouts of Krip Revolution* in 2020. He recently co-authored another book of poetry called *Studies in Brotherly Love* in 2021.

Eric J. Sanders, PhD, CCC-SLP is an associate professor in the Speech-Language Pathology program in the Department of Rehabilitation Sciences at Moravian University. He earned his MS and PhD in Speech and Hearing Sciences at the University of North Carolina at Chapel Hill. As a speech-language pathologist, Dr. Sanders worked for the Miami-Dade County Public Schools and in private practice. In those roles, he specialized in working with children who required augmentative and alternative communication. Dr. Sanders' research focuses on service provision and language and literacy development for individuals who require AAC, and those with intellectual disabilities. Additionally, he studies the scholarship of teaching and learning with a focus on graduate education in speech-language pathology.

Contributors

Cheri Wild Blue, MS, CCC-SLP
University of Utah
Doctoral Student
Salt Lake City, UT
Chapter 2

Adele F. Dimian, PhD
University of Minnesota
Associate Director
TeleOutreach Center
Research Associate
Institute on Community Integration
Chapter 3

Cindy Gevarter, PhD, BCBA-D
Associate Professor
Speech and Hearing Sciences
University of New Mexico
Albuquerque, NM
Chapters 4, 5, and 6

Jay Grochala
PRC-Saltillo Ambassador
Self-Employed
Hamilton, NJ
Chapter 7

David J. Hajjar, PhD, CCC-SLP
Assistant Professor
Department of Speech-Language and
    Audiology
Ithaca College
Ithaca, NY
Chapter 9

Gretchen Hanser, PhD, MS, OTR/L
Assistive Technology and Literacy
    Specialist
New York, NY
Chapter 12

Jennifer W. Hanson, MS, CCC-SLP
Speech-Language Pathologist
Alburquerque, NM
Chapter 6

Krista Howard
AAC Mentor/Consultant
We Speak AAC
Goodyer, AZ
Chapter 9

Vanessa J. Ince, PhD
Licensed Clinical Psychologist
Ince Health and Wellness, LLC
Maui, HI
Chapter 1

Susan S. Johnston, PhD, SLP
Professor and Early Childhood Special
    Education Program Coordinator
Department of Special Education
University of Utah
Salt Lake City, UT
Chapters 1, 2, 3, and 13

Monica Kaniamattam, PhD, CCC-SLP
Assistant Professor of Speech-Language
    Pathology

Department of Rehabilitation Sciences
Moravian University
Bethlehem, PA
Chapter 12

Ashley R. McCoy, PhD, BSBA-D, COBA
Assistant Professor of Special Education
Bowling Green State University
Bowling Green, OH
Chapter 3

Stephanie M. McDougle, MS, CCC-SLP
Speech-Language Pathologist
University of New Mexico Hospital
Albuquerque, NM
Chapter 6

Lateef McLeod, MFA
Doctoral Candidate
Department of Anthropology and Social
   Change
California Institute of Integral Studies
San Francisco, CA
Chapters 7, 8, 9, 10, 11, and 12

Cas McNamara, M.Ed
Salt Lake City, UT
Chapter 1

Cassandra Medrano
Project Manager
Office of Commissioner Representing
   Employers
Texas Workforce Commission
Austin, TX
Chapter 4

Caroline Ramsey Musselwhite, EdD, CCC-SLP
AAC and Literacy Consultant
AAC Intervention

Litchfield Park, AZ
Chapters 9 and 12

Joanne K. Niemkiewicz, MS, CCC-SLP
Doctoral Candidate
The Pennsylvania State University
University Park, PA
Chapter 9

India Ochs
Human Rights Attorney and Advocate
Annapolis, MD
Chapter 10

Jamie Preece
Service User Representative
Barnsley Hospital Assistive Technology
   Department
Barnsley, Great Britain
Chapter 7

Toña Rivera
Founder and Executive Director
Every Ability Plays Project
Albuquerque, NM
Chapter 4

Christina Royster, EdD, CCC-SLP
Speech-Language Pathologist/AAC
   Consultant
Owner/Founder
Play on Words Therapy
Silver Spring, MD
Chapter 12

Eric J. Sanders, PhD, CCC-SLP
Associate Professor and Program
   Director
Speech-Language Pathology Program
School of Rehabilitation Sciences
Moravian University
Bethlehem, PA
Chapters 7, 8, 9, 10, 11, and 12

Samuel Sennott, PhD
Associate Professor
Universal Design Lab Director
Department of Special Education
College of Education
Portland State University
Portland, OR
Chapters 7, 8, 9, 10, 11, and 12

Mariah Siciliano, MS, CCC-SLP
Speech-Langauge Pathologist
Charleston, SC
Chapter 6

Jessica J. Simacek, PhD
Director MIDB TeleOutreach Center
Research Associate Institute on
    Community Integration
University of Minnesota
Minneapolis, MN
Chapter 3

Melinda R. Snodgrass, PhD
Assistant Professor
Department of Special Education

Illinois State University
Normal, IL
Chapter 3

Brandi Wentland, MA, CCC-SLP
Speech-Language Pathologist
AAC Consultant and Trainer
WeSpeak AAC, LLC
CEO and U.S. Distributor
PicSeePal USA, LLC
Cleveland, TN
Chapter 9

Bob Williams
Policy Director
Communication First
Washington, DC
Chapter 10

Kevin Williams
Vice President Leadership Chair of
    ISAAC
People Who Use AAC
Charlotte, NC
Chapter 7

We dedicate this book to individuals with complex communication needs and the family members and professionals who are committed to breaking down AAC opportunity barriers.

Section I

Understanding and Addressing Knowledge/Skill Barriers

Section Overview

Knowledge barriers refer to insufficiencies in understanding how to address the communication needs of individuals who use AAC; while skill barriers occur due to lack of competency when supporting these individuals, despite having adequate knowledge. Knowledge and skill barriers are often interconnected and strategies to address these barriers are interrelated. Further, the knowledge and skills needed by different communication partners (e.g., family members, peers, teachers, speech-language pathologists, para-educators, community members, health care professionals) will vary. For example, the knowledge/skills that a peer needs to interact with an individual who uses AAC is very different from the knowledge/skills that a speech-language pathologist who is taking the lead on vocabulary selection and device programming needs for that same individual.

This section is devoted to knowledge/skill barriers with a specific focus on understanding and addressing barriers related to (a) identifying AAC knowledge/skill needs and accessing resources to address those needs, and (b) using principles of instructional design, instructional coaching, virtual instruction and telepractice to address the unique knowledge/skill needs of professionals and communication partners. Upon completion of this section, readers will be able to:

- Describe the impact of knowledge/skill barriers and facilitators on the lives of individuals who use AAC and their families.
- Summarize the research on knowledge/skill barriers.
- Identify effective strategies for addressing knowledge/skill barriers.

1

Knowledge/Skill Barriers: Learning From Individuals Who Use AAC and Their Families

Susan S. Johnston, Vanessa J. Ince*, and Cas McNamara*

Understanding the impact of knowledge/skill barriers and facilitators on the lives of individuals who use AAC and their families can assist practitioners as they design effective and efficient interventions to address those barriers. Although the barriers and facilitators experienced by individuals who use AAC and their families will vary based upon the unique situations that they encounter, the following interviews provide the reader with insight into knowledge/skill barriers from the perspective of two parents whose children use AAC.

Vanessa J. Ince—Parent of a Child Who Uses AAC

In the first interview, Vanessa Ince, the parent of a young child with a rare chromosomal disability, shares information about the knowledge/skill barriers and facilitators that she has encountered in supporting her daughter's use of AAC. Vanessa's interview draws attention to the importance of training support staff and being knowledgeable about the unique needs of individuals who use AAC.

Will you introduce yourself including your name, age, gender, and race/ethnicity?

I'm Vanessa Ince. I am 55 years old. I'm Caucasian and I live in Hawaii.

Can you share a little bit about who you are as a person, what you are doing in your life, and what you enjoy doing?

I'm a licensed clinical psychologist and I have a private practice. I'm married to Scott, who does ultrasounds in a local clinic. I personally enjoy doing triathlons because it's a big stress reliever for me. My husband is a fisherman, and we have a boat. We enjoy swimming and spending time together outdoors as a family. We really enjoy life in Maui, and we try to be outside whenever we can.

---

*These authors have contributed equally to this work and share senior authorship.

As a parent of an AAC user, can you also tell us a little bit about your daughter who uses AAC, who they are as a person, and what they enjoy doing?

Alexis is 11½ years old and is very small and spunky (Figure 1–1). She's a happy little girl, even when things are not great. She really enjoys music and things that light up. She has two dogs and likes swimming. She loves her peers at school and interacts well with them. She just loves interacting with people in general. Even though she can't verbalize anything, she has a very unique sense of humor. She likes being a little devious and playing mischievous games. As she is approaching her teenage years, she's getting a bit more active in her defiance, which is good because she's expressing her opinions and her desires. And while she used to be very slow in her movements, now she's very quick. She's always on the go even though her coordination isn't great.

As a parent of an AAC user, can you tell me a little bit about your daughter's use of AAC over the years, and her current AAC system?

Alexis was born with a rare chromosomal disability. She's missing a piece of chromosome one. It's called chromosome one deletion q24.1 q25.3, which is the piece that's missing. She's hearing impaired and vision impaired. She also has developmental delays, epilepsy, really small hands, and is nonverbal. We started her with Snap Core Software from Tobii Dynavox on

Figure 1–1. Alexis, Vanessa, and Scott Ince.

an iPad about four years ago and she still uses it today. The iPad is quite heavy but she needed to have a fairly sizable display that she could both see and also touch with some degree of accuracy. When she started using it, she had a paraprofessional that served as her communication aide. The communication aide's job was to help her navigate the AAC device. They taught the communication aide how to use the program and work collaboratively with the speech therapist. That went well, initially, and she made good progress. We started with only two or three symbols and then, over the course of maybe the first two and half years, she gradually was able to select from a field of nine. But then staff changed, and, over the years, the new communication aides haven't gotten any training and they don't seem to know how to use the AAC device.

> "But then staff changed and, over the years, the new communication aides haven't gotten any training and they don't seem to know how to use the AAC device."

In previous years, we tried to have some consistency between how the AAC device was used at home and how it was used at school. But, because of staff changes and lack of communication, that fell by the wayside. The way we're using it at home seems to be different now than the way they're using it at school. What they have her doing at school is kind of back to where she was in the beginning with only two or three symbols. At home, we have it set up for things like greetings,

making choices, and body parts (so that she can tell us if something doesn't feel good). And we have it set up so it navigates automatically. For example, she selects "greetings," and then she selects "hi mama," and then it automatically navigates back to the main page.

Can you tell me about any challenges that you have experienced related to different communication partners/professionals having the necessary content knowledge in AAC?

There have been some speech therapists who have been really good. The way they instructed us to set up the device seemed to make sense and they collaborated with us on the use of the AAC device. But I think part of the problem is that everybody quits and then we get a brand new speech therapist and they know nothing about AAC or the AAC system. They're unable to create meaningful learning experiences to help Alexis develop her communication skills, and they're unable to train the communication aide. We end up with very isolated parts on her IEP and none of it comes together in a meaningful way to promote learning. We've had about five different speech therapists in the last two years alone. And most of them haven't known enough about AAC to facilitate meaningful communication for Alexis.

I think it's also important to recognize that many individuals who are nonverbal and need AAC have numerous other disabilities as well. For example, Alexis has cognitive, visual, hearing, and physical impairments. Teaching the use of AAC for Alexis is far more complicated than teaching a child who doesn't have multiple disabilities. Because of that, professionals need to have a deeper, and more nuanced, knowledge of AAC.

Can you tell me about any challenges that you have experienced related to teaching communication partners/professionals how to effectively support and interact with AAC users?

In the beginning, we had team meetings so that everybody was familiar with the use of the AAC system and the different purposes of communication. And, at that time, the communication aide was really well trained on how to use AAC and how to help Alexis to communicate. We also had someone once who taught Alexis to use the AAC device with peers. They would show the device to Alexis and a peer, and Alexis could select the peer and choose a task to do with a peer, like read a book. That was very, very good. She had these little peer learning partners who were all familiar with Alexis' AAC system, and that was very successful. When things were going well, I think it was because the speech therapist was educated in the theory of communication and how that can be translated into an AAC system. And she taught others what to do. But now I don't think anyone is doing that anymore, and things have really fallen apart.

Can you tell me about any challenges that you have experienced related to ensuring communication partners/professionals have access to deeper/individualized/ongoing knowledge to support AAC users?

This has been a big issue for us. One of the initial barriers was that the school district didn't have anybody who knew how to do an AAC assessment. It took two years of asking and asking and asking. And then they finally found a person. But that person never showed up. And then they found another person. And that person never showed up either. Ultimately, we had to file a lawsuit in order to receive the proper assessment that she should have had years before. And when we've asked for a follow-up reevaluation it's just been denied. Flat out denied. When we've asked for training, it's kind of dismissed. Sometimes they have referred us to the Tobii Dynavox representative and said that he can help program. But he doesn't know our child's unique special needs, and he's not an educator. He can tell us how to program a system, but he can't tell us how to make it work with our child. And I think part of the problem is that the people who don't know, don't know what they don't know.

> "And I think part of the problem is that the people who don't know, don't know what they don't know."

What do you see as the role of technology for improving outcomes related to knowledge/skill barriers?

Because of COVID, I think we've learned that we can do so much online. It's such a perfect opportunity to be able to provide online training in AAC to anyone, no matter where they live. It's no longer the case where people have to travel somewhere to get appropriate training. And it wouldn't have to be this big financial burden for somebody to go to a training because they could access it from wherever they live.

What equity issues do you want to bring up connected to knowledge/skill barriers?

Scott and I have the benefit of being highly educated. We know what to fight for. We did our research, we did our homework, and we know what our rights are and we fight for them. But I think a lot of people don't even realize what their rights are for their children, let alone being able to fight for them. And I think the other problem is lack of access to attorneys. In Hawaii there are very few attorneys. In previous years, we were able to access attorneys through Hawaii Disability Rights so that we didn't have to pay a fortune to get what we needed for Alexis. But now they're no longer a functioning entity and there's not really a lot of attorneys in this field. Some families may be bogged down with working two or three jobs and they don't have the time or energy to fight for this. And the whole idea of getting a device and learning technology themselves to be able to teach that to their child may be just unobtainable.

What do you think people need to know or do to overcome knowledge/skill barriers?

I think there has to be some recognition, and some understanding, of what it must be like to be nonverbal. I think it has to start with understanding what it must be like for a four- or five-year-old to be trapped inside a body and not be able to communicate what they want. You need to start with realizing this person has something to communicate and then you need to make sure they have a voice. And so that's starting from the bottom. And then from the top end, I would say that it all comes down to IDEA law and having proper policies that recognize that children have a right to communicate. I mean it sounds so basic, but it should be on par

with math and English and social studies and history. Giving children a voice through AAC should be part of a curriculum that professionals are expected to know and to implement.

How do you see knowledge/skill barriers being overcome? What do you envision for the future?

I think it's a combination of people's attitudes being different, having a basic expectation for people to be treated with respect, and having the tools to be able to do so. New technology is also probably important. I think technology could be improved quite a bit. AAC should be easy to use and easy to have around all the time so that the device is used in an interactive manner. You know, if a person is blind and uses a cane, you don't send them out into the world without the cane. And you shouldn't send a child that is nonverbal out into the world and expect them to function without their device, without their voice.

I also think that there needs to be a resource where parents and professionals can get answers to questions. Questions like what icon size do we use, and how can we teach our child to use the device in a meaningful way instead of just swiping at it. Maybe even like a Center where parents and professionals can tap into the knowledge of experts. Connecting the experts to individuals who use AAC, professionals, and parents would really help.

Key Points From Vanessa's Interview

Vanessa's interview highlights the positive impact of facilitators as well as the detrimental impact of barriers. When communication partners and professionals possessed appropriate levels of knowledge/skills, positive outcomes with regard to the integrated and meaningful use of AAC were observed. However, the integrated and meaningful use of AAC declined when knowledge/skill barriers were encountered. Specific barriers that Vanessa encountered included (a) identifying professionals that had the requisite AAC knowledge/skills in the areas of assessment and intervention, (b) ensuring that AAC training was provided when faced with staff turnovers, and (c) accessing deeper levels of AAC knowledge to meet the specific learning needs of her daughter.

Cas McNamara—Parent of a Child Who Uses AAC

The interview with Vanessa provides several examples of the impact of knowledge/skill barriers and facilitators on her daughter's use of AAC. The following interview with Cas, a parent of an adult son with autism, provides additional insight into the impact of knowledge/skill facilitators and barriers, including barriers that exist for adults who use AAC.

Will you introduce yourself including your name, age, gender, race/ethnicity? My name is Cas McNamara. I'm 63 years old, Caucasian and a single mom.

Can you share a little bit about who you are as a person, what you are doing in your life, and what you enjoy doing? I'm not working right now, however, I don't consider it retirement because

I don't feel being a single mom of an adult child with disabilities is actual retirement. I have two children, a daughter who's 26, and my son, Will, who's 24. Will has autism and has a secondary diagnosis of anxiety. Because I am Will's sole caretaker, and due to limited services for young adults with disabilities, I currently don't have much free time. However, Will has a wonderful aide that comes about 10 hours a week, so I do love to go for walks and hikes. I also have an incredible support group of friends that I enjoy spending time with. I've been in the same book group for about 30 years. One of my brand-new hobbies is watching Korean dramas.

As a parent of a child that uses AAC, can you also tell us a little bit about your son, who he is as a person and what does he enjoy doing? Will is generally a happy and pleasant young man. He enjoys being around people and social interaction in small doses, but also requires quiet time and time alone. His favorite things in the world are water, videos, and computers. He has loved water ever since he was a little boy and loves to skip rocks into the water. All year long, we venture to parks, streams, lakes, and puddles to play. For the last several years, we have traveled to the Tetons, our perfect location, and we wander from lake to stream. Additionally, Will has always liked videos and technology. When he was young, he would watch VHS tapes and rewind them so that he could watch the meaningful parts over and over. Currently, Will's technology includes a VHS player, a laptop, a desktop, and an iPod. Often, he interacts with all of these devices at the same time. He has memorized and indexed thousands of movies, clips, visuals, and lines from videos. He's fascinated by animation, specifically, and the stories they tell, particularly Disney and Pixar.

Can you tell me a little bit about your son's use of AAC over the years, and about his current AAC system?

Will developed normally as a baby. He walked early, loved to climb, was very active, and could eat all sorts of foods. He met all his milestones. At about 15 months or so, everything changed. He started screaming, stopped playing with toys, and limited his food choices. In those early years he totally withdrew into himself and it was difficult to get his attention. His typical play was tapping magnetic alphabet letters on the wall.

Will never developed much spoken language. In the early years he would say a few words and sometimes put a few phrases together, but they never really stuck. Therefore, in terms of intervention, the most essential thing was encouraging him to engage. This was his first use of AAC—engaging him with body language and responding to any of the ways he chose to communicate such as through movement, eye contact, even responding to his tapping. Responding and encouraging two-way communication, emotions, and interest in the world through gestures and movement were Will's first AAC lessons.

Will began private speech therapy around the age of 4 where he was introduced officially to the Picture Exchange Communication System (PECS). He learned the basic concepts fairly quickly and continued to use PECS as the basis for his communication throughout preschool, elementary school, and into junior and high school with varying success. PECS was used to communicate his basic needs and to make simple choices. He also had schedule boards with picture symbols for both at home and school. Over time, technology that allowed him to point to symbols that would talk was added. But, even with technology, the AAC system only addressed basic needs like requesting. I think professionals (and myself), at the time, thought Will couldn't progress further with PECS because he didn't understand it, so we made it simpler through different pictures or fewer buttons. But, looking back, I came to understand that PECS wasn't meeting his needs because it didn't allow him to say what he needed to say. He knew how to get his basic needs met, but he wanted to say more. So, Will created his own communication system using his beloved videos.

Currently, Will uses a combination of his AAC device as well as video clips on his iPod, computer, VHS, and laptop to communicate his emotions, needs, questions, and to develop relationships (Figure 1–2). For on the go, he has a communication app on an iPod that he wears on a strap around his neck. It also has photos and video clips. He can ask for basic needs like "I want a Diet Coke," and "I want to go to the park." He can also pull up a line from a video clip or movie, in order to tell me that he is a "bright little lamp" (a line from the movie, the *Brave Little Toaster*). At home, he has access to all his devices, which he uses creatively to express what he wishes. For example, there was a time that his computer was broken, and he wanted his sister to fix it. He could have just asked for his sister by pointing to her picture on his communication app. But instead of doing that, he found a video on

Figure 1–2. Will's multifaceted AAC system that includes an AAC Application and video clips on an iPod, a computer, VHS tapes, and a laptop.

YouTube that said, "I want the computer fixed" and then went to the photos on his iPod to select his sister's photo. So, on his own, he used all the different tools that he has available so that he could communicate the way he wants to, not the way someone else had programmed his device.

Can you tell me about any challenges that you have experienced related to communication partners/professionals having the necessary content knowledge in AAC?

One challenge is certainly people's understanding of AAC, but equally essential is having content knowledge related to disabilities. In Will's case, that means understanding autism. I think people have a perception that individuals with autism are either high functioning or low functioning. Because Will is often viewed as low functioning, professionals and communication partners make assumptions

about his abilities and don't often try as hard to provide the supports he needs. I think we do a real disservice to people with disabilities who are nonverbal if we don't work hard to understand them as individuals and understand what they are trying to say.

Can you tell me about any challenges that you have experienced related to teaching communication partners how to effectively support and/or interact with AAC users?

I think because Will's traditional ways of communicating look low functioning, expectations are lowered and communication partners don't try to get to know him or give him a chance. I know that AAC is difficult and that teachers are frequently overwhelmed, but I think it's essential to know a person as an individual and try to connect with them on a human level. Once you really know the person, you can more successfully implement the technology and the supports needed. I think sometimes we do it the opposite way. We say, "Oh we've got these new iPads," or "We have this new technology" and we try to make the child fit the technology instead of really looking at the technology and seeing if it's going to fit that child.

> "Another challenge that I've experienced is educating professionals and communication partners how to encourage and elicit communication."

Another challenge that I've experienced is educating professionals and communication partners how to encourage and elicit communication. You can have the technology, but if you don't know how to encourage someone to communicate, and provide a trusting environment, it will be less motivating to the student. One of Will's teachers was good at this. They kept track of every video that he watched so that they could identify his interests. Then they developed his curriculum around what he was watching. They even let him take over teaching the class utilizing technology. Again, I think that has to do with really knowing the child and understanding how to get them to want to communicate. I think a lot of training and resources needs to go to training people to support interactions with different AAC users.

Can you tell me any challenges that you have experienced related to ensuring that communication partners have access to ongoing knowledge to support AAC users?

For Will, part of his success was that he had people that he could trust, and he went to school every day knowing that people would listen to him and value what he was saying. If you don't have that, and you know nobody's really listening to you, then you're going to give up and you're not going to try. We've been very lucky because Will's had a lot of awesome teachers and speech therapists. His high school teachers and then his postsecondary teachers were amazing; they really worked hard to build trust so that Will felt safe to communicate. If trust isn't there or if you don't feel like somebody's going to respond to you, you're not going to communicate. It becomes particularly frustrating if there are a lot of staff changes because you finally get somebody who truly knows the child, and knows their AAC system, and then they're gone. You must then find someone else; and the child must build trust and start the process again. Imagine being that person with disabilities and having to do something that's extremely difficult, physically or emotionally, to communicate, and then you must do it with somebody that you don't know or don't trust.

What do you see as the role of technology for improving outcomes related to knowledge/skill barriers?
I think that technology can play a big role in helping others to understand AAC. As a parent of a child that uses AAC, I've been invited to talk to university students in their classes. I found that to be so valuable, and I think the students did also because they always had tons of questions. And so that same kind of thing can be done through technology, like through ZOOM. Or maybe videotaping families

and individuals using AAC so that people can really see how it all works, because I don't think that professionals can ever get enough exposure on how to use AAC.

What equity issues do you want to bring up connected to knowledge/skill barriers?

I think that there's a big equity disparity for adults that use AAC. When kids with disabilities are in school, they have access to a variety of resources. When Will was in school, we had access to resources such as the technology center and the speech therapist. But that's not the case now that he's older. After kids turn twenty-one, a lot of the resources just aren't there.

What do you think people need to know or do to overcome knowledge/ skill barriers?

I think that the most important thing that people need to do is to understand that barriers are real and that the barriers are different for every person. Will's barriers are going to be different from the barriers of other people who use AAC. But it doesn't make the barrier any less or more important. I think people need to at least recognize that barriers exist if we are going to find ways to address them.

> "I think people need to at least recognize that barriers exist if we are going to find ways to address them."

How do you see knowledge/skill barriers being overcome? What do you envision for the future?

I think we need to make sure that people with disabilities can advocate for themselves. And that includes advocating for

AAC systems that really work for them. Making sure that we teach kids with disabilities to advocate, rather than relying solely on professionals and their parents, will allow them to have more control over their lives.

Key Points From Cas's Interview

Cas's interview provides readers with examples of knowledge/skill barriers as well as facilitators. With regard to barriers, Cas identified challenges that she encountered in ensuring that professionals and communication partners have the knowledge and skills needed to individualize AAC systems and to ensure that individuals who use AAC can communicate beyond the expression of basic requests. It is interesting to note that positive outcomes were observed once her son had access to several different tools that allowed him to communicate for a wide array of purposes. Cas also identified specific challenges that she faced when professionals and communication partners lacked the knowledge/skills needed to encourage and support meaningful communicative interactions for her son and emphasized the importance of training communication partners on strategies for supporting interactions.

Conclusion

In summary, Vanessa and Cas provide insight into the knowledge/skill barriers as well as facilitators that may be encountered when supporting their children who use AAC. Further, Vanessa and Cas both shared experiences illustrating that knowledge/skill barriers often occur in tandem with attitude barriers (e.g., recognizing the challenges faced by individuals who use AAC), policy barriers (e.g., ensuring implementation of existing policies such as IDEA), and practice barriers (e.g., developing infrastructures that support collaboration). Although the knowledge/skill barriers and facilitators that Vanessa and Cas experienced varied based upon the unique situations that they encountered, common themes were evident. Specifically, both identified barriers related to professionals and communication partners (a) having necessary levels of AAC content knowledge, (b) developing and refining the skills needed to support individuals who use AAC, and (c) building upon their knowledge/skills in order to address the unique and ongoing learning needs of individuals who use AAC. Additional information regarding these specific knowledge/skill barriers, and strategies for addressing them, will be discussed in the chapters that follow.

2 Knowledge/Skill Barriers: Exploring the Evidence Base

Susan S. Johnston and Cheri Wild Blue

Elias is a 3-year-old boy with cerebral palsy who attends an inclusive preschool classroom. His current communication modes include facial expressions, body movements to express preferences, and four spoken words intelligible to familiar listeners. He also has a voice output aided AAC system, but he rarely uses it at home or in preschool. Elias enjoys interacting with his peers and teachers, but it is evident that his limited communication is negatively impacting his social interactions and development. Elias' educators and parents recognize that something needs to be done to support his complex communication needs but are unsure how to proceed. They question if they have the knowledge/skills needed to support Elias and worry that they "don't know what they don't know."

Based upon the information provided, it is evident that Elias' educators and parents are experiencing knowledge and skill barriers. As previously discussed, knowledge barriers refer to insufficiencies in understanding how to address the communication needs of individuals who use AAC. In contrast, skill barriers occur due to a lack of competency when supporting

these individuals, despite having adequate knowledge. Research suggests that Elias' team is not unique, and that many professionals experience knowledge/skill barriers that prevent them from fully supporting individuals who use AAC (Assistive Technology Industry Association, 2012; Cameron et al., 2018; Norburn et al., 2016; Sanders et al., 2021; Soto et al., 2001).

Offering AAC coursework as part of preservice training is an important step in addressing knowledge/skill barriers. The field of communication sciences and disorders has experienced an increase in the proportion of programs offering dedicated AAC courses from 73% of programs in 1995 (Ratcliff & Beukelman, 1995) to 86% in 2018 (Johnson & Prebor, 2019). However, despite this notable positive increase, only 51% of faculty surveyed in 2019 reported that their preservice SLP students were fully prepared to support AAC by graduation (Johnson & Prebor, 2019). Further, even when preservice training equips practitioners with foundational knowledge and skills for serving **individuals with complex communication needs**, they must stay up to date with advancing technologies and practices (McNaughton & Light, 2013). Moreover, it is important to note that many professionals and communication partners (e.g., paraeducators, parents, peers, individuals in the community) will not have had the benefit of AAC preservice training. Thus, although preservice training is critically important, it is likely insufficient for fully addressing barriers. Addressing knowledge/skill barriers may initially seem overwhelming. However, the task can be made easier by first considering strategies for breaking down the barrier of lacking necessary AAC knowledge, and then considering strategies for breaking down the barrier of lacking the skills needed to support individuals who use AAC.

> Individuals who have complex communication needs are unable to communicate effectively using speech alone.

Breaking Down Barriers: Identifying AAC Knowledge/Skill Needs

When addressing barriers that stem from inadequate AAC knowledge, it may be helpful to start by identifying the AAC knowledge needed by the professionals and communication partners who interact with an individual who uses AAC. In order to accurately identify AAC knowledge needs, it is important to recognize that the professionals and communication partners who interact with individuals

who use AAC have diverse backgrounds and experiences that will, in turn, impact their needs. For example, Sanders et al. (2021) surveyed 272 school-based SLPs to examine confidence levels and predictors of increased confidence related to AAC assessment. Results revealed that SLPs had varied levels of confidence in different aspects of assessment and that several variables (e.g., self-identification as an AAC specialist, percentage of caseload of students with complex communication needs, length of longest continuing education experiences, etc.) contributed to predicting confidence. Further, it is equally important to recognize that the professionals and communication partners who interact with and support individuals who use AAC will not always need the same breadth and depth of knowledge. For example, professionals who support individuals with complex communication needs in finding/accessing services (e.g., physicians, teachers, etc.) will not need the same knowledge/skills as the AAC service providers who design and implement AAC assessments and interventions (Binger et al., 2012; McNaughton et al., 2019).

Given that the professionals and communication partners who interact with individuals who use AAC will have varied backgrounds and experiences and will not always need the same breadth and depth of knowledge, it becomes important for "everyone involved in the process to know what they do and do not know and be aware of when to act independently and when to seek additional assistance" (McNaughton et al., 2019, p. 37). One strategy for supporting professionals and communication partners in determining what they do and do not know is to conduct a self-assessment of AAC knowledge/skill barriers.

Figure 2–1 provides an example of an AAC knowledge/skill barrier assessment based upon content presented in Beukelman and Light (2020) that may assist individual practitioners and interprofessional teams as they identify AAC knowledge/skill needs. As illustrated in Figure 2–1, knowledge and skills in AAC can be organized into categories, with specific topic areas within each category. Recognizing that some knowledge/skill needs may be unique to a given situation, an opportunity to add additional topics within each category is provided. In completing the needs assessment, an individual or group of individuals (e.g., team) will start by identifying whether or not the topics listed within each category are a knowledge/skill barrier. An option of not applicable (NA) is also available for each topic since not all topics will be applicable for all individuals who use AAC. After identifying the topics that are resulting in knowledge/skill barriers, the individual (or group) can prioritize the topics to decide which barrier(s) to address first. As specific knowledge/skill barriers are tackled, the individual or team can return to this assessment to identify the next topic(s) to address based upon priorities.

Readers with a more limited familiarity with AAC may find it helpful to refer to Beukelman and Light (2020) in order to support their understanding of the topic areas listed in Figure 2–1.

Elias' SLP and special education teacher each took courses in AAC at the pre-service level. Because of the coursework they completed, their AAC knowledge needs differ from the other team members. As a result, they each chose to complete their own knowledge/skill barrier assessment (see Figure 2–1). Based upon this assessment, they pinpointed several areas of need and decided that addressing their personal knowledge/skill deficits with regard to training others/instructional coaching was a high priority.

The rest of Elias' team, including his parents, have minimal knowledge of AAC and have not had any training related to AAC assessment or intervention. As a result, Elias' SLP and special education teacher decide to complete one knowledge/skill barrier assessment with all of them during a group meeting. Based on this assessment, they identified several knowledge/skill barriers that were common across all members of the group, including the use of AAC modeling and prompts/prompt fading.

Breaking Down Barriers: Identifying AAC Resources

Identifying AAC knowledge/skill needs is an important first step. However, equally important, is accessing information and resources designed to address those needs. Prior research suggests that lack of access to AAC resources has contributed to knowledge/skill barriers (Dada et al., 2017; O'Neill & Wilkinson, 2020; Singh et al., 2017). Several resources are accessible to assist practitioners and teams

AAC KNOWLEDGE & SKILL BARRIERS SELF-ASSESSMENT

The purpose of this self-assessment is to assist individuals or interprofessional teams in identifying AAC knowledge/skill needs.

Begin the self-assessment by indicating whether each topic is a knowledge/skill barrier (Yes or No), or is not applicable (N/A) based upon the skills and abilities of the individual with complex communication needs or the situation.

Then, for each topic that is identified as a barrier, indicate the level of priority by selecting either (a) high priority (must be addressed promptly in order to move forward), (b) medium priority (should be addressed as soon as possible), or (c) low priority (should be addressed after addressing topics of high and medium priority).

Topic	Knowledge/Skill Barrier?			Priority of Identified Barrier?		
	Yes	No	N/A	High	Medium	Low
Features of AAC						
Modes of Communication (e.g., facial expressions, gestures, sign language, communication boards)						
Communicative Competence						
Communication Bill of Rights						
Vocabulary Selection						
Symbol Systems (e.g., pictures, objects, written words)						
Unaided AAC						
Aided AAC						
Symbol Systems						
Symbol Displays and Organization						
Symbol Encoding and Prediction						
Access/Selection Methods (direct select, scanning)						
Alternative Inputs (e.g., switches)						
Selection Output/Speech Output						
Positioning to support access						
Other:						
Effective Communication and Collaboration with Team Members & Communication Partners						
Collaborative Teaming						
Cultural Competency						
Collaboration with Families & Other Communication Partners						
Service Coordination						
Training Others/Instructional Coaching						
Other:						
Identifying Resources and Supports						
Organizations/Specialists that Support Individuals who use AAC						
Legal assistance						
State Assistive Technology Programs						
Device Manufacturers and Apps						

Figure 2–1. AAC knowledge and skill barriers self-assessment. *continues*

Funding for AAC Systems and Services						
Other:						
Conducting AAC Assessments						
Assessment Models *(e.g., Participation Model, SETT Model)*						
Person-Centered Planning						
Identifying Participation Patterns and Communication Needs						
Assessing Opportunity Barriers and Facilitators *(e.g., knowledge/skill, practice, attitudes, policy)*						
Assessing Capabilities and Access Barriers *(e.g., expressive communication, receptive language, symbol knowledge, cognitive skills, motor skills, etc.)*						
Other:						
Selecting and Personalizing AAC Systems						
Summarizing Assessment Results						
Feature Matching *(e.g., matching the skills and needs of the individual to the features that are available across an array of AAC options)*						
Device Trials						
Writing Reports for Insurance Funding						
Personalizing AAC Systems						
Programming and Troubleshooting Technology						
Other:						
Identifying and Prioritizing Goals (Deciding What to Teach)						
Range of Communication Functions *(e.g., comment, request, reject, etc.)*						
Symbolic Communication						
Conversational Skills *(e.g., initiate, maintain, terminate)*						
Social Skills *(e.g., conflict resolution, empathy, social awareness, etc.)*						
Linguistic Skills *(e.g., semantics, syntax, morphology, etc.)*						
AAC system operational skills						
Digital Communication skills						
PsychoSocial Skills *(e.g., motivation, attitude, resilience, etc.)*						
Visual Schedules/Visual Supports						
Alphabet Supplementation						
Language comprehension						
Literacy Skills *(e.g., emergent, conventional, advanced)*						
Other:						
Using Instructional Strategies for Supporting Individuals who use AAC (How to Teach)						
Ensuring Access to AAC						
AAC Modeling						
Milieu/Incidental Teaching						
Scaffolding						
Systematic Prompts and Prompt Fading						

Figure 2–1. *continues*

Planning for Generalization and Maintenance					
Environmental Adaptations					
Meaningful Opportunities					
Activity-Based/Routine based instruction					
Involving Peers in interventions					
AAC Mentors					
Communication Partner Strategies					
Role Play					
Functional Communication Training					
Conversational Coaching and Strategy Instruction					
Adapting materials to support participation and engagement					
Addressing Opportunity Barriers					
Evaluating intervention effectiveness					
Other:					
Considerations for Different Disabilities					
Motor impairments					
Genetic disorders					
Intellectual disabilities					
Autism spectrum disorder					
Sensory disabilities					
Apraxia of speech					
Acquired disabilities					
Degenerative conditions					
Other:					
Considerations for Different Ages/Settings					
Birth-3					
Preschool					
Elementary					
Secondary					
Post-Secondary					
Employment					
Home					
Community					
Medical					
Other:					

Figure 2–1. *continued*

(Table 2–1 provides select resources that may be of interest). Although readers may have familiarity with the range of books, journals, and professional organizations listed in Table 2–1 that are available to advance their knowledge, they may be less familiar with resources available through federal grants, technology technical assistance training centers, device manufacturers, and social media/blogs.

As illustrated by Table 2–1, resources are available through national centers/ federal grants such as RERC on AAC, the AAC Learning Center, and the Communication Matrix. As an example of resources that are available to assist professionals and communication partners, RERC on AAC has developed a series of free, web-based interactive modules on evidence-based practices across a broad range of topics, including intervention strategies (e.g., literacy and language development), considerations for individuals with different disabili-

Table 2–1. A Quick Reference Guide for Breaking Down Knowledge/Skill Barriers

Barrier	Examples	Solutions	Select Resources
AAC Knowledge	Insufficient preservice or inservice training for professionals who provide AAC services Limited opportunities for communication partners to develop AAC knowledge	Books	Beukelman, D., & Light, J. (2020). *Augmentative and alternative communication: Supporting children and adults with complex communication needs* (5th ed.). Brookes Publishing. Dodd, J., (2017). *Augmentative and alternative communication: An intensive, immersive, socially based service delivery model.* Plural Publishing. Ganz, J., & Simpson, R. (2019). *Interventions for individuals with autism spectrum disorder and complex communication needs.* Brookes Publishing. Johnston, S., Reichle, J., Feeley, J., & Jones, E. (2012). *AAC strategies for individuals with moderate to severe disabilities.* Brookes Publishing. Karanth, P., Roseberry-McKibbin, C., & James, P., (2017). *Interventions for toddlers using augmentative and alternative communication: Practical strategies.* Plural Publishing. Ogletree, B. (2021). *Augmentative and alternative communication: Challenges and solutions.* Plural Publishing.
		Professional Organizations and National Committees	American Association on Intellectual and Developmental Disabilities (AAIDD) https://www.aaidd.org/ American Occupational Therapy Association (AOTA) https://www.aota.org/ American Physical Therapy Association (APTA) https://www.apta.org/ American Speech-Language-Hearing Association (ASHA) https://www.asha.org/ ASHA Special Interest Group 12: Augmentative and Alternative Communication. https://www.asha.org/sig/12/ ASHA online continuing education courses in AAC https://apps.asha.org/eWeb/OLSDynamicPage.aspx?Webcode=olsresults&cat=CE%20Courses&tpc=aac Assistive Technology Industry Association https://www.atia.org/ Association of Assistive Technology Act Programs https://ataporg.org/ Council for Exceptional Children https://exceptionalchildren.org/

continues

Table 2–1. *continued*

Barrier	Examples	Solutions	Select Resources
AAC Knowledge *continued*		Professional Organizations and National Committees *continued*	International Society for Augmentative and Alternative Communication (ISAAC). https://isaac-online.org/english/home/
			National Joint Committee for the Communication Needs of Persons with Severe Disabilities http://www.asha.org/njc
			TASH https://tash.org/
		National Centers and Federal Grants	RERC on AAC https://rerc-aac.psu.edu/
			AAC Learning Center https://aac-learning-center.psu.edu/welcome/
			Communication Matrix https://communicationmatrix.org/
			Communication Partner Instruction
			Project Core http://www.project-core.com/
		Technology Technical Assistance Training Centers and Device Manufacturers	National Assistive Technology Act Technical Assistance and Training Centers https://exploreat.net/
			List of AAC device manufacturers with links to their websites https://allaboutaac.wordpress.com/aac-companies/
		Social Media & Blogs	AAC for the SLP https://www.facebook.com/groups/1539830846285663/
			AAC Intervention http://www.aacintervention.com/
			Jane Farrell Consulting http://www.janefarrall.com/
			Practical AAC http://praacticalaac.org/
			Rachel Langley, AAC Specialist https://www.facebook.com/RachaelLangleyAAC/?fref=ts
			Stories of a Seasoned AAC SLP https://gvantatenhove.wordpress.com/
			Teaching Learners with Multiple Special Needs http://teachinglearnerswithmultipleneeds.blogspot.com/
			Uncommon Sense Blog http://niederfamily.blogspot.com/

Table 2-1. *continued*

Barrier	Examples	Solutions	Select Resources
AAC Skills	Limited applied experiences with AAC during preservice or inservice training	Coaching	Kent-Walsh, J., & McNaughton, D. (2005). Communication partner instruction in AAC: Present practices and future directions. *Augmentative and Alternative Communication, 21,* 195–204.
			Rush, D. D., & Shelden, M. K. (2011). *The early childhood coaching handbook.* Brookes Publishing.
	Limited opportunities to develop fluency in the applied use of AAC knowledge		Rush, D.D, & Shelden, M.K. Webinar on Coaching
			https://www.earlychildhoodwebinars.com/webinars/coaching-in-early-childhood-by-dathan-rush-and-mlisa-shelden/
			Frank Porter Graham Handouts on Coaching
			https://inclusioninstitute.fpg.unc.edu/sites/inclusioninstitute.fpg.unc.edu/files/handouts/Using_a_Coaching_Interactive_Style_with_Families.pdf
			YouTube playlist on Foundations of Coaching
			https://youtube.com/playlist?list=PLsNbrldMdU2t5z7t6M9d3DEfeNYXaxwiC
		Online Training & Telepractice	Clark, R. C., & Mayer, R. E. (2016). *E-Learning and the science of instruction: Proven guidelines for consumers and designers of multimedia learning* (4th ed.) John Wiley & Sons, Inc.
			Hall, N., Juengling-Sudkamp, J., Gutmann, M., & Cohn, E., (2020). *Tele-AAC: Augmentative and alternative communication through telepractice.* Plural Publishing.
			Parsons, M. B., Rollyson, J. H., & Reid, D. H. (2012). Evidence-based staff training: A guide for practitioners. *Behavior Analysis in Practice, 5,* 2–11.
			ASHA Conference Session on Getting Started in Tele-AAC https://asha.zoom.us/rec/play/75Ukc7v8-z43SdLAtQSDVv8vW43pLq6s0ylNrvJZnU62AHQCMwavYeQWarcPPJu2Z0RqMbmGY5GScY7x?autoplay=true&startTime=1585093951000

ties (e.g., aphasia, physical disabilities, autism), considerations for different settings (e.g., workplace, employment success), and strategies related to technology (e.g., funding, communication apps). Further, both the RERC on AAC and the AAC Learning Center (also listed in Table 2–1) have compiled webcasts that include perspectives of AAC users on a wide range of topics and information/supports related to translating research to practice.

Table 2–1 also provides contact information for the Assistive Technology Act Technical Assistance and Training Center (AT3) and device manufacturers. The AT3 Center serves as a clearinghouse for information and resources on assistive technology, including but not limited to AAC. In addition, it provides contact information for each state's assistive technology program, which provides free assistive technology assistance for individuals within the state.

Device manufacturers are another resource for addressing knowledge/skill barriers in AAC. Manufacturer's websites typically include information designed to provide practitioners and communication partners with information regarding the AAC devices they sell, with particular attention to device functions, programming, and troubleshooting. Further, device manufacturer websites often include contact information for technical support and/or local AAC vendor representatives. Establishing relationships with AAC vendor representatives can be helpful when obtaining devices on loan so that team members and individuals who use AAC can actively engage with the technology.

Finally, Table 2–1 provides a select list of social media sites that may be of interest to readers seeking to advance their AAC knowledge and network with professionals. Popular social media platforms used by the AAC community include blogs, Facebook pages/groups, Pinterest, and YouTube. However, it is essential to note that social media content does not always undergo review prior to posting. Therefore, readers must critically evaluate the content provided, including the knowledge, skills, and experiences of the author(s) of the content.

Based upon their identified (and prioritized) AAC knowledge/skill needs, Elias' team decides to gather information and review resources designed to address those needs. In order to increase efficiency, individual team members volunteer to take the lead on different topics. For example, Elias' SLP volunteers to gather information on training others by reviewing resources listed in Table 2–1, while Elias' special education teacher reviews resources related to instructional strategies by viewing several of the free webcasts provided by the RERC on AAC. After AAC content resources were accessed and reviewed, the next step was to consider the process for providing instruction to support other members of their team.

Breaking Down Barriers: Instructional Design

Instruction to professionals and communication partners can be provided in a range of contexts, including individually or in groups, in-person or online, and synchronously (everyone learning at the same place or same time) or asynchronously. Each of the different instructional contexts have relative advantages and disadvantages. For example, providing instruction individually increases opportunities for highly personalized support, but decreases opportunities for team-based learning. Further, online instruction allows access for individuals who live in remote locations and eliminates transportation costs, but creates challenges for those who do not have access to necessary technology or lack requisite technological skills. Research reveals that, despite relative advantages and disadvantages, these contexts (or combinations of contexts) can be used effectively to address knowledge/skill barriers. For example, online synchronous and asynchronous instruction (McCoy & McNaugton, 2021), online individual instruction (Akemoglu et al., 2018), and in-person individual instruction (Ganz et al., 2013) have all been used effectively to address specific knowledge and skill barriers.

Given research suggesting that a range of effective instructional contexts are available for addressing knowledge/skill barriers, examining effective strategies (regardless of instructional context) to support learning may be helpful. Instructional design is the process of considering how individuals learn and what materials and methods will most effectively help them learn (Klepsch & Seufert, 2020). There are several different instructional design models that offer steps and strategies for creating effective learning experiences (see Merrill, 2013, for a review). Although the models have distinct differences, they each describe activities within the common overarching components of

planning, implementing, and evaluating (Hilgart et al., 2012). Table 2–2 provides a checklist of considerations within each of these common overarching components when addressing knowledge/skill barriers. As illustrated by Table 2–2, some considerations may not be relevant for a given training situation (e.g., not applicable). There may also be unique considerations to a given training that are not included in the checklist (e.g., other).

When engaged in planning, it is helpful to ask yourself (or others) several open-ended questions to identify specific training needs. These questions might include: "What knowledge/skill barrier(s) will be addressed in the training? What are the objectives of the training? Who will participate in the training, and what knowledge or experiences do they already have? Should the training be conducted to a group or an individual? Should the training be conducted online or face-to-face? Should the training be conducted in a synchronous and/or asynchronous fashion? What logistical matters should I consider related to scheduling and access to technology?" Once training needs and objectives have been identified, instructional content can be collected that is consistent with needs (see Table 2–1 for possible resources). After collecting existing content, additional content can be created (as needed) before implementing the instruction.

Although implementing the instruction may take many forms (e.g., online and/or in person, with a single or multiple participants, asynchronously and/or synchronously), Table 2–2 identifies several considerations regardless of form. Included among these considerations are

Table 2–2. A Checklist of Instructional Design Considerations	Yes	NA	Comments
Plan			
Specify the knowledge/skill barrier			
Develop learning objectives			
Identify who will participate in the training (including their background/experience)			
Determine the training environment (e.g., online or in person, asynchronous or synchronous, group or individual, etc.)			
Attend to training logistics (e.g., access to technology, space for training, scheduling needs, etc.)			
Gather resources (e.g., textbooks, videos, data collection tools) to support learning			
Create and organize content (e.g., handouts, videos) and activities to support learning			
Create informal/formal assessments			
Other (please specify):			
Implement			
Focus on current challenges/situations			
State learning objectives			
Build upon prior knowledge			
Pre-teach vocabulary (as needed)			
Provide multiple examples and explanations			
Provide multiple opportunities for practice and feedback			
Allow participants to control the pace of instruction			
Promote generalization and maintenance			
Other (please specify):			
Evaluate			
Measure learner performance on instructional targets and adjust instruction based on performance			
Obtain learner feedback on instructional design			
Other (please specify):			

central tenets for teaching adult learners, such as (a) focusing on real-world challenges that apply to their current situation, (b) ensuring active engagement through the use of practice activities and discussions, (c) building upon prior knowledge, (d) creating opportunities for participants to explore and direct their learning, and (e) scaffolding instruction by starting with more simple/concrete practice opportunities and then moving to more complex opportunities as participants demonstrate mastery (McCall et al., 2018).

The instructional design process should also include steps for evaluating participant performance on stated objectives and obtaining participant feedback. Evaluating participant performance on the objectives can include informal assessments (e.g., information collected based on instructional activities and discussions), participants' self-assessment of their acquisition of knowledge/skills, and formal assessments. Participant feedback can also be formal and/or informal. However, it should obtain insight from the participant(s) regarding what is working, what is not working, and what can be done differently to support learning. Data collected can then be used in subsequent planning and implementation stages.

Based upon their newly acquired knowledge regarding teaching others and the data indicating barriers for the other team members in AAC modeling and prompts/prompt fading, Elias' special education teacher and SLP work together to prepare and deliver a short workshop with the entire group. In designing the workshop, they attend to the considerations listed in Table 2–2 for the overarching components of planning, implementing, and evaluating. Assessment data suggest that their workshop was successful, and all members met the learning objectives. However, participant feedback provided by Elias' paraeducator and parents indicated that they needed some additional instructional coaching to further refine their knowledge/skills.

Breaking Down Barriers: Instructional Coaching

Instructional coaching is a term used to describe interventions where a person with expertise (coach) observes a teacher or facilitator's instruction or implementation of a strategy and then provides feedback (Kraft et al., 2018). The term instructional coaching is used to describe a wide range of practices; therefore, it is essential to identify and describe empirically supported instructional coaching practices. Kraft et al. (2018) conducted a meta-analysis of 60 studies to examine the effect of instructional coaching programs on general education teachers' (pre-K through grade 12) instructional practices and students' academic achievement. Results from the meta-analysis suggested that instructional coaching positively influenced instructional practices and that common features of effective interventions included coaching that (a) was individualized, (b) occurred in the context in which teachers implemented taught strategies, (c) was sustained over an extended period, and (d) focused on discrete skills. Although the meta-analysis conducted by Kraft et al. (2018) focused solely on the impact of coaching general educators, research supports the use of instructional coaching in a wide range of contexts. For example, research suggests that **instructional coaching:**

- **positively impacts the instructional practices of a wide range of professionals and communication partners**, including SLPs (Hanline et al., 2018), behavioral therapists (Ganz et al., 2013), special education teachers (Hanline et al., 2018; Muttiah et al., 2018), parents/caregivers (Binger et al., 2008; Kent-Walsh, Binger, & Hasham, 2010; Kent-Walsh, Binger, & Malani, 2010), general education teachers (Muttiah et al., 2018), paraprofessionals (Chung & Carter, 2013; Hanline et al., 2018), and peers (Chung & Carter, 2013).
- **is effective in supporting the needs of a wide range of persons who use AAC,** including individuals with cerebral palsy (Binger et al., 2010; Kent-Walsh, Binger, & Hasham, 2010; Muttiah et al., 2018), intellectual/developmental disabilities (Chung & Carter, 2013; Hanline et al., 2018; Muttiah et al., 2018; Sennott & Mason, 2016), motor speech disorders (Binger et al., 2008; Kent-Walsh et al., 2010; Sennott & Mason, 2016), autism spectrum disorders (Ganz et al., 2013; Hanline et al., 2018; Wermer et al., 2018), orthopedic disabilities (Hanline et al., 2018), and multiple disabilities (Bingham et al., 2007; Muttiah et al., 2018).
- **can be used effectively across a range of settings,** including home (Kent-Walsh, Binger, Hasham, 2010), school (Binger et al., 2010; Chung & Carter, 2013; Ganz et al., 2013; Hanline et al., 2018) and community

(Ballin et al., 2012; Ballin et al., 2013) settings.

- **can be used effectively across an array of routines/activities**, including conversations (Ballin et al., 2012), academics (Chung & Carter, 2013), play (Trottier et al., 2011; Wermer et al., 2018), and snack/mealtime (Nunes & Hanline, 2007; Wermer et al., 2018).
- **can facilitate the implementation of a wide range of AAC instructional strategies**, including creating opportunities for AAC use (Johnson et al., 2004), AAC modeling (Sennott & Mason, 2016), using gestural and physical prompts (Binger et al., 2010), using time-delay and least to most prompting (McMillan & Renzaglia, 2014a, 2014b), and consistently responding to communication acts of the person who uses AAC (Chung & Carter, 2013; Sennott & Mason, 2016).

It is important to note that, in most cases, coaching interventions are designed to teach a combination of instructional strategies. For example, in the context of shared book reading, Kent-Walsh, Binger, and Hasham (2010) taught parents of children who use AAC to (a) read and provide aided language models (e.g., combine their verbal input with the selection of symbols on the AAC system), (b) ask wh-questions and provide aided AAC models, (c) answer questions and provide aided AAC models, and (c) provide wait time to encourage responses.

Kent-Walsh and McNaughton (2005) developed an eight-stage instructional model that may be particularly useful when designing instructional coaching interventions to address knowledge/skill barriers. Based on the work of Kent-Walsh and

McNaughton (2005), Table 2–3 provides the list of stages and activities within each stage that can be used as a checklist when implementing instructional coaching. Further, Chapter 3 provides an explicit example of how instructional coaching was used to support team members of a young boy with complex communication needs to use aided AAC modeling, environmental arrangement, and systematic prompting to teach him to operate the device and locate target words/symbols.

Table 2–3. A Checklist for Instructional Coaching Based on the Stages and Activities

Coaching Stages and Activities	*Insert Date When Activity is Completed*
Stage 1—Pretest and Commitment to Instructional Program	
Coach creates data collection forms for: (a) the instructional strategy for teaching communication behaviors (b) the target communication behavior(s) for the individual with complex communication needs	
Coach collects baseline data on: (a) the communication partner's use of the instruction strategy in the natural environment (b) the target communication behavior(s) for the individual with complex communication needs in the natural environment	
Coach meets with communication partners to: (a) introduce the instructional strategy (b) discuss the coaching process (c) discuss the communication partner's strengths and areas for growth in implementing the instructional strategy (using the baseline data as a reference)	
Communication partner(s) commits orally or in writing to participating in the coaching process in order to learn the instructional strategy.	
Stage 2—Strategy Description	
Coach meets with the communication partner(s), the individual with complex communication needs, and/or parents and caregivers to: (a) describe the instructional strategy in detail (including each of the instructional components) (b) provide a method for remembering the steps of the instructional strategy (e.g., acronym, mnemonic device) (c) compare and contrast the instructional strategy being taught to prior strategies that the communication partner(s) used (d) discuss the importance and potential impact of implementing the current instructional strategy	

continues

Table 2–3. *continued*

Coaching Stages and Activities	Insert Date When Activity is Completed
Stage 3—Strategy Demonstration	
Coach meets with communication partner(s) to: (a) review the instructional strategy (including each of the instructional components) (b) model the use of the instructional strategy (c) verbally discuss and explain the thought process used when prompting, problem-solving, and collecting data by "thinking out loud" while modeling the use of the instructional strategy	
Stage 4—Verbal Practice of Strategy Steps	
Coach meets with communication partner(s) and asks them to: (a) practice naming and describing all components of the instructional strategy (b) explain the importance of each step/component of the instructional strategy	
Coach provides prompts, feedback, and encouragement to communication partner(s).	
Coach gradually fades prompting and feedback until the communication partner(s) demonstrate fluency in their ability to name all components/steps of the instructional strategy.	
Stage 5—Controlled Practice and Feedback	
Communication partner(s) practice implementing the instructional strategy in an environment that is free from distractions (e.g., a setting with only the coach, communication partner(s), and individual with complex communication needs present).	
Coach provides specific and sustained prompts, feedback, and encouragement to communication partner(s).	
Coach gradually fades prompts and feedback until communication partner(s) demonstrate competence, fluency, and confidence when implementing the strategy.	
Stage 6—Advanced Practice and Feedback	
Communication partner(s) practice implementing the instructional strategy in a variety of situations in the natural environment.	
Coach provides specific and sustained prompts, feedback, and encouragement to the communication partner(s).	
Coach gradually fades prompts and feedback until communication partner(s) demonstrate fluency and confidence when implementing the strategy.	

Table 2–3. *continued*	
Coaching Stages and Activities	*Insert Date When Activity is Completed*
Stage 7—Posttest and Commitment to Long-Term Strategy Use	
Coach meets with communication partner(s) and: (a) compares data related to the communication partner's current use of the instructional strategy with baseline data (b) compares data related to the current communication behavior(s) for the individual with complex communication needs with baseline data. (c) supports the communication partner(s) in recognizing and celebrating their success in the use of the strategy to promote changes in the communicative behaviors of the individual with complex communication needs (d) assists the communication partner(s) in developing plans to support generalization and maintenance of the use of the instructional strategy Communication partner(s) commits orally or in writing to long-term strategy use.	
Coach obtains feedback on the communication partner(s) use of the instructional strategy from the individual with complex communication needs and/or their parents/caregivers.	
Stage 8—Generalization of Targeted Strategy Use	
Coach assists communication partner(s) to: (a) identify when and where to use the newly learned instructional strategy (b) develop methods for remembering to use the newly learned instructional strategy (c) learn to modify the newly learned instructional strategy based upon challenges that arise (d) use feedback to improve upon skills when implementing the instructional strategy (e) incorporate acquired knowledge/skills into their portfolio of professional skills	
Communication partner(s) implement the instructional strategy across a wide range of contexts/settings.	
Communication partner(s) plan for long-term implementation of the strategy.	
Coach intermittently monitors communication partner's use of the newly learned strategy over time and provides prompts, feedback, and encouragement as needed.	

Source: Kent-Walsh and McNaughton (2005).

Elias' special education teacher provides instructional coaching with his paraeducator to support her use of AAC modeling and prompts/prompt fading. As a beginner coach, his special education teacher uses the checklist provided in Table 2–3 when providing the coaching. She finds the checklist particularly useful in helping her to remember the stages of coaching and the activities to implement within each stage. Elias' paraeducator learns to implement the strategies with high fidelity across multiple activities and settings. When asked to provide feedback on the instructional coaching, the paraeducator reported high satisfaction levels and felt that having the coach model the instructional strategies and receiving multiple opportunities for practice and feedback was particularly beneficial.

Elias' SLP planned to provide instructional coaching on AAC modeling and prompts/prompt fading with his parents. However, scheduling challenges made it difficult for her to provide coaching in the context of face-to-face home visits. Because of this, Elias' SLP and parents decided to engage in instructional coaching via virtual instruction and telepractice.

Breaking Down Barriers: Virtual Instruction and Telepractice

As discussed previously, one issue to consider when designing instruction to address knowledge/skill barriers is determining the training environment (e.g., virtual or in person, group or individual, etc.). The most effective and efficient training environment is likely to vary based on the skills being taught, the participants' background and expertise, and resources. However, virtual instruction can be of tremendous benefit, particularly when the individuals who have strong expertise in AAC (e.g., instructors/coaches) are not in close physical proximity to those who would benefit from instruction and support (e.g., preservice and inservice professionals, family members, etc.).

For example, if barriers exist in accessing professionals who have strong expertise in AAC (a practice barrier that will be addressed in a later section of the text), virtual meetings can be conducted to support preservice and/or inservice professionals in a group context. Chapter 3 provides a case example illustrating the effective use of online instruction for addressing the knowledge/skill barriers of a group of preservice and inservice professionals. Further, in addition to supporting preservice and inservice professionals in a group context, virtual support can be used for one-on-one coaching via telepractice. Telepractice is a term used to describe telecommunication technologies for facilitating the provision of services from professionals to patients, clients, and students from a distance (Akemoglu et al., 2018; Knutsen et al., 2016). Telepractice can occur in a synchronous format (which allows for live interactions) and/or an asynchronous format where information is shared via video recordings (American Telemedicine Association, 2020). Telepractice can effectively address a range of barriers, including allowing access for individuals who live in remote locations or have limited access to qualified personnel (Heitzman-Powell et al., 2014). Further, it allows for instruction to take place in naturalistic routines and environments and optimizes time efficiency (Akemoglu et al., 2018; Snodgrass et al., 2017). Telepractice also eliminates transportation costs of clients and practitioners (Akemoglu et al., 2018; Curtis, 2014) and can allow for services to continue when circumstances (e.g., pandemics, natural disasters, health concerns) prevent face-to-face sessions (Cason & Cohn, 2014).

Research supports the feasibility and use of telepractice for both AAC assessment and AAC intervention services (Hall et al., 2020). Further, although not specific to AAC, training and coaching via telepractice has been shown to be effective in teaching parents of children with communication delays/disabilities to implement evidence-based communication interventions with fidelity, including modeling, time delay, following the child's lead, prompting, and expansions (see Akemoglu et al., 2018 for a review).

Telepractice requires access to (a) a reliable high-speed Internet connection (minimum 384 kbps), (b) hardware such as computers, mobile devices, web cameras, microphones, and other audio accessories, and (c) a secure two-way communication platform (Akemoglu et al., 2018; Cohn & Wazlaf, 2011; Watzlaf et al., 2010). It is important to note that software used for telepractice must be compliant with HIPPA and FERPA privacy requirements (Cohn & Watzlaf, 2011; Watzlaf et al., 2010), and practitioners must take steps to ensure that telepractice is executed in a manner that emphasizes its advantages

and is in alignment with professional, ethical guidelines for service delivery such as ASHA's code of ethics. Chapter 3 provides a case example illustrating the effective use of telepractice in coaching parents of a 28-month-old girl with autism spectrum disorder to address challenging behaviors and teach the use of AAC. The case study in Chapter 3 also provides a checklist to support the use of telepractice.

Elias' SLP provided instructional coaching with his parents via telepractice. They scheduled the visits on Friday afternoons when (a) Elias was home from school (he attended preschool in the mornings), (b) his parents were able to flex their work schedule to be at home, and (c) his SLP had time in her schedule between working with other students on her caseload. As a result of coaching, Elias' parents quickly became proficient in AAC modeling and prompts/prompt fading. Further, Elias increased his spontaneous and independent use of AAC in his home environment.

Breaking Down Barriers: Response Efficiency

Sometimes, professionals and communication partners may possess AAC knowledge/skills but use those skills infrequently. For example, consider a situation where Sondra (a professional with high levels of AAC expertise) noticed that Jason (a fellow team member) immediately provided full physical prompts when supporting one of his students with intellectual disabilities who was learning to use AAC. As a result, Sondra noticed that the student was becoming prompt dependent. Sondra provided instructional coaching to Jason on the use of constant time delay prior to delivering a controlling prompt (e.g., waiting 5 seconds before providing the physical prompt). However, despite this coaching, Sondra noted that Jason continued to immediately provide a physical prompt.

One possible reason for Jason's infrequent use of learned skills may be related to the efficiency of using a newly learned behavior (e.g., using constant time delay prior to the physical prompt) compared with the efficiency of other competing behaviors (e.g., the sole use of a physical prompt). Herrnstein (1961) demonstrated that the distribution of behavior among concurrently available options depends on the history of reinforcement for each behavior (e.g., the prior reinforcement schedules each behavior). This led to the hypothesis that when individuals have a choice between two or more behaviors, they will select the option that is perceived as most efficient (Mace & Roberts, 1993). Based upon Herrnstien's (1961) theory and Mace and Roberts' (1993) hypothesis related to efficiency, Sondra wondered if Jason might perceive the immediate use of a full physical prompt as more efficient than using constant time delay prior to the delivery of the physical prompt.

Research has demonstrated that efficiency is influenced by at least four variables: response effort, rate of reinforcement, immediacy of reinforcement, and quality of reinforcement (see Johnston et al., 2004 for a review). Although much of the research has been conducted with individuals with disabilities, it seems plausible that the components of response efficiency may also influence the behavior of professionals and communication partners (Johnston et al., 2004). In order to increase the likelihood that Jason used constant time delay, Sondra considered the four variables related to response efficiency. Sondra's first step in considering the variables related to response efficiency involved collecting information on the efficiency of Jason's current behavior (immediate use of full physical prompts), including information regarding the reinforcement history for that behavior. Based on this information, Sondra then formulated a strategy that competed with the four variables of response efficiency in order to increase the likelihood that Jason would use his newly learned behavior (constant time delay prior to the delivery of the physical prompt). Table 2–4 summarizes information collected by Sondra via direct observation and conversations with Jason and illustrates how Sondra adjusted the rate of reinforcement, immediacy of reinforcement, quality of reinforcement, and response effort. This table reveals that the adjustments made by the Sondra resulted in the new behavior (using constant time delay before providing a full physical prompt) receiving (a) an equal rate of reinforcement, (b) a higher quality of reinforcement, (c) an equal (and sometimes lower) response effort, and (d) and equal immediacy of reinforcement. These changes resulted in Jason using the constant time delay before providing a physical prompt because he associated a higher level of response efficiency when using this new strategy compared to his prior strategy of immediately providing a full physical prompt.

Table 2–4. Summary of the Rate of Reinforcement, Quality of Reinforcement, Response Effort, and Immediacy of Reinforcement for Jason's Current Behavior and the Newly Learned Behavior

Factor Influencing Efficiency	Current Behavior (Immediate Use of Full Physical Prompt)	Behavior Taught During Training (Constant Time Delay Prior to Full Physical Prompt)
Rate of Reinforcement	Immediately using a full physical prompt resulted in high rates of correct responding from the student, which Jason finds reinforcing. Jason reports that this results in a **high** rate of reinforcement.	During training, Jason is coached to provide a constant time delay prior to delivering a full physical prompt. His student continues to engage in high rates of correcting responding, which is reinforcing to Jason. Jason reports that this results in a **high** rate of reinforcement.
Quality of Reinforcement	When Jason uses a full physical prompt, he indicates that the quality of reinforcement is high because the student responds correctly and, therefore, he feels like he is doing a good job with instruction. However, Jason reports that the quality of reinforcement that he receives from implementing the small group activities during which he typically prompts the student is low. He states that, in addition to supporting the student who uses AAC, another student in the small group requires a lot of attention due to significant challenging behaviors. As a result, neither he nor the other students in the group enjoy the activities. Although the quality of reinforcement for immediately providing a full physical prompt to the student is high, the quality of reinforcement that Jason receives for the conducting activity as a whole is low. As a result, Jason finds the overall quality of reinforcement **neutral**.	Jason learns the importance of designing instruction to prevent students from becoming prompt dependent and the potential for learned helplessness to occur when students are prompt dependent. Jason reports that the student's continued correct responses, in conjunction with this new understanding, provide a high quality of reinforcement because he feels like he is doing an even better job with instruction by making a difference in this student's life. The other teachers and paraeducators meet to reassign students in the small groups to ensure that students with more significant support needs are allocated evenly across groups. Due to his increased knowledge/ skills and changes to student groupings, Jason reports that he now finds the overall quality of reinforcement **high.**
Response Effort	The effort for Jason to provide a full physical prompt is **average**.	The effort for Jason to insert a time delay prior to delivering a full physical prompt is **average**. Further, the effort is **low** when the student responds prior to delivering the physical prompt.

continues

Table 2–4. *continued*

Factor Influencing Efficiency	Current Behavior (Immediate Use of Full Physical Prompt)	Behavior Taught During Training (Constant Time Delay Prior to Full Physical Prompt)
Immediacy of Reinforcement	Jason is **immediately** reinforced by his student's correct response.	Jason indicates that the pause-time when using a 5-second constant time delay is very short and still feels as though he is **immediately** reinforced by his student's correct response.

Conclusion

In summary, professionals and communication partners may experience barriers with regard to (a) having necessary levels of AAC knowledge and (b) developing and refining the skills needed to support individuals who use AAC. However, there are strategies for addressing these barriers. Included among the strategies for addressing barriers related to lack of AAC knowledge are conducting needs assessments to more precisely identify barriers and accessing resources that address identified barriers. Strategies for addressing barriers in developing and refining skills needed to support individuals who use AAC include using instructional design principles, providing instructional coaching, using online teaching and telepractice, and considering issues related to response efficiency. The following chapter will present case examples demonstrating the successful use of several of these strategies for addressing knowledge/skill barriers.

References

Akemoglu, Y., Meadan, H., Pearson, J. N., & Cummings, K. (2018). Getting connected: Speech and language pathologists' perceptions of building rapport via telepractice. *Journal of Developmental and Physical Disabilities, 30*(4), 569–585.

American Telemedicine Association, (2020). *Telehealth basics.* https://www.americantelemed.org/resource/why-telemedicine/

Assistive Technology Industry Association. (2012). *The critical need for knowledge and usage of AT and AAC among speech-language pathologists* [Survey white paper]. https://www.atia.org/wp-content/uploads/2018/12/ATIA-SLP-Survey-2011.pdf

Ballin, L., Balandin, S., & Stancliffe, R. J. (2012). The speech-generating device (SGD) mentoring program: Training adults who use an SGD to mentor. *AAC: Augmentative and Alternative Communication, 28*(4), 254–265.

Ballin, L., Balandin, S., & Stancliffe, R. J. (2013). The speech-generating device (SGD) mentoring program: Supporting the development of people learning to use an SGD.

Journal of Developmental and Physical Disabilities, 25(4), 437–459.

Beukelman, D., & Light, J. (2020). *Augmentative and alternative communication: Supporting children and adults with complex communication needs* (5th ed.). Paul H. Brookes.

Binger, C., Ball, L., Dietz, A., Kent-Walsh, J., Lasker, J., Lund, S., . . . Quach, W. (2012). Personnel roles in the AAC assessment process. *Augmentative and Alternative Communication, 28*, 278–288.

Binger, C., Kent-Walsh, J., Berens, J., Del Campo, S., & Rivera, D. (2008). Teaching Latino parents to support the multi-symbol message productions of their children who require AAC. *Augmentative and Alternative Communication, 24*, 323–338.

Binger, C., Kent-Walsh, J., Ewing, C., & Taylor, S. (2010). Teaching educational assistants to facilitate the multi-symbol message productions of young students who required augmentative and alternative communication. *American Journal of Speech-Language Pathology, 19*, 108–120.

Bingham, M. A., Spooner, F., & Browder, D. (2007). Training paraeducators to promote the use of augmentative and alternative communication by students with significant disabilities. *Education and Training in Developmental Disabilities, 42*, 339–352.

Cameron, A., McPhail, S., Hudson, K., Fleming, J., Lethlean, J., Ju Tan, N., & Finch, E. (2018). The confidence and knowledge of health practitioners when interacting with people with aphasia in a hospital setting. *Disability and Rehabilitation, 40*(11), 1288–1293.

Cason, J., & Cohn, E. R. (2014). Telepractice: An overview and best practices. *Perspectives on Augmentative and Alternative Communication, 23*, 4–17.

Chung Y., & Carter, E. W. (2013). Promoting peer interactions in inclusive classrooms for students who use speech-generating devices. *Research & Practice for Persons with Severe Disabilities, 38*, 94–109.

Clark, R. C., & Mayer, R. E. (2016). *E-Learning and the science of instruction: Proven guidelines for consumers and designers of multimedia learning* (4th ed.). John Wiley & Sons.

Cohn, E. R., & Watzlaf, V. (2011). Privacy and internet-based telepractice. *Perspectives on Telepractice, 1*, 26–37.

Curtis, T.R. (2014). Case studies for telepractice in AAC. *Perspectives on Augmentative and Alternative Communication, 23*, 42–54.

Dada., S., Murphy, Y., & Tönsing, K. (2017). Augmentative and alternative communication practices: A descriptive study of the perceptions of South African speech-language therapists. *Augmentative and Alternative Communication, 33*(4), 189–200.

Dodd, J., (2017). *Augmentative and alternative communication: An intensive, immersive, socially based service delivery model.* Plural Publishing.

Ganz, J. B., Goodwyn, F. D., Boles, M. M., Hong, E.R., Rispoli, M. J., Lund, E. M., & Kite, E. (2013). Impacts of a PECS instructional coaching intervention on practitioners and children with autism. *Augmentative and Alternative Communication, 29*, 210–221.

Ganz, J., & Simpson, R. (2019). *Interventions for individuals with autism spectrum disorder and complex communication needs.* Brookes Publishing.

Hall, N., Juengling-Sudkamp, J., Gutmann, M., & Cohn, E. (2020). Tele-AAC: Augmentative and alternative communication through telepractice. Plural Publishing.

Hanline, M. F., Dennis, L. R., & Warren, A. W., (2018). The outcomes of professional development on AAC use in preschool classrooms: A qualitative investigation. *Infants and Young Children, 31*, 231–245.

Heitzman-Powell, L. S., Buzhardt, J., Rusinko, L. C., & Miller, T. M. (2014). Formative evaluation of an ABA outreach training program for parents of children with autism in remote areas. *Focus on Autism and Other Developmental Disabilities*, *29*(1), 23–38.

Herrnstein, R. J. (1961). Relative and absolute strength of response as a function of frequency of reinforcement. *Journal of the Experimental Analysis of Behavior*, *4*, 266–267.

Hilgart, M. M., Ritterband, L. M., Thorndike, F. P., & Kinzie, M. B. (2012). Using instructional design process to improve design and development of internet interventions. *Journal of Medical Internet Research*, *14*(3), 1–18.

Johnson, J. W., McDonnell, J., Holzwarth, V. N., & Hunter, K. (2004). The efficacy of embedded instruction for students with developmental disabilities enrolled in general education classes. *Journal of Positive Behavior Interventions*, *6*, 214–227.

Johnson, R. K., & Prebor, J. (2019). Update on preservice training in augmentative and alternative communication for speech-language pathologists. *American Journal of Speech-Language Pathology*, *28*(2), 536–549.

Johnston, S., Reichle, J., & Evans, J. (2004) Supporting augmentative and alternative communication use by beginning communicators with severe disabilities. *American Journal of Speech-Language Pathology*. *13*(1), 20–30.

Johnston, S., Reichle, J., Feeley, J., & Jones, E. (2012). *AAC strategies for individuals with moderate to severe disabilities*. Brookes Publishing.

Karanth, P., Roseberry-McKibbin, C., & James, P. (2017). *Interventions for toddlers using augmentative and alternative communication: Practical strategies*. Plural Publishing.

Kent-Walsh, J., Binger, C., & Hasham, Z. (2010). Effects of parent instruction on the symbolic communication of children using augmentative and alternative communication during storybook reading. *American Journal of Speech-Language Pathology*, *19*, 97–107.

Kent-Walsh, J., Binger, C., & Malani, M. D. (2010). Teaching partners to support the communication skills of young children who use AAC: Lessons from the ImPAACT program. *Early Childhood Services*, *4*, 155–170.

Kent-Walsh, J., & McNaughton, D. (2005). Communication partner instruction in AAC: Present practices and future directions. *Augmentative and Alternative Communication*, *21*, 195–204.

Klepsch, M., & Seufert, T. (2020). Understanding instructional design effects by differentiated measurement of intrinsic, extraneous, and germane cognitive load. *Instructional Science*, *48*, 45–77.

Knutsen, J., Wolfe, A., Burke, B. L., Hepburn, S., Lindgren, S., & Coury, D. (2016). A systematic review of telemedicine in autism spectrum disorders. *Journal of Autism and Developmental Disorders*, *3*(4), 330–344.

Kraft, M. A., Blazar, D., & Hogan, D. (2018). The effect of teacher coaching on instruction and achievement: A meta-analysis of the causal evidence. *Review of Educational Research*, *88*, 547–588.

Mace, F., & Roberts, M. (1993). Factors affecting the selection of behavioral treatments. In J. Reichle & D. Wacker (Eds.), *Communicative approaches to the management of challenging behavior*. Paul H. Brookes.

McCall, R. C., Padron, K., & Andrews, C. R. (2018). Evidence-based instructional strategies for adult learners: A review of the literature. *Codex: The Journal of the Louisiana Chapter of the ACRL*, *4*, 29–47.

McCoy, A., & McNaughton, D. (2021). Effects of online training on educators' knowledge and use of system of least prompts to support augmentative and alternative communication. *Journal of Behavioral Education*, 30, 319–349.

McMillan, J.M., & Renzaglia, A. (2014a). Supporting speech-generating device use in the classroom. Part 1: Teacher professional development. *Journal of Special Education Technology*, 29, 31–47.

McMillan, J. M., & Renzaglia, A. (2014b). Supporting speech-generating device use in the classroom. Part two: Student communication outcomes. *Journal of Special Education Technology*, 29(3), 49–61.

McNaughton, D., & Light, J. (2013). The iPad and mobile technology revolution: Benefits and challenges for individuals who require augmentative and alternative communication. *Augmentative and Alternative Communication*, 29(2), 107–116.

McNaughton, D., Light, J., Beukelman, D., Klein, C. Nieder, D., & Nazareth, G. (2019). Building capacity in AAC: A person-centered approach to supporting participation by people with complex communication needs. *Augmentative and Alternative Communication*, 35(1), 56–68.

Merrill, M. D. (2013). *First Principles of Instruction*. John Wiley & Sons.

Muttiah, N., Drager K. D. R., McNaughton, D., & Perera, N. (2018). Evaluating an AAC training for special education teachers in Sri Lanka, a low- and middle-income country. *Augmentative and Alternative Communication*, 34, 276–287.

Norburn, K., Morgan, S., Levin, A., & Harding, C. (2016). A survey of augmentative and alternative communication used in an inner-city special school. *British Journal of Special Education*, 43(3), 289–306.

Nunes, D., & Hanline, M. F. (2007). Enhancing the alternative and augmentative communication use of a child with autism through a parent-implemented naturalistic intervention. *International Journal of Disability, Development, and Education*, 54, 177–197.

Ogletree, B. (2021). *Augmentative and alternative communication: Challenges and solutions*. Plural Publishing.

O'Neil, T., & Wilkinson, K. M. (2020). Preliminary investigation of the perspectives of parents of children with cerebral palsy on the supports, challenges, and realities of integrating augmentative and alternative communication into everyday life. *American Journal of Speech-Language Pathology*, 29, 238–254.

Parsons, M. B., Rollyson, J. H., & Reid, D. H. (2012). Evidence-based staff training: A guide for practitioners. *Behavior Analysis in Practice*, 5, 2–11.

Ratcliff, A., & Beukelman, D. (1995). Preprofessional preparation in augmentative and alternative communication: State-of-the-art report. *Augmentative and Alternative Communication*, 11, 61–73.

Rush, D. D., & Shelden, M. K. (2011). *The early childhood coaching handbook*. Brookes Publishing.

Sanders, E. J., Page, T. A., & Lesher, D. (2021). School-based speech-language pathologists: Confidence in augmentative and alternative communication. *Language, Speech, and Hearing Services in Schools*. 52(2), 512–528.

Sennott, S. C., & Mason, L. H. (2016). AAC modeling with the iPad during shared storybook reading pilot study. *Communication Disorders Quarterly*, 37, 242–254.

Singh, S. J., Hussein, N. H., Kamal, R. M., & Hassan, F. H. (2017). Reflections of Malaysian parents of children with developmental disabilities on their experiences with AAC. *Augmentative and Alternative Communication*, 33(2), 110–120.

Snodgrass, M. R., Chung, M. Y., Biller, M. F., Appel, K. E., Meadan, H., & Halle, J. W. (2017). Telepractice in speech-language therapy: The use of online technologies for parent training and coaching. *Communication Disorders Quarterly*, *38*, 242–254.

Soto, G., Muller, E., Hunt, P., & Goetz, L. (2001). Professional skills for serving students who use AAC in general education classrooms: A team perspective. *Language Speech and Hearing Services in Schools*. *32*(1), 51–56.

Trottier, N., Kamp, L., & Mirenda, P. (2011). Effects of peer-mediated instruction to teach use of speech-generating devices to students with autism in social game routines. *Augmentative and Alternative Communication*, *27*(1), 26–39.

Watzlaf, V., Moeini, S., & Firouzan, P. (2010). VoIP for telerehabilitation: A risk analysis for privacy, security, and HIPAA compliance. *International Journal of Telerehabilitation*, *2*(2), 3–14.

Wermer, L., Brock, M. E., & Seaman, R. L., (2018). Efficacy of a teacher training a paraprofessional to promote communication for a student with autism and complex communication needs. *Focus on Autism and Other Developmental Disabilities*, *33*, 217–226.

3 Knowledge/Skill Barriers: Studying Successful Case Examples

Susan S. Johnston, Adele F. Dimian*, Ashley R. McCoy*, Jessica J. Simacek*, and Melinda R. Snodgrass*

Introduction

This chapter presents three case examples highlighting the successful use of strategies for addressing knowledge/skill barriers. The first case illustrates the use of instructional coaching to tackle the knowledge/skill barriers experienced by a school team who served a five-year-old boy diagnosed with Angelman syndrome and a seizure disorder. The second case shares how the knowledge/skill barriers of preservice and inservice professionals were addressed through online training. The third case illustrates the use of telepractice to attend to the knowledge/skill barriers experienced by the parents of a 28-month-old child diagnosed with autism spectrum disorder (ASD). Although the case studies vary in many ways, there are similarities in that all three (a) recognized the presence of knowledge/skill barriers, (b) identified the knowledge/skill needs of professionals and com-munication partners, and (c) attended to principles of instructional design when planning, implementing, and evaluating their instruction and support.

Case Example: Instructional Coaching (Melinda R. Snodgrass, PhD)

As a former special education teacher turned teacher preparer and education researcher, I work with individuals who are learning to use AAC, the families and school teams that support them, and pre-service teachers who will support the AAC learners of the future. This case example with Eli is drawn from prior research where I supported and studied the efforts of a school team. Eli was a 5-year-old boy, transitioning from preschool into kindergarten, who was diagnosed with Angel-man syndrome and a seizure disorder. Eli was introduced to aided AAC before he

---

*These authors have contributed equally to this work and share senior authorship.

was three years old when his parents had encouraged his early intervention team to use a low-tech symbol communication book. Then, approximately a year before he started kindergarten, his parents purchased a high-tech communication app for an iPad (i.e., PODD with Compass). At that point, Eli had not used either AAC system to communicate independently. However, he was skilled at using prelinguistic communication to request (e.g., pointing or taking people by the hand to lead them to what he wanted) and protest (e.g., vocalizing or crying when he did not want something or pushing away unwanted items). Eli needed to learn how to engage in communication exchanges with his AAC device and his other communication modes (gestures, vocalizations, paper-based symbol book) with people who did not know him well, including his new educational team and classmates. He also needed to learn how to operate his AAC device. For example, he did not know how to locate words, clear messages, navigate to and from different screens, and change the volume. Finally, he needed instruction to build the language skills and vocabulary to communicate with others more effectively.

In kindergarten, Eli received instruction and support from multiple professionals. Eli spent his day in the general education kindergarten classroom with some pull-out time in the special education resource room. He was supported in the kindergarten classroom by a general education teacher and a team of four paraprofessionals who rotated in and out. He also received support from the speech-language pathologist (SLP), an occupational and physical therapist, and his special education teacher, mostly in pull-out sessions away from his kindergarten class.

Eli's new educational team had limited experience with or knowledge of AAC. Of the adults supporting Eli in kindergarten, only the SLP and the special education teacher had received any previous AAC training, and only the SLP had direct experience with AAC. In addition, there were logistical challenges because of limited overlap in adult time with Eli and with one another. Although at least one adult was always present to support Eli, that adult changed throughout the day, and the adults overlapped with one another only in the transition to the next person. Further, although the general education teacher and a paraprofessional worked together as they co-supported Eli, they also shared the responsibility to support the rest of the kindergarten class. Thus, the team's biggest challenge was efficiently and effectively teaching all these adults the knowledge and skills they needed to support Eli's communication. The following section summarizes the strategies used to address these knowledge/skill barriers.

Strategies

The team began work on their knowledge and skill barriers by **identifying a team leader.** The most knowledgeable and experienced members of Eli's team with the most training in AAC were his SLP and me, a researcher studying and supporting this team's efforts. Thus, we served together as team leaders. Next, the team **specified who would be on the primary AAC team**. That is, they discussed who would play an active role in the initial activities for supporting Eli's AAC learning. Some team members felt overwhelmed at the prospect of learning how to support AAC, but other members were excited to take on this challenge. Thus, the team members who were willing to take on the challenge were put on the primary team, with the understanding that the rest of the team would learn later. Eli's mother, the SLP, two of his paraprofessionals, and his special education teacher were on the primary AAC team. The team then **held a planning meeting** focused on Eli's AAC. Everyone on Eli's education team was invited to participate, but only the primary AAC team was required to attend. The meeting was scheduled for two hours and had three main goals:

1. Specify the communication vision for Eli (i.e., long-term communication goals) and this year's priorities for working toward that vision (i.e., short-term goals).
2. Identify the strategies the team would use to teach Eli the skills required to meet this year's goals.
3. Train all members of the primary AAC team to use these strategies.

The team began the meeting by listening to Eli's parents describe their long-term vision for his communication and then discussing what the team could focus on this year to help move toward that vision. The team specified that, by the end of kindergarten, they wanted Eli to use at least two of six specific words/phrases (i.e., hello, goodbye, let's go, done, help, more) that his mother had already been working on teaching him to use on

his AAC device. The team then discussed what instructional strategies might help him learn to do this. They decided to use (a) aided AAC modeling, focusing but not limiting their modeling on those six words; (b) environmental arrangement, in which team members would create opportunities for Eli to use the target words; and (c) systematic prompting to teach him to operate the device and locate target words/symbols. The team leads then taught the whole team how to use these three strategies by (a) describing the steps in the strategy, (b) demonstrating the strategy using role-play and videos, and (c) having everyone rehearse strategy steps aloud. By the end of the meeting, everyone who attended knew the plan for supporting Eli's AAC learning and why they were doing it. Further, everyone had been exposed to the strategies and knew their basic steps. Now it was time to ensure that this new knowledge and new skills were used to support Eli throughout his day.

Thus, the team leaders began **coaching** each member of the primary AAC team to use the three strategies they had identified in the planning meeting. Each school-based team member identified a time in the school day when they were with Eli during a predictable routine. Eli's mother and the team leaders also identified a routine that occurred at a time that worked with their schedules so that Eli's mother could receive coaching via a home visitor video call. Each coaching session was short, usually lasting 15 to 25 minutes, and was structured the same way each time. The steps in the coaching process are described below and illustrated in checklist format in Figure 3–1.

Coaching Session Checklist

Pre-Observation Conversation (2–5 minutes)
- ☐ Decide which instructional strategy to focus on today.
- ☐ Review the strategy procedures. If you've coached on this strategy before, review previous feedback.
- ☐ Ask if there are any questions and respond to questions.
- ☐ Decide when to have the post-observation conversation.

Observation (5–10 minutes)
- ☐ Coach observes the interaction with the student.
- ☐ Take notes (written preferred, but mental notes are okay if necessary) each time the strategy identified in the pre-observation conversation is used.
  Note:
    - ☐ Was the strategy used at the right time/under the correct conditions?
    - ☐ Was the strategy used correctly (e.g., followed all the steps; responded to errors correctly)?
    - ☐ How did the student respond to the strategy?
    - ☐ Any other things you want to remember for the post-observation conversation.

Post-Observation Conversation (5–10 minutes)
- ☐ Ask the team member to reflect on the session related to how they used the selected strategy and the student's response to the strategy.
- ☐ Discuss their reflection.
- ☐ Offer supportive feedback (things they did well).
  Note. Focus this feedback on how they used the strategy correctly and/or how they responded to the student.
- ☐ Offer constructive feedback (things they can improve next time).
  Note. Focus this feedback on how to use the strategy correctly and/or how to respond to the student.
- ☐ Give them the opportunity to ask questions. Respond to questions.
- ☐ Ask them to describe how they are using the strategy in other routines and interactions with the student.
- ☐ Set date, time, and location for next session if needed.

Figure 3–1. Coaching session checklist.

1. Pre-Observation Conversation (approximately 2–5 minutes). The team leader and the team member speak briefly to identify which of the three strategies to focus on in that session, review the steps in the strategy, and ask/respond to any team member questions.
2. Observation (approximately 5–10 minutes). The team leader watches the team member interact with Eli during the chosen routine and watches for instances when the team member uses the identified strategies to check if the team member used the strategy correctly (i.e., completed all the steps in the proper order and in the correct way; fidelity of implementation). The team leader also collects data on how Eli responds to the strategy and any other commu-

nication he engages in during the observation.

3. Post-Observation Conversation (approximately 5–10 minutes). As soon as the team member can step away (which sometimes meant waiting until after school, but usually happened right away), the team leader and team member debrief about the observation. First, the team member reflects on how the session went and how using the strategy felt from their perspective. Then, the team leader offers both supportive (e.g., comments on a step in the strategy done particularly well) and constructive (e.g., reminds about a strategy step) feedback. They briefly discuss how the team member is using the strategy in other routines or interactions with Eli and address any questions the team member has about using the strategy any time they are with Eli. If not already set, they set up the next coaching session and then part ways.

The team leaders continued to coach each team member until they used all three strategies correctly for at least three coaching sessions in a row and told the team leaders that they felt confident using the strategies across Eli's routines.

Outcomes

As a result of the team's efforts to support Eli's communication through planning and coaching, everyone got better, but no one got perfect. The primary AAC team members learned to use the strategies they had selected in the planning meeting. In fact, they got good at using them in a relatively short amount of time. Only 5 to 8 coaching sessions were needed for the primary AAC team members to master the three strategies they had chosen (8 sessions for Eli's mother, 5 for one paraprofessional and his special education teacher, and 7 for the other paraprofessional). This meant that they were supporting Eli in working toward the goals they had set at the planning meeting and were **providing support for Eli's AAC learning across multiple settings** (Eli's home, his general education kindergarten classroom, the playground, the lunchroom, his special education classroom, and even the hallway). Eli was getting lots of AAC language models and was learning to use the six target words across many contexts and with multiple communication partners in these different settings.

In addition to these direct benefits, the team identified several outcomes of planning and coaching that they had not expected. First, **Eli always had access to his AAC device.** The common practice barriers of AAC devices left in backpacks, on shelves, or uncharged that had plagued Eli's preschool experience were not an issue at all in kindergarten. Because multiple team members knew what to do, everyone pitched in to ensure he had his device and that it was charged and ready to go. In addition, **everyone continued to respect and encourage Eli's gestural and vocal communication**. By discussing the importance of multi-modal communication in the planning meeting and the team leads providing feedback during coaching sessions about how to respond to Eli's gestures and vocalizations, the whole team honored the many ways Eli already communicated and was learning to communicate. Another unintended consequence of so many adults on Eli's team knowing how to support his AAC learning was that **Eli's peers got on board with AAC.** The school allowed Eli's communication app to be downloaded onto the kindergarten classroom's iPad so that his peers could model for him. As a result, his peers started using the classroom device to communicate. This not only created authentic models for Eli but also supported the communication and social-emotional development of many of his peers.

The team also noted that **onboarding reticent team members to support Eli's AAC learning was easier** after watching so many of their colleagues support him. The primary AAC team was an effective model of what it took to support Eli for the rest of his team (two more paraprofessionals, general education teacher, and other related service providers). Finally, the team realized that **coaching the primary team members had also created more coaches**. Because the coaching process ensured that each person mastered the use of the selected strategies, those team members could then quickly be trained in the coaching process and coach others when scheduling conflicts arose. In addition, most of the team members also started informally coaching other people in Eli's life to support his AAC, including a lunchroom supervisor, Eli's bus monitor, and his peers. Eli's mom reported that she, too, was coaching Eli's siblings to use the strategies.

Discussion

Although planning and coaching won't remove all barriers to supporting a student's AAC learning, this team experienced some important successes. First, due to planning and coaching, **AAC was integrated, essential, and supported** across Eli's life, both at home and at school. Second, communication was broadly defined by all members of Eli's educational team and his peers. **Everyone honored Eli's communication regardless of modality**, be it using his AAC device, gestures and actions, or vocalizations. It is important to note that the team also experienced some challenges that may be useful to consider before replicating this case example. These challenges included (a) practice barriers related to coordinating multiple schedules to set the planning meeting and to coach the mother within contract hours, as well as (b) policy barriers related to amending Eli's IEP to adjust the SLP's time from direct service to consultation, which required negotiations with the principal (and would require negotiations with parents/guardians, although Eli's parents were supportive and instrumental in advocating for this to school administration). An additional challenge was encountered in identifying the strategies used to support AAC learning. In the present case example, this challenge was addressed through the combined knowledge of the team leads. If team members did not possess this knowledge, they would need to seek support to identify strategies, learn them, and teach them to the rest of the team.

Based upon these successes and challenges, key lessons learned from Eli's kindergarten experience include **distributing the load** and **creating AAC access for all**. Learning new skills is time-consuming and takes effort, both from teachers and learners. However, the more people who work together to learn how to support AAC, the lighter that load feels and the more time-efficient it becomes. Eli's team benefited from having multiple people learning to support his AAC, and Eli benefited from receiving consistent, frequent instruction across his day. Further, ensuring classroom access to an AAC device that matched Eli's had beautiful consequences for Eli (he got peer models of AAC use) and for his peers (they had another way to communicate, several children learned new vocabulary, etc.). Learning to communicate is a huge undertaking, and learning to use AAC presents a unique set of challenges. But planning and coaching can go a long way toward ensuring that knowledge/skill barriers are taken down.

Case Example: Online Preservice and Inservice Training (Ashley R. McCoy, PhD)

As a former special educator and autism coordinator, whose responsibilities included providing professional development and instructional coaching, I became acutely aware of the need for teachers, paraprofessionals, and related service providers to receive increased quality and quantity of training as a way to address knowledge/skill barriers. This need resulted in my pursuit of a PhD and continues to be a focus in my current role as a faculty member in higher education. This case example is drawn from my research examining the use of online instruction to provide training to professionals on instructional strategies that can be used to support individuals who use AAC (McCoy & McNaughton, 2021).

Although there are advantages to online training, such as flexible and convenient access, cost-efficiency, and global accessibility, online training in and of itself is not inherently superior in providing quality instruction and producing effective outcomes (Johnson, 2004; Meyen et al., 1997). In support of this, Ally (2008, p. 15) states, "learning is influenced more by the content and instructional strategy in the learning materials than by the types of technology used to deliver instruction." Therefore, this case example consciously applies instructional strategies to online training. Specifically, online instruction was used to teach 20 trainees to utilize the system of least prompts to support communication of individuals who use AAC in a manner that is effective (i.e., increases knowledge and skill), efficient (i.e., appropriate time and resources for both the communication partner and trainer), and socially valid (i.e., training delivered in a meaningful and acceptable way). All trainees were enrolled in a university-affiliated online assistive technology course. Thirteen were graduate students, and six were undergraduate students. Twelve graduate students were teachers or paraprofessionals (i.e., general education, special education, inclusive education), and one was a social worker. Six undergraduate students were majoring in education (i.e., elementary and early childhood education, secondary education), and one was majoring in rehabilitation and human services.

Strategies

In the week prior to beginning the training, trainees completed a pretest that included two asynchronous and one synchronous components. Trainees were then given one week to asynchronously complete the online AAC training, which was divided into three parts; introduction to prompting and the system of least prompts, introduction to planning, and introduction to implementation (Figure 3–2). In the week following training, trainees completed a post-test, again with two asynchronous and one synchronous components.

Based on the work of Kent-Walsh and McNaughton (2005), each part of the training included instructional elements related to description, modeling, rehearsal, and feedback. These elements are discussed in the following sections, with a particular focus on how the elements were incorporated into the online instruction to teach the use of the system of least prompts.

Describe & Model

Describe and model was an important initial training step for establishing the foundational knowledge needed to develop related skills. Our online training included short instructional text about the system of least prompts (with definitions of related terminology) and short video clips modeling the technique. Additionally, as illustrated in Figure 3–2, acronyms were used to help trainees focus their attention on crucial information and recall the instructional strategy and related steps.

Rehearsal & Feedback

Comprehension Checks and Verbal Rehearsal. Throughout all of the online training, we created frequent opportunities to check for learning via comprehension checks. In addition, comprehension checks provided opportunities for verbal rehearsal by asking the participants to pause and practice (e.g., when the trainee was asked to verbally practice naming the acronym and describing each step of the instructional strategy).

Guided Practice. Building upon the comprehension checks and verbal rehearsal, guided practice was embedded into our online instruction to provide learning opportunities that supported the transition from *knowledge about* to *performance of* skills. As noted in Figure 3–2, the guided practice opportunities went beyond foundational knowledge and directly engaged the trainees in utilizing the acquired knowledge. Relatedly, the guided practice learning opportunities were scaffolded so that the trainees were initially fully supported, and then the support was gradually removed.

During the development of the guided practice opportunities, we carefully considered how and when feedback to the trainees was provided. Specifically, pre-programmed feedback was embedded within the guided practice opportunities. For example, each quiz question had written text confirmation for correct responses and error correction text for incorrect responses. Then, when the quiz was submitted, the feedback was immediately presented to the trainee. Additionally, for open-response items, text

System of Least Prompts Online Training Outline (McCoy & McNaughton, 2021)	
Training Section	**Activities**
Pre-Test	Knowledge Quiz Planning Document Implementation Role Play (conducted as a synchronous online activity)
Part 1a: Introduction to Prompting	Describe • Define and provide examples of prompts Model • Video examples of prompts and how prompts can be used during instruction Rehearsal & Feedback • Multiple choice questions designed to check understanding about prompting and types of prompts • Preprogrammed, immediate feedback (correct/incorrect with explanations)
Part 1b: Introduction to Systematic Prompting Procedures	Describe • Define "systematic prompting" • Define and describe system of least prompts, when it can be used, and how it differs from other prompting systems • Define other relevant vocabulary used when planning and implementing system of least prompts Rehearsal & Feedback • Multiple choice questions designed to check understanding of system of least prompts terminology • Preprogrammed feedback (correct/incorrect with explanations) Model • Video examples of system of least prompts instruction with AAC Rehearsal & Feedback • Multiple choice questions designed to check understanding of system of least prompts core components (i.e., what it is, when it can be used) • Preprogrammed feedback (correct/incorrect with explanations)

Part 2: Introduction to Planning	Describe
	• Introduction of Case Study 1 (written case study)
	Describe & Model
	• Introduction of planning acronym: SADD IDx3
	  o Select 3 prompts
	  o Arrange selected prompts in least to most order
	  o Determine cue
	  o Determine response interval
	  o ID communicator & communication partner responses (correct, incorrect, and no response) across the 3 levels of prompts
	• Describe each step of the planning process for Case Study 1 (separate videos for each planning step – describe step and model think aloud decision-making process)
	Rehearsal & Feedback
	• Multiple choice questions designed to check understanding of system of least prompts planning acronym
	• Preprogrammed feedback (correct/incorrect with explanations)

Figure 3–2. System of least prompts online training outline (McCoy & McNaughton, 2021). *continues*

	Guided Practice 1 & Feedback
	• Introduction of Case Study 2 (written case study)
	• Guided practice activity with highly scaffolded supports
	   o Provided beginning planning steps and communication partners were asked to identify the next step
	   o Preprogrammed feedback (correct/incorrect with explanations)
	Guided Practice 2 & Feedback
	• Introduction of Case Study 3 (written case study)
	• Guided practice activity with moderate scaffolded supports
	   o Communication partners were responsible for progressively building parts of their own plan
	   o Preprogrammed feedback (correct/incorrect with explanations)
	Independent Practice & Feedback
	• Introduction of Case Study 4 (written case study)
	• Independent practice activity without scaffolded supports
	   o Preprogrammed feedback (example plan and comparison activity)

Part 3: Introduction to Implementation	Describe & Model
	• Introduction of implementation acronym: DWR
	   o Deliver the cue
	   o Wait (determined response interval)
	   o Respond to the communicator
	• Describe each step of the implementation process for Case Study 1 (multiple example videos)
	Rehearsal & Feedback
	• Multiple choice questions designed to check understanding of implementation acronym and identify/describe implementation components in example videos
	   o Preprogrammed feedback (correct/incorrect with explanations)
	Guided Practice 1 & Feedback
	• Review Case Study 2
	• Guided practice activity with highly scaffolded supports
	   o Communication partners were given a sample plan and short implementation video clips
	   o Communication partners were asked to describe the implementation components observed
	   o Preprogrammed feedback (correct/incorrect with explanations)
	Guided Practice 2 & Feedback
	• Review Case Study 3
	• Guided practice activity with moderate scaffolded supports
	   o Communication partners were given possible implementation scenarios and asked to describe the related process
	   o Preprogrammed feedback (correct/incorrect with explanations; video examples of the implementation scenarios)
	Independent Practice
	• Review Case Study 4
	• Independent practice activity without scaffolded supports

Post-Test	Knowledge Quiz Planning Document Implementation Role Play (conducted as a synchronous online activity)
Note: Unless otherwise specified, all activities were conducted asynchronously	

Figure 3–2. *continued*

explanations and/or example videos were presented for the trainee to evaluate their own response.

Independent Practice. During this training component, the trainees assumed full responsibility for demonstrating the instructional strategy without scaffolding or other supports. In this context, it is important to note that the independent practice was still within a controlled environment, and the trainees were not yet attempting to use the new instructional strategy in natural environments. Figure 3–2 provides additional information regarding the comprehension checks, verbal rehearsal, guided practice, and independent practice incorporated into our online training.

Evaluation of Learning

In addition to the frequent rehearsal activities embedded in the online training as a formative assessment measure, summative assessments of knowledge and skills were also conducted. As illustrated in Figure 3–2, our summative assessments for teaching the use of the system of least prompts via online instruction included a three-part pre- and posttest (i.e., knowledge quiz, planning document, role-play implementation). The summative assessments involved trainees asynchronously completing a knowledge quiz and planning document for a novel case study (i.e., not included in the training module) and then engaging in an online synchronous session to role-play the use of the system of least prompts with a confederate (i.e., an adult who was trained to play the role of an individual who uses AAC).

Outcomes

The results of our case example suggest that the online training was effective, efficient, and socially valid. Specifically, there was an increase in trainee knowledge and skill in using the system of least prompts, with an overall group change from 49% to 85% (knowledge), 11% to 76% (planning), and 65% to 79% (implementation). Additionally, trainees rated the social validity of the online training at 4.25 on a 5-point Likert scale. Specific to the instructional strategies used, trainees liked the guided practice opportunities with multiple case studies (i.e., 4.53 out of 5.00), found the written text, video explanations, and video models effective in supporting learning (i.e., 4.22 out of 5.00), and thought the virtual role-plays were an important training element (i.e., 4.06 out of 5.00).

Discussion

Key successes in this case example were that the online instruction was effective and efficient and that the trainees felt they had learned a valuable skill that increased their confidence in working with individuals who use AAC. However, it is important to note that not all trainees had immediate access to an individual who used AAC. Therefore, advanced practice in natural environments was not included in this online training. This is a critical component in addressing knowledge/skill barriers and should be included to support generalization of the online training to natural environments and across communication goals. Further, it would be worthwhile to consider if individuals who use AAC could be brought into online advanced practice activities. For example, an individual who uses AAC may be able to engage in an online session in which the communication partner practices and receives immediate feedback on the implementation of the new instructional strategy.

Additionally, there are several considerations for replicating this case example with other professionals. Specifically, in our case example, trainees were provided one week to complete all portions of the online training and practice activities. Some individuals expressed that this was not enough time and did not complete parts of the training. To address time constraints, the amount of instructional content and the complexity of the practice activities should be carefully considered when developing an online training schedule. Furthermore, progression within the online training should depend on the completion of prior activities and/or a required minimum performance on comprehension checks. This could be accomplished by locking portions of the training module until key criteria are met (i.e., completion, accuracy). In addition, in our case, the online training was provided at no additional cost to the trainee (i.e., trainees were recruited from a university course). However, adult confederates were paid for the time spent conducting the role-play implementation conferences with the trainees. Small group role-plays (where trainees take turns serving as confederates) could be an effective alternative to reduce this cost.

A related "cost" consideration is the time demands associated with the online instruction for the trainees and the instructors. In our case example, trainees spent an average of 180 minutes engaged with the online training materials and approximately 75 minutes completing the assessments. We did not calculate the number of hours spent developing instructional materials. However, approximately five hours were spent planning, recording, and editing videos, and four hours were spent training adult confederates. When evaluating these estimates, it is important to note that time spent developing instructional materials is a variable component (i.e., training components that can be used in future training) rather than a fixed component (i.e., time that the trainer must invest every time the training is given). Initial development of a training will require more time and cost demands as both variable and fixed components will need to be developed. However, subsequent trainings will likely be able to utilize the same instructional text, example videos, practice activities, and embedded feedback, which greatly reduces these demands. Instructors could consider using already-made resources publicly available on the Internet to minimize the time and cost demands of initial training development. When doing so, instructors should carefully consider how these resources can be utilized within a strategy instruction framework (i.e., describe, model, guided practice, independent practice). For example, as discussed in Chapter 2, free, online assistive technology modules and webcasts are available from https://atinternetmodules. org/ and https://aac-learning-center.psu. edu/. Trainees could complete portions of these trainings as prerequisites (i.e., establish foundational knowledge) or as part of the online training, keeping in mind that structured learning opportunities that engage the trainee in knowledge and performance of the targeted AAC skill should still be developed.

Additional recommendations when developing an online training include considering synchronous versus asynchronous delivery. Specifically, portions of the online training (i.e., describe, model, guided practice) might be best delivered asynchronously, taking advantage of the full range of online training benefits (i.e., flexible and convenient access). Conversely, some elements of the training could also be delivered synchronously. For example, verbal rehearsal could be incorporated as an introduction/warm-up activity during the synchronous sessions. Additionally, to supplement the preprogrammed feedback within the guided practice activities, a synchronous session could contain additional opportunities to practice and receive individualized feedback.

Lastly, one important consideration is the motivation of trainees. As noted in Chapter 2, Kent-Walsh and McNaughton (2005) address this in Stage 1: Pretest & commitment to the instructional program and Stage 7: Posttest and commitment to long-term strategy use. In the current case, our trainees completed the online training as part of their university course enrollment. However, this is not likely the case for many trainees. Therefore, it is recommended that instructors initially engage trainees about their motivation for completing the training. Not only can this commitment help trainees persist in

completing all elements of the training, but it can also improve trainees' acquisition of the targeted skill (Kent-Walsh & McNaughton, 2005). Similarly, it is recommended that after the training is completed, trainees be provided an opportunity to reflect on the skills learned during the training and how this can positively impact individuals who use AAC (Kent-Walsh & McNaughton, 2005).

In summary, providing effective, efficient, and socially valid training is critically important in addressing knowledge/skill barriers. Although there can be challenges to developing a new online training (i.e., time/cost) and important considerations to ensure quality instruction (i.e., instructional strategy, development of practice opportunities/feedback), online instruction is a viable strategy for ensuring that preservice and in-service professionals receive training on instructional strategies that can support individuals who use AAC.

Case Example: Telepractice to Support Families (Adele F. Dimian, PhD and Jessica J. Simacek, PhD)

As former early intervention service providers who now work at a federally designated University Center for Excellence in Developmental Disabilities (UCEDD), our work includes a focus on using telepractice to support the families of young children with intellectual and developmental disabilities and complex communication needs. As discussed in

Chapter 2, telepractice involves the use of video conferencing or other technology to connect remotely to deliver services. We use telepractice to address barriers that many families face due to waitlists, lack of access to professionals with specialized knowledge, and geographic location. This case example, with Alitha and her family, illustrates how we used telepractice to address knowledge/skill barriers.

When Alitha was 18 months old, her parents spoke to their pediatrician about concerns regarding her lack of expressive language skills, tantrums, and repetitive behaviors. Alitha was ultimately diagnosed with autism spectrum disorder (ASD), and we met her when she was 28 months. At that time, Alitha was receiving early intervention services for two hours per week and had an individualized family service plan (IFSP) through her school district. Alitha's early intervention team had primarily focused on goal setting and teaching routines, and no one on the team specialized in AAC. Because of the family's concerns with Alitha's expressive language skills and her tantrums, Alitha was referred for in-home, community-based, early intensive behavioral intervention and speech-language services. However, there were no providers available to serve Alitha and she was placed on a waitlist. While Alitha and her family were waiting, we provided telepractice support for 12 weeks and engaged in communication assessment and intervention activities. The following section summarizes how we utilized telepractice as a tool to address knowledge/skill barriers, with a focus on how we design and implement telepractice sessions to teach AAC strategies to family members.

Strategies

Figure 3–3 provides a checklist that describes our process for using telepractice to support families of young children with disabilities. It is important to note that each component of this process may require more than one session. As illustrated by Figure 3–3, the initial step in our process is **telepractice onboarding**. For Alitha's family, onboarding involved talking via phone to discuss communication and scheduling preferences (e.g., days and times that worked well for the child and family, and the family's preferences regarding texting, emailing, or phone calls to remind them about their session meeting time and goals for that day), any cultural or linguistic needs or preferences, and their comfort level with technology. The phone conversation also included a discussion of the family's goals and Alitha's strengths and needs related to communication and functional skills. As a result of this conversation, it was discovered that the family's access to technology was limited. To support families with limited access to technology or bandwidth, we supply loaned equipment or Internet hotspots from a lending library. For Alitha's family, we mailed them loaned telepractice equipment (e.g., an external web camera and a laptop computer) with return shipping postage included. Other means of connection to support families can include coordination with a satellite location (e.g., a care provider's office) that has adequate technology for telepractice sessions.

After the onboarding is complete, the next step is a **videoconference practice session** (see Figure 3–3). The goal of the

Telepractice Process Overview

Telepractice onboarding

- [ ] Assess the families' comfort level with using video conferencing technology.
- [ ] Ask what type of devices the family uses, and if they have a device, if they can connect to the internet for video conferencing. Ask if their device has a web camera. Additional optional equipment may include a Bluetooth headset and external microphone if the child is reactive to hearing the coaching during the session or if it is difficult to hear or understand child vocalizations.
- [ ] If the family does not have the necessary technology (e.g., internet, device, web camera, a stand for their device), work with the team or other service providers such as case managers to provide technology and a Wi-Fi hotspot or internet connection.
- [ ] Schedule a practice videoconferencing session with the family.

Videoconference practice session

- [ ] Before the session, send an advanced organizer to the family, including detailed instructions for logging in to the video conferencing platform.
- [ ] Conduct a technology check.
    - [ ] Before connecting with the family, call them on the phone to help them log in.
    - [ ] Assist with downloading any software, updates, apps, or drivers the family needs to connect on the platform.
    - [ ] Help the family run a speed test to see if their internet connection will be sufficient.
    - [ ] Troubleshoot any audio, video, and internet problems (e.g., some devices require permission to use video or microphone).
    - [ ] Walk through how to use the video conferencing settings once connected. Show the family how to turn on and off their video and microphone to help maintain their privacy if something comes up during their session.
- [ ] Conduct an environmental safety check and set up the device.
    - [ ] Have the family take the device to where the sessions will be conducted to ensure there are no safety concerns (e.g., breakable items in reach, open staircases, unlocked doors they could elope through during the session).
    - [ ] Coach the family on where to set up their device so you can see both them and the child in the video frame.
- [ ] Conduct a free play session to build trust and rapport, ask the family to play with some preferred toys.
- [ ] Set a schedule for meeting with the family each week. Send a reminder and an advanced organizer for what you will be working on via email or text (ask caregiver preference) before each session.

Assessments and observation sessions

- [ ] Identify routines the family typically does every day with their child, and the skills that are important for the child to learn.
- [ ] Conduct baseline observations within identified routines (e.g., free play, snack time, taking turns with a preferred item or clean up, activities of daily living). Observe each routine or context for approximately 5–10 minutes.
- [ ] Identify communication goals and target behaviors, develop an intervention plan, and provide the family with AAC systems and materials (e.g., send electronic page sets or low-tech symbols).

Figure 3–3. Telepractice process overview. *continues*

Coaching sessions
☐ Present the session's goal (e.g., we will be focusing on requesting and taking turns with toys today).
☐ Model by having the same AAC materials as the family and physically showing them how to use the AAC system during coaching sessions.
☐ Provide coaching and give encouragement and feedback.
☐ Fade prompts as both family and child demonstrate mastery and troubleshoot any challenges.
☐ Reflect with the family about what went well and what strategies they can work on before their next session.
☐ End each session on a positive note.

Figure 3–3. *continued*

practice session is to ensure that the family knows how to log on to the videoconferencing platform, interact within the platform, and troubleshoot technology issues (i.e., sound, video, internet connectivity). During the practice session, an environmental scan is also completed to identify the best location(s) for conducting the sessions and ensure there are no safety issues present in those locations (e.g., an open staircase, breakable objects, etc.). The practice session also provides an opportunity to further refine goals and continue developing rapport.

As illustrated by Figure 3–3, **assessments and observation sessions** are conducted after the practice session. For Alitha and her family, we started by assessing routines using an approach called structured descriptive assessment (SDA; Anderson & Long, 2002). SDAs were originally developed with a focus on identifying potential contexts that relate to challenging behavior. Our team has used SDA via telepractice for this purpose, but also expanded its use to identifying contexts or routines in which a child may

use potentially communicative behavior (Simacek, Dimian, & McComas, 2017). In this specific case example, we observed Alitha and her family via telesupport during free play sessions that were approximately five minutes long. During free play sessions, preferred activities were available to Alitha without demands or restrictions (aside from ensuring safety). We also watched Alitha during daily routines (snack time, turn-taking with toys, clean-up time, activities of daily living) to observe her use of communicative behaviors. Further, because Alitha was engaging in challenging behaviors (e.g., tantrums and self-injury), we completed a functional behavior assessment (FBA) through a combination of parent interview and antecedent-behavior-consequence data collection during the SDA sessions.

When coaching families via telesupport, we encourage caregivers to respond to situations as they occur in the environment (e.g., take a break for a diaper change) and teach them how to turn off their camera and sound to maintain privacy. Further, for very active children who consistently move away from the camera frame, we identify and utilize preferred activities that involve less movement. Breaks are also encouraged throughout the sessions, and assessment/training opportunities within any given session are intentionally short.

An intervention plan is then developed with the family based on the assessments and observations. The development of the plan includes discussions with the family about (1) goals, (2) target behaviors, including the contextual fit of AAC modality and alternative responses (e.g., assessment of AAC modalities that meet the needs of the communicator and is feasible for them to use independently within their environment), (3) routines and contexts for intervention, and (4) instructional strategies. An important component of our model is that it is intended as a supplemental intervention. Therefore, the intervention plan is written to focus on initial, high-priority communication skills, not a comprehensive plan of skills. For Alitha and her family, the intervention plan involved using a low-tech AAC system (e.g., a communication board with picture symbols) that we sent to the family via mail. Further, we decided to focus on teaching the use of symbols representing "more," "break," and "my turn" during three routines; snack time, playtime, and during clean-up of toys (where she was prompted to clean up a preferred activity and transition to a different activity). To address Alitha's engagement in challenging behavior, we developed proactive, antecedent-based instructional strategies (e.g., using a timer to signal transitions) and implemented differential reinforcement of alternative behavior (i.e., AAC responses were reinforced with the functional reinforcer, and reinforcement for tantrum behavior was withheld).

Once developed, the intervention plan is implemented in the context of **coaching sessions** (see Figure 3–3). During coaching sessions, we support families as they learn to (a) create opportunities for communication (e.g., taking turns with a toy), (b) prompt the use of target behaviors and AAC via models and verbal/gestural/physical prompts, (c) reinforce new skills and behaviors, and (d) fade prompts as mastery and independence are demonstrated. In Alitha's case, we started by coaching her parents to prompt Alitha to point to symbols on her communication board. Once Alitha was consistently pointing to symbols when prompted, we coached her parents to use a time delay (e.g., wait 10 seconds before providing the prompt). Over the course of several sessions, we coached Alitha's family to develop additional knowledge/skills such as positioning the communication board within Alitha's reach on her dominant side, placing multiple communication boards around their house to increase ease of access, modeling the use of the AAC, and saying the written word on each symbol when Alitha selected it. Alitha's parents expressed interest in having her early education team trained in the AAC methods. Following signed permission from Alitha's parents, we provided Alitha's early intervention team with training on the intervention strategies used, allowed them to observe the coaching sessions conducted with the family, and provided access to a report generated for the family with the data on Alitha's communication use during participation.

Outcomes

As a result of our efforts to support Alitha and her family via telepractice, we successfully coached Alitha's parents to (a) teach their daughter to use a low-tech AAC system, and (b) prevent/respond to challenging behaviors. We met with Alitha and her family two to three times a week for 12 weeks, which would not have been possible in a face-to-face context given how far away they lived. Alitha acquired all three target AAC symbols within 12 weeks and independently used each symbol with multiple communication partners. Alitha's challenging behaviors decreased in frequency, length, and severity (although she continued to protest at times during transitions to new activities). Alitha also started to use symbols that had been modeled but not explicitly taught and generalized her use of AAC to new routines.

Alitha's family reported that they liked using videoconferencing and were comfortable doing sessions remotely. Further, they shared that the use of telepractice offered several benefits, including not having to travel or schedule childcare for Alitha's sibling. At times, sessions were difficult if Alitha had skipped a nap and was tired. In these instances, the team ended the sessions early. Another area of noted difficulty was coaching the parents to prompt and to fade prompts via telesupport. For untrained interventionists, such as caregivers, prompting and prompt fading may be easier to model in-person.

It is important to note that we only taught three initial communicative behaviors using AAC in order to address the challenging behavior immediately. This was only a starting place to introduce

AAC to Alitha and her family. The telesupport was intended to be supplemental to give Alitha's family skills and strategies that they could use while waiting for more comprehensive services, not a replacement for comprehensive support.

Discussion

This case example illustrates how we used telepractice to address knowledge/skill barriers experienced by the parents of a young child with disabilities. In this case, telepractice was particularly helpful in addressing challenges due to waitlists, limited provider expertise, and geographic barriers. Essential components of our telepractice process include onboarding, videoconference practice, assessments and observations, and coaching. Many families that we work with have indicated that, due to the coaching they received via telepractice, they have an increased sense of empowerment and confidence in supporting their child with disabilities. Further, in general, the families we work with rate telepractice sessions as highly effective and easy to implement. They also indicate that they like doing sessions via telepractice because it feels less intrusive compared to having providers come to their homes in person. Although our case example focused on providing support to a family, telesupport can also be used to address knowledge/skill barriers experienced by professionals and team members. For example, telepractice can be used to provide service providers with synchronous and asynchronous training and coaching while they are supporting individuals with complex communication needs in face-to-face contexts. In summary, telepractice can be an effective tool for breaking down knowledge/ skill barriers. Although there are challenges to implementation (e.g., technology access and support), these challenges can often be overcome.

References and Additional Resources

Ally, M. (2008). Foundations of educational theory for online learning. In T. Anderson (Ed.), *Theory & practice of online learning* (2nd ed., pp. 15–44). AU Press.

Anderson, C. M., & Long, E. S. (2002). Use of a structured descriptive assessment methodology to identify variables affecting problem behavior. *Journal of Applied Behavior Analysis, 35*, 137–154. https://doi .org/10.1901/jaba.2002.35-137

Dimian, A. F., Elmquist, M., Reichle, J., & Simacek, J. (2018). Teaching communicative responses with a speech-generating device via telehealth coaching. *Advances in Neurodevelopmental Disorders, 2*, 86–99. https://doi.org/10.1007/s41252-018-0055-7

Johnson, L. R. (2004). Research-based online course development for special education teacher preparation. *Teacher Education and Special Education, 27*, 207–223. https://doi .org/10.1177/088840640402700301

Kent-Walsh, J., & McNaughton, D. (2005). Communication partner instruction in AAC: Present practices and future directions. *Augmentative and Alternative Communication, 21*, 195–204. https://doi.org/10 .1080/07434610400006646

*McCoy, A., & McNaughton, D. (2021). Effects of online training on educators' knowledge and use of system of least prompts to support augmentative and alternative communication. *Journal of Behavioral Education, 30*, 319–349. https://doi.org/10.1007/ s10864-020-09374-6

Meyen, E. L., Lian, C. H. T., & Tangen, P. (1997). Developing online instruction: One model. *Focus on Autism and Other Developmental Disabilities, 12*, 159–165. https:// doi.org/10.1177/108835769701200304

Reichle, J., Simacek, J., Wattanawongwan, S., & Ganz, J. (2019). Implementing aided augmentative communication systems with persons having complex communicative needs. *Behavior Modification, 43*, 841–878. https://doi.org/10.1177/0145445519858272

Rush, D. D., & Shelden, M. L. (2020). *The early childhood coaching handbook*. Brookes.

Simacek, J., Dimian, A. F., & McComas, J. J. (2017). Communication intervention for young children with severe neurodevelopmental disabilities via telehealth. *Journal of Autism and Developmental Disorders, 47*, 744–767. https://doi.org/10.1007/s108 03-016-3006-z

Simacek, J., Wattanawongwan, S., Reichle, J., Hyppa-Martin, J., Pierson, L., & Dimian, A. F. (2021). Supporting aided augmentative and alternative communication interventions for individuals with complex communication needs via telepractice: A tutorial. *Perspectives of the ASHA Special Interest Groups, 6*, 1170–1181. https://doi .org/10.1044/2021_PERSP-21-00050

Snodgrass, M. R. (2016). *Supporting a school team in planning and implementing AAC for a child with intellectual disability* [Dissertation, University of Illinois at Urbana-Champaign]. Illinois Digital Environment for Access to Learning and Scholarship. http://hdl.handle.net/2142/93024

Snodgrass, M. R., & Meadan, H. (2018). A boy and his AAC team: Building instructional competence across team members. *Augmentative and Alternative Communication, 34*(3), 167–179. https://doi.org/10.1080/07 434618.2018.1491059

Stoner, J. B., Meadan, H., & Angell, M. (2013). A model for coaching parents to implement teaching strategies with their young children with language delay or developmental disabilities. *Perspectives on Language Learning and Education, 20*(3), 112–119. https://doi.org/10.1044/lle20.3.112

Wainer, A. L., & Ingersoll, B. R. (2013). Disseminating ASD interventions: A pilot study of a distance learning program for parents and professionals. *Journal of Autism and Developmental Disorders, 43,* 11–24.

NOTE: Electronic supplementary materials (e.g., knowledge assessments, datasheets, social validity questions and participant responses, sample instructional content, and practice activities) are also available as a free download from the publication website.

Section II

Understanding and Addressing Practice Barriers

Section Overview

AAC practice barriers involve common processes, rules, and methods used by professionals, organizations, schools, communities, and families during AAC assessment and implementation. Although these practices are not written as formal policies, they are typically accepted as the standard approach in a given context. For example, it may be clear that a particular method, process, or rule is a common practice when AAC team members use phrases such as "this is how we do it." Whereas some processes can facilitate AAC use and acceptance, other common practices can become barriers when the accepted approaches do not support successful AAC implementation. Examples of practices that may be seen in schools, private organizations, and medical settings include adopting one type of AAC system for all individuals, providing insubstantial time for professionals to work in teams, and developing unclear processes for supporting and communicating with families. Such practices can lead to barriers that limit (a) AAC individualization, (b) interprofessional collaboration, and (c) the ability to meet cultural and/or familial needs.

In this section readers will be able to:

- Describe the impact of practice barriers and facilitators on the lives of individuals who use AAC and their families.
- Summarize the research on practice barriers.
- Identify effective strategies for identifying and addressing practice barriers.

4 Practice Barriers: Learning From Individuals Who Use AAC and Their Families

Cindy Gevarter, Cassandra Medrano*, and Toña Rivera*

The following interviews demonstrate how the common practices of organizations, schools, individuals, companies, and families can either serve as facilitators or barriers to successful AAC implementation. Interviewees include an adult who relies on AAC and the parent of a child who relies on AAC.

Toña Rivera—Adult With Cerebral Palsy Who Uses AAC

In the first interview, Toña Rivera, a bilingual adult with cerebral palsy who has been using AAC since her childhood, details how positive outcomes occur when there are few practices limiting individualization and collaboration between professionals and families. However, Toña's story also highlights how the practices of companies creating AAC devices can limit the ability of AAC teams to select systems that meet an individual's unique needs. Additionally, Toña provides examples of how attitude and policy barriers can influence family practice barriers.

Will you introduce yourself including your name, age, gender, race/ethnicity? My name is Toña Rivera. I am 41 years old. I am a woman. I call myself Mexican-American. Spanish was my first language.

Can you share a little bit about who you are as a person, what you are doing in your life, and what you enjoy doing? I am a very strong, loving, and caring person. I am the Founder and Executive Director of an organization called Every Ability Plays Project. We purchase special playground equipment for children with disabilities for their neighborhood parks, homes, and schools. I am also teacher certified in DanceAbility®. I teach dance to people with all abilities. I enjoy spending time with my family and friends. I enjoy emailing, writing, being outside, and dancing on stage.

---

*These authors have contributed equally to this work and share senior authorship.

Can you share information about your use of AAC over the years and your current AAC system?

When I was in kindergarten, I used only a board that had pictures on it to talk with. I pointed to the pictures with my eyes, and someone had to guess what I was saying. That was very difficult. Two years later I got a LightTalker (Prentke Romich Company). I liked it because it was easier to talk with. I liked programming things into it that I wanted to say. I liked using the icons. When I was in eighth grade, I got a laptop. When I was in high school, I had a talking device, called a Freestyle (Assistive Technology Inc.). I did not like using the Freestyle because it was too slow. It did not have a word list, so I had to type, letter-by-letter. In 2004, my speech therapist applied to Medicaid to get me a Mercury (Tobii). I really liked using this device better than the other ones I had, because I talked with it and at the same time, I could use it like a computer. I used two programs to communicate. One was called Word-Power™, and the other was called Talk Boards (Mayer Johnson). I really liked the pop-up answers and questions. In 2013, I got a Dynavox device. I really liked it because I could program each button by myself. What I didn't like about that Dynavox was that it had a cross-scanner mouse, so it was difficult for me to use the computer part of it. In 2019, I got the Dynavox i-110 that I'm using now. I really love it because I have a mouse that I can use easily. I use two programs to talk. To give my speeches, and to store my stories, I use a program called Communicator 5 (Dynavox). To talk with my friends in-person and to email, I use WordPower™. I really like using these programs. The only thing I don't like about this Dynavox is that I cannot program each button by myself now, and I really miss my independence to do that. Each time that I need a button programmed, I need to call on my speech therapist.

Can you tell me about any experiences that you have had where practices of professionals or organizations led to one-size-fits-all approaches to AAC?

Through all my communication devices, my speech therapists have programmed them in the way I can use them, with scanning, which meets my needs. My speech therapists have gotten to know my mind which has been very helpful to me. I think the only hard experience was in high school with the Freestyle, which was really slow, because I had to type letter by letter. I think if I had a better AAC system, I could have been involved in high school activities instead of being embarrassed by the fact that I couldn't express myself in the way I would have liked. In 11th grade, I took an Internet class at the Career Enrichment Center. I was finally in a class with students who didn't have disabilities. I felt like my lack of communication kept me from wanting to go up to them and start talking with them.

I also use an ASL (Adaptive Switch Laboratories) head rest to drive my wheelchair. I should be able to use my head rest to use my computers. Instead, I use a Specs switch (AbleNet) that is wrapped around one of the wings of my head rest. I like how my Specs switch clicks when I use it. My head rest doesn't click when I use it on my computers. I consider this a barrier because I think I would be more independent if I could use my headrest for my Dynavox especially when I am out in the community.

> "My speech therapists have gotten to know my mind which has been very helpful to me."

Can you tell me about any positive or negative experiences related to professionals on your AAC team effectively collaborating with each other to meet your needs?

As long as I have had a Dynavox device, my speech therapists have worked very closely with the Dynavox representative. All through my school years, my speech therapists would teach my helpers how to use my computers.

Can you tell me about any positive or negative experiences you've had with professionals working with you and your family to meet cultural or familial needs?

All of my experiences and my family's experiences with my speech therapists and the Dynavox representatives have been very good ones. One concern is that I just recently got my first bilingual device. I couldn't fully express myself to my dad the 33 years I had him with me because he spoke only Spanish. When I had something very important to tell him (my dad), he would do his very best to read what I was writing in English. I could use my communication device with one of my dad's sisters because her girls would translate. In 2016, when my great aunt and cousin came, Omar (my cousin) got

a little impatient with me when I tried to talk with him even though I tried using an online translation program.

> "One concern is that I just recently got my first bilingual device. I couldn't express myself to my dad all of the 33 years I had him with me because he spoke only Spanish."

Are there any equity issues you want to bring up connected to practice barriers?

My parents would take my sister and me to Mexico up to [when] I was 23. They took me for the first time when I was three years old. My mom never took any of my communication devices [to Mexico] as she was scared they would have been stolen. I think I was very blessed in that both sides of my family saw my parents' leadership in terms of how to communicate with me. I think that was my base. Some of my aunts and all of my cousins could communicate with me as if I had a device. The only time I really wished I had my talking device in Mexico was when my cousin told me that she wanted to become a nun. Her words to me were "Toña, guess who I am going to marry. He is with us in this room." At that moment, I just wanted to congratulate her, and ask questions. She is our first cousin who entered the religious life, so I really looked up to her.

What do you think people (e.g., speech-language pathologists, people who use AAC, teachers, family members) need to know or do to overcome practice barriers like those mentioned?

When I get asked this question by the students who are going into the field of speech-language pathology, I always tell them to study the people who they are going to work with. That is so important, as each individual has different skills.

In the summer of 2016, it was the first time for my great aunt and cousin Omar (who is a priest) to visit us from Mexico. That Tuesday, we went to the mall to eat. As we were eating, I noticed a couple who had a young boy who was in a wheelchair. I saw he had a round neck pillow and that he had to be tube fed. After we were done eating, my mom told me to go ahead of them and find Erin, my sister's friend, so that we could introduce Tia Chole (my aunt) and Omar (my cousin) to her. As I was going, I saw this family ahead of me and they kept looking at my power wheelchair. I stopped and waited for my family to catch up to me. The other family stopped to talk to us. This family also spoke Spanish. My mom understood right away that this young boy in the wheelchair could understand everything, but unfortunately, the mom said her son couldn't understand anything. I got a little sad about that and I took Omar's hand at that point. At the end, we got close to the boy and Omar gave him a blessing.

I know another mom who really thinks that her son has the ability to go to college. In reality, he may not have that ability. I met him when he was 6 years old. Now, he is a young man. Ever since he was little, this mom gave all of the teachers a very difficult time thinking they weren't doing a good job teaching her son. That is why the therapists wanted me to meet this family. A few years after I started my Every Ability Plays Project, I started getting to know an OT (occupational therapist). One day, she told me about a young man who wanted an accessible treehouse with an adaptive swing attached. I told her I would love to work with this young man. When she told me his name, I knew it was this same boy who I met years ago. The OT tried to get me to meet the family, but it never happened. A year later, my speech therapist told me that she would like me to volunteer at the school where this little guy was going, so I could work with him using his communication device. When I would talk to him about the treehouse, his eyes would get so big and bright. I think I went three times to work with him. On the day his mom found out that I was going every Monday to work with him, she told me she didn't want me to go at all. She said since it was the last year of him being in the public schools, she just wanted him to work on reading and math. That made me sad. Especially for parents reading this book, my advice to you is to get to know your child very well, please accept their skills; I assure you that they will lead a very happy life being a part of the disability community.

What do you see as the role of technology for improving outcomes related to practice barriers?

I think technology is already improving for AAC users. However, when I got the talking program called Communicator 5, it only had keywords that covered the whole screen, so I couldn't use any of them. The Dynavox representative had to let me transfer Tiny Scan from Communicator 4. The makers of the special computer programs have to realize that people with disabilities have different abilities.

Figure 4–1. Toña at an inclusive playground with equipment funded by Every Ability Plays Project.

Key Points from Toña's Interview

Toña's story provides evidence that AAC teams can implement practices that facilitate successful AAC system use throughout child and adulthood. For instance, Toña indicated that throughout her childhood, her speech-language pathologists (SLPs) collaborated with school staff, AAC representatives, and her family. Additionally, she notes that her SLPs used individualized approaches (i.e., getting to know her mind) to select AAC systems that best meet her unique needs. Toña did, however, also discuss practice barriers she has encountered or witnessed. First, Toña noted that it was common practice for her mother to not bring her

AAC devices on family trips to Mexico. For many families, the use of similar practices may be impacted by policy barriers (i.e., limited or no insurance coverage for lost or stolen devices). Luckily, in Toña's case, other family practices (e.g., her parents modeling how to communicate with her in other ways) helped alleviate this barrier. Although not her direct experience, Toña also cited examples of how, in other cases, she has seen attitude barriers lead to family practices that limit a child's inclusion and access to the disability community. Other barriers Toña faced directly relate to the practices of companies that design AAC systems. For instance, it has only recently become common practice for AAC systems to include multilingual vocabulary options. Due to this barrier,

Toña was unable to independently communicate in Spanish with several family members for years. Additionally, even though Toña describes improvements in AAC system design, she notes that some systems are limited in their options for customizing access methods and facilitating the ability of the person who relies on AAC to program their own vocabulary.

For more information about Toña Rivera and to see some videos of her using various AAC systems you can visit her YouTube channel at tonyaeapp or visit her personal website (http://tonyarivera5 .yolasite.com). Go to http://everyability playsproject.org for information about the Every Ability Plays Project.

Cassandra Medrano—Parent of a Child Who Uses AAC

Whereas Toña's experience indicated few school-related barriers, the following interview with Cassandra Medrano details numerous practice barriers that can occur in school settings. Cassandra specifically describes barriers she has encountered while advocating for the needs of her son with autism, who relies on AAC. Her story highlights how knowledge, attitude, and practice barriers can influence one another. Importantly, Cassandra's case also brings intersectional considerations regarding disability and culture to the forefront.

Will you introduce yourself including your name, age, gender, race/ethnicity?
My name is Cassandra Medrano. I am 49 years old. I'm African American.

Can you also tell us the name, age, gender, race/ethnicity, and diagnosis of your son who uses AAC?
I have a son, Andrew. He is 12 years old and biracial (African American and white). He is diagnosed with autism spectrum disorder. He's nonverbal and he has [challenging] behaviors. With therapy, he's been able to regulate. He has some auditory processing issues and has been diagnosed in school with intellectual development disorder.

Can you share a little bit about who you are as a person, what you are doing in your life, and what you enjoy doing?
I'm a native Texan, born and raised in Austin, Texas. I'm an identical twin and I ended up having two sets of twins, so Andrew has a twin brother and twin older brothers. I enjoy running. I've run over 36 marathons now. I've been a marathon running coach for over 15 years so that's my passion. I also like arts and crafts and I've been working with the State of Texas government for over 20 years. I love photography and being outdoors. And then Andrew, the love of my life!

Can also share a bit about who your son is as a person, what he enjoys?
Andrew enjoys being outdoors as well, and he is a lovable child. He loves going to the movies, going to see Santa at Christmas time, and going to the mall. We get popcorn at the movies, which is his favorite. He enjoys the park, and loves being active and spending time with his twin brother and his family and friends. He loves school, believe it or not, and loves riding the bus! He enjoys when people around him are enjoying living life—he feeds off that! Being taught to commu-

nicate with this iPad also makes his life much more enjoyable.

Can you share information about your son's use of AAC over the years and his current AAC system?

So, when he was first diagnosed [with autism] he was like a year and a half old, and they started him out with sign language. That was okay, and he was learning sign, but if people in the environment that he was in weren't prepared to answer him in sign, he grew increasingly frustrated and that caused a lot of behaviors. So, around the age of five, we started with an AAC device, the iPad with Proloquo2Go, and that's changed our life tremendously. It's quick and he has the option to search for words. He also has the option to have the main core home board. He started with two to four icons and now he's up to like 30 or 48 on a page and he can navigate through the pages. It's worked wonders. He enjoys it and his behaviors have gone down since using the iPad.

Can you tell me about any experiences that you have had where practices of professionals or organizations led to one-size-fits-all approaches to AAC?

So, in the very beginning when he was 5, it was magical. We got his iPad through the charity organization Zach's Voice. And then we had a private speech therapist who knew how to use it and taught me how to navigate the iPad. And we had an ABA (Applied Behavior Analysis) therapist who assisted on that as well. But, the first practice barrier is that after we got his iPad, the school didn't want to use it. They just included it in his IEP (Individualized Education Plan) last year for the first time. So that's five years lost of not having it included.

> "The first practice barrier is that after we got his iPad, the school didn't want to use it. They just included it in his IEP (Individualized Education Plan) last year for the first time. So that's five years lost of not having it included."

With remote learning [during the Covid-19 pandemic] I got to see what they were doing and how they dismissed actually teaching the use of the iPad. They just said things like "tell me what the right answer is?" but they weren't teaching him how to go through the process by using reminders like "Andrew get your iPad, go to the numbers, and tell me which number is correct." I had to go through a full training process of how to get them educated and trained on how to communicate with Andrew and how to use the iPad.

Now he's back in school and they stopped using the iPad again. I went to the school to confront them about that, and they said they use PECS (Picture Exchange Communication System) cards. I said that's why he's having [challenging] behaviors. He's more advanced than the PECS cards. With the PECS, they have like 10 to 20 cards, and what he wants is not always there. I told them he knows how to search, he knows how to use this home button, and he knows how to navigate to school folders, sensory activity folders, everything! And I know he wants to tell me, "Mama they're not advanced, I'm advanced." So, that's the frustrating part because now we're starting to see increasing behaviors at school. I was so happy because I could see he thrived during the pandemic [with remote learning]. He was able to communicate via his iPad, he saw all the kids lined up in Zoom, and he imitated their behaviors. And his speech and his skills on the actual computer keyboard improved.

No one's ever explained to me why they won't use the iPad. I don't know if they just don't want to do it because it takes a lot of work. What they saw during remote learning is that it takes a lot of commitment to sit there and be patient for him to type out a word or answer a question. If you ask him a question, you have to follow through to get the answer. Sometimes, he's quick, but you probably have to use some time management on the teacher's end to complete lessons.

Can you tell me about any positive or negative experiences related to professionals on your son's team effectively collaborating with each other to meet his communication needs related to his device use?

We've had some good experiences with private therapies. The private therapists did collaborate. When I asked, "can you get with the school?" or, "can you email his school?" they almost always did. But it was the school interacting with them that there was a problem. He has a speech therapist in school, she uses the iPad so she's trying to incorporate training with the teachers. But, to my knowledge, they're saying they're busy or they don't have time. And I know it's tough. The pandemic has caused all kinds of strain and there's a teacher shortage. Special education services are under the microscope because they're looking at why it is failing, why evaluations have backed up, why special educators are quitting on a daily basis. So, I know there are limitations, but you still can't ignore the communication and collaboration.

> "He has a speech therapist in school, she uses the iPad so she's trying to incorporate training with the teachers. But, to my knowledge, they're saying they're busy or they don't have time."

Can you tell me about any positive or negative experiences you've had with professionals on your son's team working with you and your family to meet cultural or familial needs?

Yes, every day. I know the school staff are busy, but they need to make time to work with me and include me in meetings. I can help, like I did remotely. The school could touch base with me on cultural differences. Andrew is used to our culture, the way we speak, the way we interact with each other. We're a family where we hug each other, we support each other like other families. But of course, being African American, I teach my sons about black history and black leaders in our community. I also teach them about some of the challenges we have as African Americans. For example, I teach him that sometimes we are second guessed, that our voices are not seen as being as strong as other people's, and we are sometimes treated differently. So, I'm trying to explain that to Andrew in a way that he understands. And I'm trying to communicate with the school that it is important to let him know there are racial disparities, there is racism. But they shy away from that topic.

> "The school could touch base with me on cultural differences. Andrew is used to our culture, the way we speak, the way we interact with each other."

Andrew is big. He is almost 5′11″, African American, and he has an afro. So I have to teach him about safety at school, and police officers, and how to behave when approached by an officer. Trying to explain that to the school, they said that's not important. I said no, I'm teaching these things to Andrew because, if he has a meltdown at school, he could possibly be restrained by a police officer, handcuffed. They don't understand that racial part of it that I'm concerned about. So that's what I'm teaching him. I teach him on his iPad that there are differences in people—no one looks just like Andrew. I teach him about differences in race, culture, and backgrounds.

Are there any other equity issues you want to bring up connected to practice barriers?

I don't like thinking like this, but I can't help but think that race has something to do with why my voice is not listened to, even if I ask for something that's ordinary, like using the iPad at school. African American students are less than 1% of the population at my son's school. That means there's only probably 20 to 30 kids in the school that are African American. I wonder, if I was another parent of a different race, if it [not using the iPad] would be addressed sooner. I have to send 20 to 30 emails, and I know they're busy, but Andrew needs advantages in school. This

is a key moment of his life, where we're trying to teach independence and I just can't get anywhere, I can't get answers. I even had to take it up with the superintendent. I have gotten responses from people outside the school that they will look into it, so they're responding, but I still don't have any answers.

I don't know why African Americans, or minorities, or people with economic disadvantages get low priority when it comes to services. I wonder where Andrew would be at this time—he might be talking. I mean, maybe it would only be a few words, but we'd be a lot further along than we are now if I had the resources or financial means, or if I had high credentials, like I was a doctor or a lawyer. If you are African American, you get priority if you are more educated and wealthier—you are respected instantly. Seeing how I don't have all those accolades or those credentials behind my name, I have to prove that I'm worthy of my son being taught. That's through talking and giving them my history—how long I've been in Austin, that I am a member of the community, and a taxpayer. I have to basically wear my resume on my back. I'm a mom who loves my children. And so, I say please provide me with equal services, but it's just not happening. With private services, when you're paying out of pocket, you're getting the services. You have to shop around, but you are going to get the services if you're paying, or if insurance covers it. But with the school, it's still a tug-of-war with the IEP and to fight for services.

> "I'm a mom who loves my children. And so, I say please provide me with equal services, but it's just not happening."

What do you think people (e.g., speech-language pathologists, AAC users, teachers, family members) need to know or do to overcome practice barriers like those mentioned?

Practices should include a solid plan for meeting a child's needs. Especially for nonverbal kids, but also kids on the spectrum or any kid needing speech. There needs to be a solid plan, even if it's a week or a month—start small. And there has to be communication and collaboration about whether that plan is going okay, check-in points, so we can say "oh let's change the plan, because this is not working." Sometimes that doesn't happen in school or with private services, so then you lose weeks. You also have to make it a practice to learn about families— learn about their cultural differences, learn about their triggers. Sometimes parents have trust issues with the system because of something they've faced. Everybody's experienced trauma, like racial or financial trauma, or even like the pandemic has caused a type of social trauma. If someone's coming to you and being honest saying, "look I want you to know I want my child to excel, but there's a problem," you need to listen to that because they're telling you their true experience—what they're up against. To be fully inclusive, you may need to gain trust, because once someone's comfortable with services and they believe that their child is going to be taken care of, that makes the process go so much smoother.

> "There needs to be a solid plan, even if it's a week or a month—start small. And there has to be communication and collaboration about whether that plan is going okay, check-in points, so we can say 'oh let's change the plan, because this is not working.'"

What do you see as the role of technology for improving outcomes related to practice barriers?

I think that the technology is working and it's here, so the technology needs to be utilized. You know, we don't have to reinvent the wheel, the technology is already there so let's make it a practice to use the technology we have that's in place. I mean Proloquo2Go for us has been a life changer and Proloquo updates have been even better. They update all the time, but we just have to use it, be educated, trained on it. And that needs to be across the board on all levels I talked about. You would be amazed how many people I've talked to that don't know about AAC technology like Proloquo on the iPad. The technology is there. We just need to bring awareness to the technology, make it a practice to use it on a more frequent basis as a form of language.

> "The technology is there. We just need to bring awareness to the technology, make it a practice to use it on a more frequent basis as a form of language."

How do you see practice barriers being overcome and what do you envision for future AAC users?

I'm a big advocate for AAC devices, and so I envision that it is not going to be a foreign concept to see people communicating with devices—it's not going to be frowned upon. Once the use of AAC becomes a common practice, it's going to be accepted everywhere and there's not going to be a stigma that it can't be done or it's hard, or it's impossible. I envision the iPad and the communication devices are going to be more mainstream. You're going to see them at the mall and at the movie theater. And people on the spectrum will have it in their IEP in school as a resource. But then it won't stop at 18. They're still going to be able to communicate with their device past elementary, junior high, and high school. It's going to be a language, a utilized device and language that's going to be accepted. It should be widely part of awareness education that this has been around, it can be used, and it's helpful.

Key Points From Cassandra's Interview

Cassandra described several school-based practice barriers. First, the school failed to meet Andrew's individual needs when, for several years, they did not include his iPad-based AAC system in his IEP, despite the fact that he had been using the device successfully with private therapists and at home. Even after the device was added to his IEP, his needs continued to be unmet as his classroom teachers and staff opted to use alternative AAC options (e.g., PECS). Although it is unclear why teachers and other school staff made these practice decisions, attitude and knowledge barriers may have impacted practice. For instance, negative assumptions about the abilities of children with autism (especially those with challenging behaviors) to use high-tech systems may have impacted decision-making. Alternatively, if teachers and school staff had limited knowledge of technology or how to use Andrew's AAC system, this might have influenced the adoption of a one-size-fits-all low-tech approach. Unfortunately, in Andrew's case, additional school practices limiting interprofessional collaboration may have prevented these barriers from being addressed. More specifically, Cassandra noted that time and staffing limitations have hindered the school SLP's ability to

Figure 4–2. Andrew using his AAC device.

provide AAC device training to classroom staff. While Cassandra advocated for AAC device use and staff training, she faced additional barriers related to the school's lack of a clear process for parent communication and collaboration. Intersectional considerations regarding how AAC teams interact with families of children who rely on AAC who are culturally or linguistically diverse are also highlighted in this case. The fact that culturally relevant practices have not been regularly incorporated into Andrew's AAC plans led to additional barriers to meeting cultural and familial needs.

Conclusion

Together, Toña and Cassandra's experiences provide examples of how the prac-

tices of schools, SLPs, private practice clinicians, families, and AAC companies can serve as either facilitators or barriers to successful AAC implementation. Toña and Cassandra's stories also both highlight the importance of gaining client and family perspectives. Although these interviews provide personal case examples, several practice barriers discussed (e.g., limited time for interprofessional collaboration) may be common across schools and other settings. However, practice barriers may also look different across other contexts (e.g., hospitals) or populations (e.g., adults with acquired disorders). Additional examples of practice barriers that promote one size fit all approaches, limit interprofessional collaboration, and prevent cultural and familial needs from being met will be discussed in the chapters that follow.

5 Practice Barriers: Exploring the Evidence Base

Cindy Gevarter

As evidenced from the preceding interviews, the practices of organizations, schools, communities, professionals, and families can either limit or promote effective AAC selection and implementation. Commonly accepted practices (e.g., methods, approaches, rules) that have the potential to restrict or prevent successful AAC adoption, are referred to as practice barriers. To address these barriers, AAC teams must first identify limiting practices. For instance, if a team is not consistently conducting comprehensive assessments, prior to brainstorming solutions, a team must determine what practices (e.g., a school providing limited time to conduct evaluations or not providing access to AAC specialists) are creating barriers. Although practice barriers can impact many elements of AAC service delivery, in this chapter we highlight practices that limit (a) AAC system individualization, (b) interprofessional collaboration, and (c) the ability to meet cultural and/or familial needs. Each of these areas will be broken down to identify specific limiting practices and alternative approaches that can promote effective AAC service delivery. Throughout this chapter, tables will also provide links to examples of AAC resources that can be used to address practice barriers.

Practices That Limit AAC individualization

Given the varying developmental, cognitive, linguistic, motor, and social abilities of individuals with complex communication needs, there is a wide range of AAC systems (Beukelman & Light, 2020). AAC includes unaided options, low-tech aided systems, and high-tech electronic aided systems. Although it is important to aim toward a precision approach to AAC that emphasizes the individualization of systems, decisions, and interventions, such personalization requires time, expertise, resources, and collaboration (Light, McNaughton, et al., 2019). In real-world contexts, when practice barriers limit such facilitating supports, teams may adopt one-size-fits-all approaches in which AAC decisions are not based on individual needs. The failure to individualize AAC can be impacted by practices that limit a team's ability to (a) conduct comprehensive assessments, (b) select high-tech systems with appropriate features, and (c) customize AAC systems.

> **Unaided modes of communication,** such as signs or gestures do not require access to materials external to one's body. **Aided modes of communication** include external low-tech aids and materials (e.g., picture exchange books and communication boards) as well as electronic high-tech devices such as dedicated **speech generating devices (SGDs)** and mobile technology devices with AAC applications.

Breaking Down the Barrier: Identifying Practices That Limit Comprehensive AAC Assessments

In addition to identifying opportunity barriers and supports, key components of the Participation Model for AAC include conducting comprehensive assessments of (a) communication and participation patterns and (b) capabilities and access barriers (Beukelman & Light, 2020). Unfortunately, organizations often do not adopt practices that support comprehensive AAC assessments (Andzik et al., 2019; Gormley & Light, 2019). For instance, in hospitals, limited time with patients, busy schedules, and a lack of resources impact assessments (Gormley & Light, 2019; Gormley & Fager, 2021). Furthermore, although it is recommended that speech-language pathologists (SLPs) with AAC expertise lead assessments, access to specialists varies across settings and geographical regions (Binger et al., 2012; Sanders et al., 2021). In schools, when specialists are available (often via district-wide assistive technology teams) they are frequently given inadequate time to conduct evaluations, observe students, and build rapport (Dodd et al., 2015; Theodorou & Pampoulou, 2020). Lengthy wait times for evaluations or difficulty scheduling with specialists can also lead to teams delaying the adoption of any form of AAC in both school and hospital settings (Chung & Stoner, 2016; Gormley & Light, 2019). Although general practice SLPs can coordinate AAC assessments, generalists may need additional time to prepare for evaluations or require consultative support (Binger et al., 2012). Unfortunately, additional time and support may not be commonly provided. In school contexts, it may also be common practice for special education teachers to be assigned the primary responsibility of identifying appropriate AAC systems (Andzik et al., 2019). This may be due to schools not having any SLPs on staff, high turnover of clinicians, or only having access to SLPs with limited AAC knowledge (Andzik et al., 2019). Even though special education teachers are often highly knowledgeable about individual student needs, and many have AAC experience, they must possess additional expertise to lead a comprehensive AAC assessment (Binger et al., 2012).

Breaking Down the Barrier: Practices That Promote Comprehensive Assessment

Ideally, when an organization does not have an AAC specialist on staff, team members should make a referral or seek consultation (Binger et al., 2012). One resource for finding specialists is the American Speech-Language Hearing Association's (ASHA) ProFind website, which allows users to search for SLPs by location and areas of specialty (Table 5–1). Some state-level assistive technology programs funded by the Assistive Technology Act of 2004 also accept referrals or provide lists of providers who conduct evaluations. Additionally, one of the positive outcomes of the COVID-19 pandemic is that more feasible and accessible telehealth options for AAC evaluation and consultation have been developed (Russell et al., 2020). Finally, although clinicians working at AAC companies should not take the lead in evaluations, if consultation with or referral to independent specialists is not possible, AAC vendors can provide consultative services to support SLPs in completing assessments (Binger et al., 2012).

Even when AAC specialists are available, there is a need to build capacity for collaborative assessment approaches. A team approach can counteract specialists' restricted time to conduct assessments (Binger et al., 2012; Dodd et al., 2015). By actively seeking the input of team members across disciplines, critical system features related to different areas of need can be identified (Beukelman & Light, 2020). Team members might also take more ownership of decisions and recognize challenges with one-size-fits-all options. Teams must, however, consider efficient and streamlined assessment processes (Ogletree et al., 2018). In school settings, the SETT Framework (Student, Environments, Tasks, and Tools) can be used to collect and organize team member input during assessment (Zabala, 2020). AAC specialists and companies have also created free or low-cost assessment checklists, protocols, and data forms to aid in efficient team-based assessment (Table 5–1 provides examples). Additionally, AAC team members can utilize commonly available assessment tools that do not require extensive training or time to complete. Such tools allow team members to collect information that can (a) be used as part of the comprehensive evaluation or (b) inform initial communication goals and intervention when there are delays to a full evaluation. Several of these tools are freely available. For instance, the Aphasia Needs Assessment allows communicators or partners to describe communication contexts, strategies, and challenges for adults with acquired disorders (Garrett & Beukleman, 2006). Further, the Communication Matrix is a frequently used tool for evaluating an individual's current communication forms (e.g., vocal speech, unaided and aided AAC modalities) and functions (e.g., request, reject, comment) that can be completed by a variety of AAC team members (Rowland, 2011). A free online version is available for family members or others who do not need to complete multiple assessments. Another free, brief assessment is the Dynamic AAC Goals Grid 2 or DAGG-2

Table 5–1. Resources for Practices That Limit AAC Individualization

Limiting Practices	Positive Practices	Resources
Limited time, resources, personnel, or support to conduct **comprehensive AAC assessments**	Consult with AAC specialists and state assistive technology programs.	**ASHA tool for locating SLPs** • https://www.asha.org/profind/ **State Assistive Technology Program Finder** • https://www.at3center.net/stateprogram
	Use team-based models, assessment checklists, and data gathering tools.	**Understanding AAC assessment team roles** • Binger et al. (2012) https://doi.org/10.3109/07434618.2012.716079 **SETT Framework resources** • https://www.joyzabala.com/ **Communication Supports Inventory- Children & Youth (CSI-CY)** • http://www.icfcy.org/aac **AAC assessment checklists and data gathering resources** • https://saltillo.com/uploads/AAC_Evaluation_Data_Gathering_Worksheet7.17.19.pdf • https://my.vanderbilt.edu/specialeducationinduction/files/2011/09/IA.AAC-assessment-checklist1.docx • https://coe.uoregon.edu/cds/files/2016/09/ADULT-AAC-Eval-Protocol.docx
	Utilize easy-to-implement assessments for initial information gathering.	**Aphasia Needs Assessment** • https://cehs.unl.edu/documents/secd/aac/assessment/aphasianeeds.pdf **Pre-assessment for adults with acquired disorders** • http://www.vantatenhove.com/files/papers/Assessment/PreAssessmentAdultAcquired.doc **Communication Matrix** • https://www.communicationmatrix.org/ **DAGG-2** • http://tdvox.web-downloads.s3.amazonaws.com/MyTobiiDynavox/dagg%202%20-%20writable.pdf

Limiting Practices	Positive Practices	Resources
Limited time, resources, personnel, or support to **select and fund high-tech AAC systems with features matched to communicator needs**	Seek support from AAC companies and state assistive technology programs.	**List of AAC companies** • https://www.atia.org/about-atia/membership-directory/ **State Assistive Technology Program Finder** • https://www.at3center.net/stateprogram **Other sources of funding** • https://www.aacfunding.com/alt-funding-sources **Funding evaluation samples and templates** • https://www.aacfunding.com/templates-samples
	Use feature matching charts, dynamic assessment, and device trials to conduct continuous assessment of device needs.	**Feature matching resources** • https://www.childrenshospital.org/centers-and-services/programs/a-_-e/augmentative-communication-program/downloads • https://talcaac.com/SGD%20Features%20Checklist.pdf • https://coe.uoregon.edu/cds/files/2016/09/FeatureMatchComparisonChart.pdf **Articles describing AAC dynamic assessment** • Binger et al, (2017) https://doi.org/10.1044/2017_JSLHR-L-15-0269 • Gevarter et al. (2020) https://doi.org/10.1080/07434618.2020.1845236 **Device trial data sheets** • https://ksha.org/docs/AAC_assessment_4.pdf • https://www.prentrom.com/assets/uploads/SGD-Device-Trial-Data-Collection-Sheet.pdf
	Work with AAC finders to promote early referral.	**AAC finder checklist** • https://www.assistiveware.com/learn-aac/finding-aac-for-those-who-need-it

Table 5–1. *continued*

Limiting Practices	Positive Practices	Resources
Limited time, resources, personnel, or support to **customize AAC systems**	Utilize efficient vocabulary assessments to gain stakeholder input.	**Preschool vocabulary assessment** • https://aackids.psu.edu/_userfiles/file/VocabularySelection/index.pdf **School-age vocabulary assessment** • https://www.dropbox.com/s/fpudr0dh0wg6qtn/Vocabulary%20Questionnaire.doc **Adult Interests Checklist:** • https://devices.aphasia.com/hubfs/Downloadable_Content/InterestInventory_Feb2021.pdf
	Involve person who relies on AAC in customization process	**Strategies for involving clients in customization** • https://praacticalaac.org/praactical/thoughts-on-involving-our-clients-in-aac-vocabulary-selection/ **Talking Mats free resources** • https://www.talkingmats.com/research/free-resources/ **Steps for using just-in-time programming with beginning communicators** • Holyfield et al. (2019) https://doi.org/10.1080/17549507.2018.1441440
	Utilize customization resources provided by AAC companies	**Example customization resources from different AAC companies** • https://www.assistiveware.com/support/proloquo2go/overview • https://www.tobiidynavox.com/pages/product-support-devices • https://touchchatapp.com/accessories/chat-editor • https://www.aphasia.com/training-and-support/

(Tobii Dynavox, 2015). The DAGG-2 allows practitioners to determine communication levels across a range of skills and select goals across modalities and communicative competencies (e.g., linguistic, operational, social).

Breaking Down the Barrier: Identifying Practices That Limit Use of Feature Matched High-Tech Systems

Although barriers to conducting comprehensive assessments can impact the adoption and individualization of any form of AAC, there are unique practice barriers that directly impact the use of high-tech systems. In hospital settings, the use of unaided and low-tech systems may be common practice because these systems are readily accessible and easy to introduce to patients and families with limited time available (Gormley & Light, 2019). Medical-based SLPs often have limited access to high-tech devices that meet their population's needs (Gormley & Light, 2019). This issue is highlighted in the hospital-based case example presented in the following chapter. Similar barriers may also occur in school-based settings. In a national survey of special education teachers in the United States, it was reported that 40% of children who rely on AAC used unaided AAC forms such as signs and gestures, 36% used low-tech pictorial systems, and only 26% used SGDs (Andzik et al., 2018). Although the study did not describe whether systems selected were matched to individual needs, the low rates of SGD use suggest potential barriers to the adoption of electronic systems. In the interview with Cassandra Medrano, presented in Chapter 4, she noted that it took her several years for her son's school to add a high-tech AAC system to his individualized education plan (IEP). Even though this decision may have been impacted by attitudinal and knowledge barriers, practice barriers related to funding may have also played a role. Schools may have limited special education funds to purchase devices or have not adopted practices to support insurance funding. For instance, as the insurance funding process is lengthy and complex (Dodd et al., 2015), schools may not allocate enough time to complete the process.

In response to funding concerns, some organizations, including school districts, have adopted the practice of providing low-cost mobile technology AAC applications for all individuals with complex communication needs (Abbot & McBride, 2014; Johnston et al., 2020). Although the relatively lower cost of mobile devices with applications (compared to dedicated SGDs) has made AAC more accessible for many, the ease of obtaining these technologies has created new barriers to the selection of systems that have features (e.g., access methods, organizations, symbol sets, and voice options) matched to individual needs (Ogletree et al., 2018). For example, some organizations may forgo conducting AAC evaluations because family members download AAC apps on their own (Ogletree et al., 2018). Other organizations or clinicians may recommend one "standard" AAC application for most individuals without conducting individualized feature matching (Johnston et al., 2020). In the next chapter, a case example suggests that recommending a particular application may be common in schools due to potential benefits of consistency across students. However, the case study also highlights that, although one application might meet the needs of many students, the failure to match AAC system features to individual needs can have negative effects for students whose needs differ from peers. Unfortunately, the feature matching process requires additional time to assess and determine what device attributes are critical for meeting an individual's needs. A lack of access to AAC specialists may further complicate this issue, as general practice SLPs report low levels of confidence in their ability to use feature matching with high-tech AAC (Sanders et al., 2021).

> **Feature matching** is the process of determining what AAC system characteristics are needed for a given individual and selecting systems that have these critical features.

Breaking Down the Barrier: Practices That Promote Use of Feature Matched High-Tech Systems

Several practices support the selection of individually appropriate high-tech AAC systems. First, teams can reach out to AAC companies to request loaner devices or free versions of AAC applications that can be used for evaluation and feature matching purposes. Many AAC compa-

nies offer free trainings so that teams can learn about device features and functions. Loaner devices and demonstrations are also available from state assistive technology programs. To increase the likelihood that the AAC team selects a high-tech system that is appropriate for a given individual, practitioners can also utilize freely available feature matching charts (see Table 5–1) that list a variety of device capabilities (e.g., the ability to customize grid size, select voices, or use alternative access). Given the time constraints for conducting initial assessments, continuous assessment and identification of critical features can be embedded into intervention. For instance, recent research has supported the use of dynamic assessment to determine individually appropriate AAC targets, grid sizes, and organizational systems (Binger et al., 2017; Gevarter et al., 2020). Requesting device trials from AAC companies also allows teams time to embed continuous assessment into daily routines. Free data collection sheets for conducting device trials are often available from AAC companies and other resources (see Table 5–1).

> **Dynamic Assessment** is an approach that embeds active teaching (e.g., the use of test-teach-retest models or graduated cueing hierarchies) into the assessment process to determine an individual's learning potential when provided with supports.

To aid in the efficiency of funding requests, most AAC companies will offer funding support and guidance. For example, Prentke Romich Company and Satillo have a website that provides templates and examples of funding reports as well as resources for alternative funding (see Table 5–1). State assistive technology programs may also help in completing insurance reports or providing other funding resources. Although some families have the financial resources to purchase mobile technology devices with AAC applications on their own, to limit the likelihood of families selecting applications that do not meet individual needs, AAC teams should consider adopting practices that promote early referral (Ogletree et al., 2018). AAC finders (e.g., family members, early intervention providers, teachers) play a critical role in supporting the assessment process by identifying individuals who may require AAC and making referrals to specialists (Binger et al., 2012). AssistiveWare has created an AAC finders' checklist that may aid finders in making earlier identifications and referrals for AAC assessment (see Table 5–1).

Breaking Down the Barrier: Identifying Practices That Limit System Customization

Even though the use of comprehensive AAC assessments and feature matching for high-tech AAC systems can limit one-size-fits-all approaches, system customization is still needed to ensure that AAC systems have (a) personally relevant vocabulary; (b) developmentally, cognitively, or culturally appropriate symbols; and (c) efficient and effective organizational and access systems (Donato et al.,

2018; Light, Wilkinson, et al., 2019; Gormley & Fager, 2021). Limited vocabularies and AAC systems that are not designed to promote easy and efficient use are common barriers to adoption (Baxter et al., 2012; Donato et al., 2018). Unfortunately, SLPs report that employers do not set aside paid time to program and customize high-tech devices or create low-tech systems (Chung & Stoner, 2016; Gormley & Light, 2019; Moorcraft et al., 2019). With high-tech systems, it may become common practice for teams to rely on default options (e.g., preset vocabularies, symbol organizations, or voices). Although default systems often include access to high frequency core words, research suggests that beginning communicators also need access to a wide range of content vocabulary that is often specific to an individual or context (Laubscher & Light, 2020). Adults with acquired disorders also need quick access to coverage vocabulary for essential messages (Beukelman & Light, 2020).

Breaking Down the Barrier: Practices That Promote System Customization

Practitioners can support customization by using vocabulary checklists that allow the person with complex communication needs and communication partners to efficiently make recommendations for personally relevant vocabulary (Beukelman & Light, 2020). For instance, Fallon et al., (2001) created and field-tested a questionnaire for determining vocabulary for preschool children. Teams can also conduct ecological inventories (e.g., observing and recording the vocabulary words an individual and peers need to communicate in typical contexts) and have individuals or family members complete communication diaries (Beukelman & Light, 2020). The Reinforcer Assessment for Individuals with Severe Disabilities (RAISD) can also be used to identify preferred items/activities for individuals with developmental disabilities (Fisher et al., 1996), which would allow for further customization of vocabulary.

AAC teams can also advocate for practice changes to support additional time to complete critical team functions such as customization (Chung & Stoner, 2016). However, if advocating for paid time to personalize systems is unsuccessful due to additional policy barriers (e.g., insurance companies not reimbursing for these activities), AAC teams can incorporate customization into communication intervention sessions. One way to do this is to directly involve the person who relies on AAC and their communication partners in the customization process. In both the school and home-based case examples presented in the following chapter, clinicians describe instances in which individuals with complex communication needs successfully made choices regarding the selection of different AAC symbols or voice options during intervention or family training sessions. Presenting these options to individuals not only allows for ownership of their own system, but also creates opportunities to practice choice making, model new vocabulary, and demonstrate how to use newly added device features. Zangari (2013) provides a brief list of strategies (e.g., using sorting tasks and yes/no questions) that can be used to elicit client opinions about cus-

tomization options. A more formal tool to help communicators express opinions about preferred topics, interests, or symbols, utilizing picture-based rating scales, is Talking Mats™ (Murphy & Boa, 2012). Recent research has also involved communication partners and young children in just-in-time programming, which focuses on adding new vocabulary to a device as it becomes needed (Caron et al., 2016; Holyfield et al., 2017). Just-in-time research has included AAC systems that allow users to quickly create visual scene displays (VSDs) by using device camera functions to photograph a scene (e.g., child swinging outside) and add speech output hotspots (e.g., *Swing me higher!)* to the photograph (Holyfield et al., 2019). Just-in-time programming may also be possible with grid-based systems, especially when camera and image search features are easily available (Holyfield et al., 2019). Although research has not yet examined the use of just-in-time programming in hospital settings, the approach might be helpful for meeting the fast-paced demands associated with medical contexts (Gormley & Fager, 2021).

Visual Scene Displays (VSDs) embed language concepts and vocabulary into contextual photographs or pictures that can depict places, events, activities, and social interactions.

AAC team members should also consider utilizing customization resources provided by AAC vendors. For instance, AAC application companies often have multiple resources (e.g., how-to-guides and video models) that provide support for customization skills such as adding and editing symbols and folders, creating templates, changing voices, or enabling switch access (see Table 5–1). Companies that focus primarily on dedicated SGDs, may also be able to use team input to pre-customize trial devices and make further customizations following the trial. The home-based case example presented in the next chapter (written by an SLP who works for an AAC vendor) highlights this option. In many instances, practitioners can also make use of existing device features that promote easy customization. For instance, Proloquo2Go (Assistive-Ware) has a progressive language feature that guides users in gradually increasing the vocabulary size for communicators who may benefit from starting with a smaller number of symbols. TouchChat® (Saltillo) also has a supplemental computer program that can be used to customize vocabulary when the device is not present. Additionally, many systems allow users to create communication templates that can be shared with other users who have overlapping personally relevant vocabulary sets (e.g., two students in the same classroom or two adults in the same hospital). Shared templates may be particularly useful for reducing programming time constraints associated with the creation of schematic grids organized by topic, activity, or context (e.g., circle time or cafeteria) that meet the needs of a group of individuals.

Finally, customization is also supported when team-based approaches are prioritized. In the school case example in the next chapter, an SLP describes how seeking input from team members benefited customization decisions. For instance, in one case, an access customization was successfully implemented based on the recommendation of an occupational therapist. Of course, successful teaming requires time and support for interprofessional collaboration. In the following section, we will discuss barriers related to working with other professionals.

Practices That Limit Interprofessional Collaboration

In the sections above, we emphasized the importance of a team approach when addressing practice barriers that prevent comprehensive AAC assessments. In addition to SLPs, professionals who play a role in AAC assessment and implementation include teachers, educational assistants, occupational therapists, physical therapists, vision specialists, vocational support staff, behavior analysts, doctors, and nurses. Unfortunately, across a variety of settings, practice barriers may limit the ability of professionals to collaborate (Johnston et al., 2020; Uthoff et al., 2021). Barriers may occur due to practices that limit (a) shared understanding and responsibilities, and (b) time for collaboration.

Breaking Down the Barrier: Identifying Practices That Limit Shared Understanding and Responsibilities

It is critical for AAC teams to have a shared understanding of team member functions (Chung & Stone, 2016; Soto et al., 2001). Unfortunately, in practice, roles and responsibilities are often not well-defined and team members may be unclear about their own duties or the functions of other professionals (Andzik et al., 2019; ASHA, 2021; Moorcroft et al., 2019; Uthoff et al., 2021). This may lead to disagreements, inconsistent service delivery, or one team member making AAC implementation decisions without team feedback (Andzik et al., 2019; Moorcroft et al., 2019). As highlighted in the medical-based case study in the following chapter, limited understanding of SLP or AAC specialist roles may also limit referrals and opportunities for collaboration. In some contexts, such as hospitals, when certain team members (e.g., doctors) act in a gatekeeper role, this may also lead to disputes (Uthoff et al., 2021).

AAC teams may also experience challenges when they are inflexible in recognizing when roles might overlap or when team members should share responsibilities (Chung & Stoner, 2016; Soto et al., 2001). In practice, the adoption of certain approaches to teaming may limit such flexibility and shared responsibility. For instance, some AAC teams may rely solely on multidisciplinary team approaches in which professionals select and intervene on their own goals and only collaborate with other team members when sharing results (Batorowicz & Shepherd, 2008; Robillard et al., 2013). In contrast, an interdisciplinary approach incorporates more shared intervention planning and implementation, but team members still have specific roles and responsibilities (Batorowicz & Shepherd, 2008; Robillard et al., 2013). In a transdis-

ciplinary approach, AAC implementation is highly collaborative and all team members, regardless of discipline, are responsible for implementing a variety of goals (Batorowicz & Shepherd, 2008; Robillard et al., 2013). Although a multidisciplinary approach may involve the least amount of collaboration and role flexibility, conflict in interdisciplinary or transdisciplinary teams may occur if individuals do not understand the challenges faced by other team members. For instance, whereas an SLP who has limited time to work directly with clients may expect classroom staff to address communication goals, educational assistants who spend much of their time assisting with basic student needs (e.g., feeding) may not feel that they have the time to address communication (Andzik et al., 2019). Alternatively, classroom teachers frustrated by the lack of time SLPs spend in their classroom may be unaware of therapist caseload and paperwork burdens.

Breaking Down the Barrier: Practices That Promote Shared Understanding and Responsibilities

To better understand roles and responsibilities during the assessment process, teams can use the descriptions of appropriate team member functions provided by Binger et al. (2012). For both assessment and intervention, AAC teams can also make use of implementation plans that are developed collaboratively to establish what needs to be done and what role each team member will play (Bausch & Ault, 2008). Implementation plans allow for accountability by making clear which team members are responsible for specific tasks and which responsibilities are shared (Bausch & Ault, 2008). By involving all team members in the creation of the plan, individuals can also discuss and troubleshoot additional barriers. For instance, if an educational assistant expresses concerns regarding the time needed to implement communication goals while also addressing activities of daily living, the team might select intervention targets that can be easily embedded into/support current routines (e.g., teaching the student to request the bathroom). Implementation plans can also include information such as training needs or delineate responsibilities across categories like equipment management, classroom use, and progress monitoring. Table 5–2 includes links to plan templates and Figure 5–1 provides an example of an implementation plan for a child in a preschool setting. In a study by Hunt et al. (2002), AAC team members created plans for students utilizing AAC in general education classrooms. Plans included (a) educational and social support strategies for different contexts (e.g., creating communication opportunities, using modifications and accommodations), (b) a list of who was responsible for implementing strategies, and (c) rating scales to evaluate progress. There were positive effects on outcomes, such as AAC use and academic engagement (Hunt et al., 2002).

To further support collaboration between professionals, AAC teams should determine the types of teaming approaches that best meet team and client needs under different circumstances and constraints (Robillard et al., 2013). For instance, when introducing an AAC device to a client with significant motor needs in an in-patient setting, given the likelihood for overlap in AAC-related goals, an SLP and occupational therapist (OT) might consider an interdisciplinary or transdisciplinary approach. At the same time, the SLP and OT might take a multidisciplinary approach with the client's doctor, as the unique nature of that role might prevent more integrated collaboration. A medical SLP gives examples of this approach in the following chapter. Teams must also evaluate the effectiveness of models employed. The Team Decision Making Questionnaire (TDMQ) was developed to help AAC teams evaluate the effectiveness of transdisciplinary models (Batorowicz & Shepherd, 2008). Recent research demonstrated that the TDMQ was able to detect differences in the quality and usefulness of transdisciplinary assessment practices for AAC mobile technologies across educational, private, and medical settings (Mansfield, 2019). The Index of Interprofessional Team Collaboration for Expanded School Mental Health (Mellin et al., 2010) has also been used to evaluate the effectiveness of interdisciplinary AAC teams (Kocanda, 2021). Although the adoption of teaming models

> An **AAC Implementation Plan** is a written document that describes (a) specific activities, tasks, or strategies team members will use for AAC assessment, intervention, training, or maintenance purposes, and (b) each team member's role in implementing the plan.

Table 5–2. Practices That Limit Interprofessional Collaboration

Limiting Practices	Positive Practices	Resources
Roles and responsibilities are poorly defined, and approaches to teaming do not support shared responsibility	Use implementation plans.	**Implementation plan templates** • https://iris.peabody.vanderbilt.edu/wp-content/uploads/modules/at/pdfs/NATRI_Assistive_Technology_Implementation_Plan.pdf#content • https://docs.google.com/document/d/1J6gZgQVFznvj7q48o5KmxTRSKQioCcZlRfcTqpQZqoE/edit **Resources for learning more about implementation plans** • Bausch & Ault (2008) https://doi.org/10.1177/004005990804100101 • https://www.ctdinstitute.org/library/2017-12-06/aac-implementation-plans-preparing-successful-communication-0 • https://praacticalaac.org/praactical/how-i-do-it-setting-up-an-aac-implementation-plan/ • https://www.slpnerdcast.com/episodes/aac-implementation-plans
	Use and evaluate collaborative teaming models that meet the needs of client and context.	**Assessment of team approaches** • Mellin et al. (2010) https://doi.org/10.3109/13561821003624622 • Batorowicz & Shepherd (2008) https://doi.org/10.1080/13561820802303664 **Interprofessional Practice (IPP) resources** • https://www.asha.org/practice/ipe-ipp/what-is-ipp/ • https://www.asha.org/practice/ipe-ipp/how-to/

Limiting Practices	Positive Practices	Resources
Limited time for collaboration	Advocate for additional time.	**Resources for advocacy** • Chung & Stoner (2016) https://doi.org/10.1080/07434618.2016.1213766 • https://www.asha.org/practice/ipe-ipp/how-to/Advocate-for-IPP-in-Your-Clinic-or-School/
	Use technology and informal methods to supplement formal meetings.	**Technology resources for online teaming and file sharing** • https://www.google.com/drive/features/ • https://support.microsoft.com/en-us/office/collaborating-with-teams-sharepoint-and-onedrive-9ea6aa07-6e5e-4917-9267-d4d361da3dea • https://www.microsoft.com/en-us/microsoft-teams/group-chat-software
	Use efficient interprofessional training models.	**Coaching resources** • See section one Chapter 2 **Tools for creating or finding just-in-time AAC training videos** • https://www.attainmentcompany.com/govisual • https://www.youtube.com/channel/UCZ9nA7I5duHtMOl09d21ISg • https://praacticalaac.org/category/video/

Implementation Plan			
Child: Michael (4-year-old with autism)		**Current Date:** October 1st	**Next Update:** 1 month
AAC system(s)	**Primary:** TouchChat® AAC application using direct selection with finger **Backups:** PECS book; manual sign		
Long-term goal	By the end of the school year, Michael will use his AAC device, vocal speech, or signs to communicate for a variety of purposes (e.g., request, reject, comment, answer questions) using at least 3-word phrases at least 5 times per routine across at least 3 different routines.		
Short-term objective	By the end of the month, Michael will use 1-symbol AAC device responses to request or reject items, actions or social interactions, across at least 3 different routines for at least 5 consecutive days.		
Strategies	**Aided language modeling**: model AAC use during routines **Embedded instruction:** create communication opportunities during routines **Least-to-most-prompting**: pause, verbal reminder, model symbol selection		
Training resources	**TouchChat operation and editing:** https://touchchatapp.com/videos?category=3&page=1 **Aided language modeling:** https://saltillo.com/images/putting-aided-language-into-practice-aac-putting-aided-language-to-practice-handout.pdf **Embedded instruction:** https://staging.ilc.com.au/wp-content/uploads/2016/02/Communication_opportunities_in_the_Classroom.pdf **Least-to-most-prompt hierarchy:** https://communicationmatrix.org/Uploads/Posts/12372/AAC%20Prompt%20Hierarchy%209-1-16%20kb%20jl.pdf		
Targeted vocabulary	**Core words:** yes, no, all done, my turn, help, give, play, go **Contextual (Fringe) words:** Art: crayon, glue, scissors, cut, paste; Literacy centers/story time: turn page, book, read; names of preferred books (e.g., Brown Bear), letters; Snack: juice, goldfish, crackers, pretzels, water; Bathroom: potty, wash, turn on; Play/sensory: trains, dinosaur, car, spin, swing, squeeze, tickle		
Team Member Responsibilities and Feedback			
Team member	**Responsibilities**	**Contexts**	**Feedback (successes, challenges, new vocabulary needed)**
SLP	• Add new vocabulary. • Use teaching strategies during speech sessions/push-in time. • Take data during speech sessions. • Model strategies for staff using just-in-time training. • Gather team input. • Update plan and AAC system as needed. • Provide training videos to parents.	Group pull-out speech sessions with peers (peer play routines); Push-in classroom activities (art, literacy, play).	Success with requesting items and some actions during art time and peer play; consistently using *NO*, but not *YES*; likely a transition to more commenting/with known vocabulary during preferred routines; not yet navigating through category folders independently (can do with a model); staff embedding more opportunities
Teacher	• Use instructional strategies throughout the day. • Provide feedback on strategy use to educational assistants. • Provide input to SLP. • Take data on least 1 routine each day.	Classroom routines: storybook reading, literacy centers; peer play; art	Will independently request different preferred items and starting to request more actions (needs more support to recognize icons); category navigation is a challenge; could use words for circle time activities (shapes, color, greetings, calendar words)
Educational Assistants	• Make sure device is charged/available. • Use instructional strategies throughout the day. • Provide input to SLP and teacher.	Classroom routines and activities of daily living: storybook reading, literacy centers; peer play; art; mealtime; bathroom routine	Success requesting during mealtime and starting to recognize food category; difficulty with bathroom words (less preferred activity); could add more words for art (paint, paper) and play (build, blocks)

Figure 5–1. Example of an implementation plan.

may be influenced by policies (e.g., early intervention agencies requiring transdisciplinary models), ASHA recommends an interprofessional collaborative practice (IPP) model. The IPP emphasizes teams (a) developing positive cultures that nurture mutual respect, (b) using knowledge of team member roles to meet client needs, (c) communicating regularly, and (d) building relationships that support effective, efficient, and equitable service delivery (ASHA, n.d.). A focus on interdisciplinary training, understanding the roles of others, and simultaneous discussion/negotiation of client plans also differentiates this approach from others. ASHA provides resources to support an IPP model across different settings (see Table 5–2).

Breaking Down the Barrier: Identifying Practices That Limit Time for Collaboration

Although AAC implementation plans and tools for initiating and evaluating different collaborative team models can help clarify team member roles and responsibilities, teams may not be able to utilize these approaches without addressing time constraint barriers. An ASHA (2021) survey found that limited time was the number one reported barrier to using IPP models of collaboration. It is frequently reported that clinical organizations, schools, agencies, and hospitals provide limited time for AAC team members to hold collaborative meetings, co-treat clients, and provide training to team members (Andzik et al., 2019; ASHA, 2021; Chung & Stoner, 2016; Kocanda, 2021; Moorcroft et al., 2019; Uthoff et al., 2021). In school settings, co-treatment and training opportunities may be restricted due to teachers' limited access to SLPs during the school day (Andzik et al., 2019; Moorcroft et al., 2019). The interview with Cassandra Medrano presented in Chapter 4 highlights this issue, as she noted that

her child's school-based SLP reported not having enough time to train classroom staff. Similarly, in the following chapter, a school-based case study describes how the author (an SLP) had to overcome limited opportunities to train and provide feedback to classroom staff. AAC teams working in rural districts with itinerant therapists may also face additional challenges to collaboration as the full team may not all be in the same location at a given time (Chung & Stoner, 2016). Limited access to team members may also create barriers in medical settings (Gormley & Light, 2019; Uthoff et al., 2021). For example, a lack of overlap between team-member work shifts, busy schedules, and limited availability of team members such as doctors or AAC specialists may limit time to problem solve, discuss plans, or train others (Gormley & Light, 2019; Uthoff et al., 2021).

Breaking Down the Barrier: Practices That Promote Collaboration Time

An important first step for AAC teams would be to advocate for more collaboration time (Chung & Stoner, 2016). To aid in this process, ASHA created a how-to guide for advocating for IPP approaches (see Table 5–2). Chung & Stoner (2016) also suggest using a logic model to assess *inputs* (e.g., necessary resources such as time) that support critical *activities* (e.g., team meetings) needed to meet desired *outcomes* (student and team goals). Teams can use a logic model to determine commonly identified inputs and use data to advocate for supports (Chung & Stoner, 2016).

Although advocacy is important for making change, sometimes teams might need to consider ways to increase collaboration under less-than-ideal practice conditions. One solution is for teams to use technology to support communication and collaboration (Chung & Stoner, 2016). Previously, communicating via email may have been a common solution, but following the COVID-19 pandemic, AAC teams have learned new technological methods that can support collaboration (Chung & Stoner, 2016; Kocanda, 2021). For instance, during the COVID-19 pandemic some school-based AAC teams began using video-call technology (e.g., Zoom) to conduct meetings, which in some cases reduced typical scheduling barriers, allowed for more organized meetings, and led to an increase in discussions of student needs (Kocanda, 2021). For some teams, virtual meetings also allowed for more involvement of the entire team, including members who may not have been involved in the past (Kocanda, 2021). Other technological tools such as chat systems or shared drives that allow teams to collaboratively edit documents (e.g., GoogleDrive™, OneDrive) may also be beneficial. Such tools might be useful for gathering information for assessment, implementation planning, and progress monitoring. Of course, whereas technology may be helpful in some cases, in other instances it may not be as useful and present additional challenges (Kocanda, 2021). Informal methods for collaboration in in-person contexts can be used to supplement scheduled meetings (Chung & Stoner, 2016; Kocanda, 2021). For instance, school-based SLPs might consult with classroom staff when they are providing push-in classroom services or attempt to meet more frequently for short periods of time rather than wait to communicate during less frequent, longer meetings (Kocanda, 2021).

Although informal and formal methods can be used to communicate and consult with team members, AAC collaboration often also requires time for interprofessional training. In fact, to support effective IPP models, interprofessional education is necessary (ASHA, n.d.). In the previous knowledge and skills section, several approaches to training are discussed. When practice barriers limit time for collaboration, some of these approaches may be more beneficial than others. In many cases, coaching approaches may be a viable option, as they embed the teaching of instructional strategies into everyday routines. Coaching has been used, for example, to teach educational assistants and behavioral therapists to use both low-tech and high-tech AAC strategies in classroom contexts (Ganz et al., 2013; Kashinath et al., 2021). However, if one-on-one coaching is a challenge to implement due to time or staffing limitations, it can be adapted for group use. In the school case example in the next chapter, an SLP who did not have enough time to provide one-on-one AAC training to individual educational assistants created small speech groups to provide group coaching. Another efficient training approach is just-in-time instruction (Beukelman & Light, 2020; Gormley, 2019). In this approach, communication partners are provided with brief in-the-moment training that focuses on a particular intervention strategy needed in the current context (Beukelman & Light, 2020). Just-in-time training often includes multimedia components, such as the use of video models with audio or text-based instructions (Beukelman & Light, 2020; Gormley, 2019). AAC team leads can support just-in-time training by creating video models of strategy use during intervention sessions. In a recent study, just-in-time instruction was used to successfully teach health care providers (e.g., nurses, physical therapists) in inpatient settings to provide choice opportunities to children with complex communication needs (Gormley, 2019). Although more research is needed to explore just-in-time instruction to teach AAC strategies, its use across other health care professions provides evidence of its potential (Gormley, 2019).

Practices That Limit the Ability to Meet Cultural and/or Familial Needs

Although a variety of professionals serve as critical members of AAC teams, the individual with complex communication needs and their family are likely to play the most important role in the adoption of AAC. Unfortunately, individuals who rely on AAC and their families face barriers that can lead to AAC abandonment (Baxter et al., 2012; Donato et al., 2018; Moorcroft et al., 2019, 2020), and families from culturally and linguistically diverse backgrounds are likely to experience additional barriers (Kulkarni & Parmar, 2017). Below we discuss practice barriers that limit (a)

support for AAC in the home, and (b) use of culturally relevant AAC systems.

Breaking Down the Barrier: Identifying Practices That Limit Support for AAC in the Home

A variety of specific practice barriers can impact the use of AAC in home environments. First, if AAC systems are funded by schools, districts may adopt practices that limit if/how often AAC systems are sent home with families (Beukelman & Light, 2020; Johnston et al., 2020). Further, even if devices are sent home, a lack of administrative support for meetings with families and other practices that promote home-school communication can create additional barriers (Bailey et al., 2006). In the interview with Cassandra Medrano in Chapter 4, she describes how the lack of a clear and consistent process for home-school communication negatively impacted her son's use of AAC across environments. Families also report that infrequent interactions and follow-up from SLPs, along with limited opportunities for AAC training create barriers (Kulkarni & Parmar, 2017; Moorcroft et al., 2020). In the school case example in the following chapter, an SLP describes how productivity and caseload requirements limit the time she has to train parents. For culturally and linguistically diverse families, these issues are further exacerbated by the fact that organizations often do not offer training and resources in their home language (Kulkarni & Parmar, 2017). Finally, family dynamics and demands may also limit the time and resources families have to devote to AAC intervention and collaboration (Mandak et al., 2017). If professionals make negative assumptions regarding fluctuations in family involvement, this may further reduce the time clinicians devote to providing support (Mandak et al., 2017).

Breaking Down the Barrier: Practices That Promote In-Home AAC Support

The first step to facilitate AAC use in the home is to adopt practices that ensure that individuals with complex communication needs have access to systems across environments. AAC teams can advocate for such practices using resources that describe legal mandates for providing assistive technology in home environments (Table 5–3). Many of the previously discussed supports for insurance and alternative funding can also facilitate access to AAC systems in homes. Similarly, some of the resources and practices described under the section on interprofessional collaboration also apply to collaboration with families. For instance, advocacy tools such as the logic model created by Chung and Stoner (2016) can be used to gather data on resources that teams require to support families. Resources might include, for example, regularly scheduled time for parent meetings or access to technology (e.g., Google Drive, video equipment) to support communication and sharing of information. Implementation plans that include families can also be created (Bausch & Ault, 2008). These plans can incorporate links to training resources and opportunities for families to provide feedback to streamline communication. For AAC team members who have direct access to families, coaching and just-in-time training can be integrated into client intervention sessions. When direct access to families is limited (e.g., in schools), SLPs can use technology to facilitate in-home AAC use. For instance, in one of the case examples in Chapter 6, a school SLP sent parents videos of recorded intervention sessions in which the clinician modeled strategies that could be used across environments. In another case study, an SLP working for an AAC vendor suggested that companies can offer supplemental virtual training to families when access to local clinicians is limited. Referring families to private clinicians or AAC companies who offer tele-based training or consultation may also increase access to services in a family's home language.

To address the unique time demands of families, AAC teams should also adopt family centered approaches (Mandak et al., 2017). Family centered frameworks allow teams to evaluate dynamic components of family systems and subsystems and can aid in determining familial needs such as resources, flexibility in scheduling, or time to adapt to change (Mandak et al., 2017). In the home-based case example in the following chapter, an SLP describes the learning process she went through to understand that her "standard" training timeline would not meet the needs of an individual family and greater flexibility would be required. Tools such as The Family Resource Support Guide developed by Sexton and Rush (2012) can be used as part of a family-centered approach to better understand family resources (e.g., time available for AAC use and training).

Table 5–3. Resources for Practices That Limit the Ability to Meet Cultural and/or Familial Needs

Limiting Practices	Positive Practices	Resources
Limited resources, time, and supports for AAC use in the home	Advocate for the inclusion of home-based AAC in IEPs and support funding for AAC across environments.	**Resources on legal mandates for schools providing assistive technology in homes** • https://gpat.gadoe.org/Georgia-Project-for-Assistive-Technology/Pages/Legal-Mandates-for-Assistive-Technology.aspx • https://www.pattan.net/getmedia/9ba41485-7a91-4922-bd0d-6f6ee8fb0f61/AssistTech_In_IEP_0418 **Resources for funding AAC** • https://www.aacfunding.com/alt-funding-sources • https://aac-learning-center.psu.edu/moodle/funding-for-aac-in-schools/
	Advocate for additional time to collaborate with families.	**Resources for advocacy** • See Table 5–2
	Use implementation plans that involve families.	**Implementation plan templates and resources** • See Table 5–2
	Use technology and informal methods to increase communication with parents.	**Technology resources for online teaming and file sharing** • See Table 5–2
	Use efficient parent training models.	**Coaching resources** • See section one Chapter 2 **Telehealth resources** • See section one Chapter 2

continues

Table 5–3. *continued*

Limiting Practices	Positive Practices	Resources
	Use family-centered approaches to address needs of families.	**Resources for family-centered approaches to AAC** • Mandak et al. (2017) https://doi.org/10.1080/07434618.2016.1271453 • The Family Resource Support Guide https://fipp.ncdhhs.gov/wp-content/uploads/casetools_vol6_no5.pdf
Teams do not incorporate culturally relevant AAC features and family input.	Use feature matching to determine culturally relevant features of AAC systems.	**Feature matching charts** • See Table 5–1 **Resources for AAC systems with Spanish language features** • https://leader.pubs.asha.org/do/10.1044/high-tech-aac-for-spanish-speakers/full/ • https://praacticalaac.org/praactical/how-i-do-it-supporting-spanish-speaking-aac-learners/ **Commonly available customizable voice options** • https://www.acapela-group.com/voices/
	Evaluate team member cultural understandings and biases.	**ASHA Cultural Competence Check-ins** • https://www.asha.org/practice/multicultural/self/
	Gain family input using culturally relevant tools.	**Vocabulary assessments** • See Table 5–1 **The Protocol for Culturally Inclusive Assessment of AAC** • Huer (1997) https://doi.org/10.1177/152574019701900104 **Life Participation Approach to Aphasia** • Chapey et al. (2000) https://doi.org/10.1044/leader.FTR.05032000.4 **Additional culturally relevant AAC assessments** • https://aac.sfsu.edu/content/multicultural-aac

Breaking Down the Barrier: Identifying Practices That Limit Use of Culturally Relevant AAC

Culturally and linguistically diverse individuals and their families may experience barriers to AAC adoption when systems do not include: (a) their home language; (b) appropriate voice and dialect options; or (c) culturally relevant vocabulary and symbols (Kulkarni & Parmar, 2017; Soto & Yu, 2014). In the United States, limited use of culturally relevant features may have been largely impacted by the practices of assistive technology companies who have tended to design systems for the "average" or "typical" individual (Pullin et al., 2017). For instance, in the interview with dual-language speaker Toña Rivera in Chapter 4, she noted that, for all her childhood and most of her adulthood, she did not have access to a bilingual SGD. Changes to the demographics in the United States have, however, highlighted the need for more inclusive AAC systems (Ogletree et al., 2018; Pullin et al., 2017). Although more AAC companies now offer a variety of options for designing culturally and linguistically relevant systems, AAC teams may not yet have adopted AAC assessment, selection, customization, and intervention practices that support culturally or linguistically diverse learners (Kulkarni & Parmar, 2017; Ogletree et al., 2018; Soto & Yu, 2014). Such practices may be impacted by knowledge or attitudinal barriers (e.g., teams being unaware of new features or not valuing cultural differences), but professionals may also be likely to stick with "what they've always done" when they do not seek family input.

Breaking Down the Barrier: Practices That Promote Use of Culturally Relevant AAC

Given the increased availability of culturally and linguistically relevant AAC features, AAC teams should first address knowledge barriers by familiarizing themselves with the features offered in different high-tech systems by using feature matching charts. Important features may, for example, include the ability to change voices, set up bilingual vocabularies, upload personal photos, or change skin tones used in graphic symbols. Figure 5–2 provides an example of a feature matching chart focused on culturally relevant components. Searches of AAC company websites will often lead to information regarding such features. Although they need to be updated regularly, online resources listing or describing AAC systems with culturally relevant features are also available. For instance, some resources provide descriptions of AAC systems that support Spanish speakers or provide access to culturally relevant symbols (see Table 5–3).

Another critical practice is to gain family input. Prior to seeking information from families from backgrounds different than their own, AAC team members should evaluate their own cultural understandings and biases. ASHA provides resources for clinicians to conduct cultural competence check-ins (see Table 5–3). With an understanding of how culture influences decision-making, clinicians can gather information from families in a manner that values lived experiences. One way to start gathering such information is to use the vocabulary tools mentioned previously to determine culturally relevant

Culturally Relevant Feature Matching Chart				
	Required or Desired	System 1	System 2	System 3
Bilingual or multilingual options matched to client's languages				
Synthesized voice options matched to client characteristics				
Options to edit pronunciation				
Options to record speech				
Options to change skin tone of symbols				
Includes symbols relevant to client's culture				
Allows for photo upload				
Allows for image search				
Gender neutral options				
Grammatical dialect options matched to client's dialect				

Figure 5–2. Culturally relevant feature matching chart.

words and phrases. Some vocabulary checklist tools may require adaptation to allow for more open-ended questions, and differences in common vocabulary across languages must be considered. Recently, Soto and Cooper (2021) published an early Spanish vocabulary list for children who rely on AAC that could be used as a starting point for gaining further input from Spanish-speaking families.

Additional culturally relevant assessments can assist AAC teams in gathering important family information critical for system selection and design (e.g., existing communication forms, functions, and contexts; individual and family priorities and preferences; languages and dialects spoken). For instance, although some questions may require updating, Huer (1997) published a culturally

relevant AAC interview that can elicit information about family communication patterns, contexts, and preferences. Previously mentioned tools, such as the Communication Matrix (Rowland, 2011), also allow for family input and are available in languages other than English. In the home-based case study presented in the next chapter, an SLP also discusses how the Life Participation Approach to Aphasia (Chapey at al., 2000) allowed her to learn more about client and family priorities and contexts for communication while she was working with a family from a cultural background different than her own. Information gathered from such tools can be used to present clients and families with different options (e.g., AAC modalities, SGD layouts, voices, symbol sets) that may meet their needs, so that the individual with complex communication needs and their family can make informed choices.

Conclusion

Although specific barriers vary across contexts, there are patterns of practices that impact AAC team members' ability to (a) individualize systems, (b) collaborate with other professionals, and (c) meet cultural and familial needs. Of course, there are also a variety of other practices (some of which will be unique to specific organizations) that create barriers not highlighted in this chapter. For instance, in addition to promoting one-size-fits-all approaches to AAC system selection, practice barriers (in combination with knowledge, attitude, or policy barriers) can also impact the selection of one-size-fits-all intervention methods. To prevent this from occurring, AAC teams should utilize an evidence-based practice model that emphasizes the importance of considering external research evidence, client perspectives, clinical expertise, and ongoing data informed decision-making to select intervention approaches that meet the needs of an individual (Higginbotham & Satchidanand, 2019).

As the barriers, solutions, and resources discussed in this chapter are by no means comprehensive, AAC teams must also use an individualized approach to identify barriers, advocate for change, and adopt supportive practices. Examples of a process for identifying barriers, considering advocacy options, and brainstorming alternative solutions are presented in Table 5–4. As practice barriers are often influenced by knowledge/skill, attitude, and policy barriers, addressing other opportunity barriers may also be necessary for long-term practice changes. Finally, as technology and research advances, successful teams must commit to engaging in continuous learning to ensure that AAC practices are supported by current evidence.

Table 5–4. Examples of Process for Identifying and Addressing Practice Barriers via Advocacy and the Adoption of Supportive Practices

Describe context and an evidence-based AAC practice you want to use.	List practices in place that are preventing/limiting your use of the evidence-based approach.	Describe your ability to advocate for supports or resources to address barriers.	List ideas for practices that would better promote use of the targeted evidence-based practice.
I work in early intervention and want to customize AAC systems.	• My organization does not schedule paid time for customization. • My organization does not offer training in AAC customization or time for me to train others.	• May be able to advocate for a professional development session on customization for early intervention teams. • Likely will not get paid time for customization due to insurance policies.	• Embed customization and just-in-time programming into intervention sessions involving parent and communicator. • Share AAC company customization training videos with the team.
I work in a school and want to ensure that classroom staff embed AAC intervention throughout the day.	• My school does not have a clearly defined approach to teaming, and we are often unaware of roles of others. • My school provides limited time to for me to collaborate with/train other team members.	• May be able to advocate for the adoption of a defined team-based model. • May be able to suggest a group professional development session. • Likely won't get regular training time.	• Create implementation plans that define roles and responsibilities. • Use just-in-time training during times I am in the classroom.
I work in a medical setting with diverse adult patients and want to recommend culturally appropriate AAC systems	• The current AAC systems we have are outdated and do not have many culturally relevant features. • The AAC assessments our team currently uses do not focus on patient/family priorities and preferences	• May be able to work with AAC companies or state programs to acquire loaner devices with updated features. • May be able to advocate for changes to our AAC assessment process.	• Use feature matching charts to determine systems with culturally matched features we can request for trials. • Consider assessment models that allow for input from the patient and family (e.g., The Life Participation Approach to Aphasia).

References

Abbott, M. A., & McBride, D. (2014). AAC decision-making and mobile technology: Points to ponder. *Perspectives on Augmentative and Alternative Communication, 23*(2), 104–111.

Andzik, N. R., Chung, Y. C., Doneski-Nicol, J., & Dollarhide, C. T. (2019). AAC services in schools: A special educator's perspective. *International Journal of Developmental Disabilities, 65*(2), 89–97. https://doi.org/10.10 80/20473869.2017.1368909

Andzik, N. R., Schaefer, J. M., Nichols, R. T., & Chung, Y. C. (2018). National survey describing and quantifying students with communication needs. *Developmental Neurorehabilitation, 21*(1), 40–47. https:// doi.org/10.1080/17518423.2017.1339133

ASHA. (n.d).*What is interprofessional practice?* ASHA.org. https://www.asha.org/ practice/ipe-ipp/what-is-ipp

ASHA. (2021, June). *Interprofessional practice survey results.* ASHA.org. https://www .asha.org/research/memberdata/interpro fessional-practice-survey/

Bailey, R. L., Stoner, J. B., Parette Jr, H. P., & Angell, M. E. (2006). AAC team perceptions: Augmentative and alternative communication device use. *Education and Training in Developmental Disabilities, 41*(2), 139–154.

Batorowicz, B., &. Shepherd, T.A. (2008) Measuring the quality of transdisciplinary teams, *Journal of Interprofessional Care, 22*(6), 612–620. https://doi.org/10.1080/ 13561820802303664

Bausch, M. E., & Ault, M. J. (2008). Assistive technology implementation plan: A tool for improving outcomes. *Teaching Exceptional Children, 41*(1), 6–14.

Baxter, S., Enderby, P., Evans, P., & Judge, S. (2012). Barriers and facilitators to the use of high-technology augmentative and alternative communication devices: A systematic review and qualitative synthesis. *International Journal of Language & Communication Disorders, 47*(2), 115–129.

Beukelman, D. R., & Light, J. C. (2020). *Augmentative & alternative communication: Supporting children and adults with complex communication needs* (5th ed.). Paul H. Brookes.

Binger, C., Ball, L., Dietz, A., Kent-Walsh, J., Lasker, J., Lund, S., . . . Quach, W. (2012). Personnel roles in the AAC assessment process. *Augmentative and Alternative Communication, 28*(4), 278–288.

Binger, C., Kent-Walsh, J., & King, M. R. (2017). Dynamic assessment for 3- and 4-year-old children who use augmentative and alternative communication: Evaluating expressive syntax. *Journal of Speech, Language, and Hearing Research, 60*(7), 1946–1958.

Caron, J., Light, J., & Drager, K. (2016). Operational demands of AAC mobile technology applications on programming vocabulary and engagement during professional and child interactions. *Augmentative and Alternative Communication, 32*(1), 12–24.

Chapey, R., Duchan, J. F., Elman, R. J., Garcia, L. J., Kagan, A., Lyon, J. G., & Simmons Mackie, N. (2000). Life participation approach to aphasia: A statement of values for the future. *The ASHA Leader, 5*(3), 4–6.

Chung, Y. C., & Stoner, J. B. (2016). A metasynthesis of team members' voices: What we need and what we do to support students who use AAC. *Augmentative and Alternative Communication, 32*(3), 175–186.

Dodd, J., Schaefer, A., & Rothbart, A. (2015). Conducting an augmentative and alternative communication assessment as a school-based speech-language pathologist: A collaborative experience. *Perspectives on School-Based Issues, 16*(3), 105–117.

Donato, C., Spencer, E., & Arthur-Kelly, M. (2018). A critical synthesis of barriers and facilitators to the use of AAC by children with autism spectrum disorder and their communication partners. *Augmentative and Alternative Communication, 34*(3), 242–253.

Fallon, K. A., Light, J. C., & Paige, T. K. (2001). Enhancing vocabulary selection for preschoolers who require augmentative and alternative communication (AAC). *American Journal of Speech Language Pathology, 10*, 81–94.

Fisher, W. W., Piazza, C. C., Bowman, L. G., & Amari, A. (1996). Integrating caregiver report with a systematic choice assessment to enhance reinforcer identification. *American Journal on Mental Retardation. 101*, 15–25.

Ganz, J. B., Goodwyn, F. D., Boles, M. M., Hong, E. R., Rispoli, M. J., Lund, E. M., & Kite, E. (2013). Impacts of a PECS instructional coaching intervention on practitioners and children with autism. *Augmentative and Alternative Communication, 29*(3), 210–221.

Garrett, K. L., & Beukelman, D. R. (2006). *Aphasia needs assessment.* https://cehs .unl.edu/documents/secd/aac/assessment/ aphasianeeds.pdf

Gevarter, C., Groll, M., & Stone, E. (2020). Dynamic assessment of augmentative alternative and communication application grid formats and communicative targets for children with autism spectrum disorder. *Augmentative and Alternative Communication, 36*(4), 226–237. https://doi.org/10 .1080/07434618.2020.1845236

Gormley, J. (2019). *Supporting children with complex communication needs to communicate choices during an inpatient stay: Effect of a partner training on health care professionals.* (Publication. No. 28123337) [Doctoral Dissertation, Pennsylvania State University]. ProQuest Dissertations & Theses Global.

Gormley, J., & Fager, S.K. (2021). Personalization of patient–provider communication across the life span. *Topics in Language Disorders, 41*(3), 249–268. https://doi.org/ 10.1097/TLD.0000000000000255

Gormley, J., & Light, J. (2019). Providing services to individuals with complex communication needs in the inpatient rehabilitation setting: The experiences and perspectives of speech-language pathologists. *American Journal of Speech-Language Pathology, 28*(2), 456–468. https://doi.org/ 10.1044/2018_AJSLP-18-0076

Higginbotham, J., & Satchidanand, A. (2019). From triangle to diamond: Recognizing and using data to inform our evidence-based practice. *ASHA Journals: Academy.* https://academy.pubs.asha.org/2019/04/ from-triangle-to-diamond-recognizing-and-using-data-to-inform-our-evidence-based-practice.

Holyfield, C., Caron, J., & Light, J. (2019). Progra005 ming AAC just-in-time for beginning communicators: The process. *Augmentative and Alternative Communication, 35*(4), 309–318.

Holyfield, C., Drager, K., Light, J., & Caron, J. G. (2017). Typical toddlers' participation in "just-in-time" programming of vocabulary for visual scene display augmentative and alternative communication apps on mobile technology: A descriptive study. *American Journal of Speech-Language Pathology, 26*(3), 737–749.

Huer, M. B. (1997). Culturally inclusive assessments for children using augmentative and alternative communication (AAC). *Journal of Children's Communication Development, 19*(1), 23–34

Hunt, P., Soto, G., Maier, J., Müller, E., & Goetz, L. (2002). Collaborative teaming to support students with augmentative and alternative communication needs in general education classrooms. *Augmentative and Alternative Communication, 18*(1), 20–35.

Johnston, S. S., Blue, C., Gevarter, C., Ivy, S., & Stegenga, S. (2020). Opportunity barriers and promising practices for supporting individuals with complex communication needs. *Current Developmental Disorders Reports, 7 (3)*, 100–108. https://doi.org/10.1007/s40474-020-00195-w

Kashinath, S., Dukhovny, E., & Polit, P. (2021). Effects of a coaching intervention on para-educator use of aided language modeling in classroom settings: A pilot investigation. *Communication Disorders Quarterly*. https://doi.org/10.1177/15257401211046871

Kocanda, N. (2021). *School-based augmentative and alternative communication collaboration during COVID-19* (Publication. No. 28715937) [Master's thesis, The University of Wisconsin-Milwaukee]. ProQuest Dissertations & Theses Global.

Kulkarni, S. S., & Parmar, J. (2017). Culturally and linguistically diverse student and family perspectives of AAC. *Augmentative and Alternative Communication, 33*(3), 170–180.

Laubscher, E., & Light, J. (2020). Core vocabulary lists for young children and considerations for early language development: A narrative review. *Augmentative and Alternative Communication, 36*(1), 43–53.

Light, J., McNaughton, D., Beukelman, D., Fager, S. K., Fried-Oken, M., Jakobs, T., & Jakobs, E. (2019). Challenges and opportunities in augmentative and alternative communication: Research and technology development to enhance communication and participation for individuals with complex communication needs. *Augmentative and Alternative Communication, 35*(1), 1–12. https://doi.org/10.1080/07434618.2018.1556732

Light, J., Wilkinson, K. M., Thiessen, A., Beukelman, D. R., & Fager, S. K. (2019). Designing effective AAC displays for individuals with developmental or acquired disabilities: State of the science and future research directions. *Augmentative and Alternative Communication, 35*(1), 42–55.

Mandak, K., O'Neill, T., Light, J., & Fosco, G. M. (2017). Bridging the gap from values to actions: A family systems framework for family-centered AAC services. *Augmentative and Alternative Communication, 33*(1), 32–41.

Mansfield, L. J. (2019). *The quality of transdisciplinary team assessment practices for mobile technology as augmentative and alternative communication.* (Publication. No. 22587374) [Doctoral Dissertation, Liberty University]. ProQuest Dissertations & Theses Global.

Mellin, E. A., Bronstein, L., Anderson-Butcher, D., Amorose, A. J., Ball, A., & Green, J. (2010). Measuring interprofessional team collaboration in expanded school mental health: Model refinement and scale development. *Journal of Interprofessional Care, 24*(5), 514–523.

Moorcroft, A., Scarinci, N., & Meyer, C. (2019). A systematic review of the barriers and facilitators to the provision and use of low-tech and unaided AAC systems for people with complex communication needs and their families. *Disability and Rehabilitation: Assistive Technology, 14*(7), 710–731.

Moorcroft, A., Scarinci, N., & Meyer, C. (2020). 'We were just kind of handed it and then it was smoke bombed by everyone': How do external stakeholders contribute to parent rejection and the abandonment of AAC systems? *International Journal of Language & Communication Disorders, 55*(1), 59–69.

Murphy, J., & Boa, S. (2012). Using the WHO-ICF with talking mats to enable adults with long-term communication difficulties to participate in goal setting. *Augmentative and Alternative Communication, 28*(1), 52–60.

Ogletree, B. T., McMurry, S., Schmidt, M., & Evans, K. (2018). The changing world of augmentative and alternative communication (AAC): Examining three realities faced by today's AAC provider. *Perspectives of the ASHA Special Interest Groups, 3*(12), 113–122.

Pullin, G., Treviranus, J., Patel, R., & Higginbotham, J. (2017). Designing interaction, voice, and inclusion in AAC research. *Augmentative and Alternative Communication, 33*(3), 139–148.

Robillard, M., Bélanger, R., Keating, N., Mayer-Crittenden, C., & Minor-Corriveau, M. (2013). Interdisciplinary models of teamwork in augmentative and alternative communication. *The International Journal of Interdisciplinary Studies in Communication, 7*(1), 35–44.

Rowland, C. (2011). Using the communication matrix to assess expressive skills in early communicators. *Communication Disorders Quarterly, 32*(3), 190–201.

Russell, M., Donaldson, C., Pleasant, J., & Roberts, K. (2020). Using telehealth to adapt service delivery for children during the COVID-19 pandemic. *Developmental Disabilities Network Journal, 1*(2), 12.

Sanders, E. J., Page, T. A., & Lesher, D. (2021). School-based speech-language pathologists: Confidence in augmentative and alternative communication assessment. *Language, Speech, and Hearing Services in Schools, 52*(2), 512–528.

Sexton, S., & Rush, D. (2012). The Family Resource Support Guide. *CASEtools, 6*, 1–14.

Soto, G., & Cooper, B. (2021). An early Spanish vocabulary for children who use AAC: Developmental and linguistic considerations. *Augmentative and Alternative Communication, 37*(1), 64–74.

Soto, G., Müller, E., Hunt, P., & Goetz, L. (2001). Critical issues in the inclusion of students who use augmentative and alternative communication: An educational team perspective. *Augmentative and Alternative Communication, 17*(2), 62–72.

Soto, G., & Yu, B. (2014). Considerations for the provision of services to bilingual children who use augmentative and alternative communication. *Augmentative and Alternative Communication, 30*(1), 83–92.

Theodorou, E., & Pampoulou, E. (2020). Investigating the assessment procedures for children with complex communication needs. *Communication Disorders Quarterly, 42* (2), 105–118. https://doi.org/10.1177/1525740120960643

Tobii Dynavox. (2015*). Dynamic AAC Goals Grid 2*. http://tdvox.web-downloads.s3.amazonaws.com/MyTobiiDynavox/dagg%202%20-%20writable.pdf

Uthoff, S. A., Zinkevich, A., Boenisch, J., Sachse, S. K., Bernasconi, T., & Ansmann, L. (2021). Collaboration between stakeholders involved in augmentative and alternative communication (AAC) care of people without natural speech. J*ournal of Interprofessional Care, 35*(6), 821–831.

Zabala, J. (2020). The SETT framework: A model for selection and use of assistive technology tools and more. In Chambers, D., & Forlin, C. (Eds.), *Assistive technology to support inclusive education* (pp. 17–36). Emerald Group Publishing.

Zangari, C. (2013). *Thoughts on involving our clients in AAC vocabulary selection*. https://praacticalaac.org/praactical/thoughts-on-involving-our-clients-in-aac-vocabulary-selection/

6 Practice Barriers: Studying Successful Case Examples

Cindy Gevarter, Jennifer W. Hanson*, Stephanie M. McDougle*, and Mariah Siciliano*

In this chapter we present three case examples written by practicing speech-language pathologists (SLPs) with varying levels of AAC experience. The case studies highlight how some of the practice barriers discussed in the prior chapter (i.e., those that limit or prevent AAC individualization, interprofessional collaboration, or the ability to meet cultural and/or familial needs) can be addressed in real-world contexts using evidence-based and individualized solutions. Although the case example settings and populations vary greatly, there are common patterns observed across cases. For example, all three case examples discuss how practice-based time constraints or limited resources can impact either AAC evaluation, collaboration, customization, intervention, or training. The influence of the COVID-19 pandemic on existing AAC practice barriers is also highlighted in two of the three case examples in this chapter. Additionally, the strategies the case study authors used to address practice barriers across different settings and contexts also share common features. These include (a) advocating for needs; (b) embedding AAC evaluation, intervention, training or customization into context-specific routines; (c) being flexible with timelines and scheduling; (d) gaining input from family members and other professionals; and (e) making use of existing resources and supports.

Case Example 1: School-Setting Involving Children With Multiple Developmental Disabilities (Mariah Siciliano, CCC-SLP)

A blog post on the popular AAC website PrAACctical AAC entitled, "We don't do AAC" highlights the fact that school-based AAC practices are not always aligned with special education law and policies, or evidence-based practices (Zangari, 2018). Due to various practice

---

*These authors have contributed equally to this work and share senior authorship.

barriers, individualized approaches to AAC system selection and intervention are not always prioritized in school settings. For example, the PrAACtical AAC post describes the case of a child who transferred to a different school setting after having successfully learned to use a specific AAC system. Staff at the child's new school informed her parents that the school did not use the AAC system the child had learned to use to communicate, and she would have to learn to use other AAC options (Zangari, 2018). Unfortunately, this may be a common narrative. In some school contexts, it may be typical to hear statements such as, "We don't use high-tech AAC systems," "We only use Proloquo2Go/LAMP/Touch Chat," or "We don't have time to customize AAC systems." Although many AAC clinical teams aim to make individualized AAC decisions that consider family dynamics, client preferences, clinical expertise, and evidence-based research, team members often make less than ideal choices due to practices that limit the time, resources, and staffing needed to create optimal AAC implementation plans.

As a relatively new SLP gaining more experience in assistive technology and AAC, I have found it is critical to determine what successful AAC implementation really looks like. While I was a graduate student, I recall wanting professors to teach me the "right way" to select and deliver interventions. As a practicing SLP, I have learned that successful AAC implementation means something different for every individual based on factors such as the client's current communication level and preferences, family involvement and carryover, and the feasibility of strategies based on available resources. To devise an individualized AAC plan, it is critical to first identify practice barriers so that strategies can be selected and implemented early in the planning process.

Currently, I work with students with varying AAC needs at a specialized public charter school for children with multiple developmental disabilities. Many children at the school have high support needs, and all students receive comprehensive therapy services, including physical therapy, occupational therapy, and speech-language therapy. These services are provided via push-in delivery systems (i.e., the clinician embeds therapy sessions into a classroom contexts). The therapy team is comprised of a physical therapist (PT) and a PT assistant, an occupational therapist (OT) and certified OT assistant, and two SLPs. Most therapists carry an average of 25 students on their caseload, which is relatively small compared to the expectations placed on SLPs in many public-school settings. The communication profiles of the students at this school vary from emerging communicators who use gestures, switches, and picture symbols to communicate, to children who can produce words and phrases using high-tech speech generating devices. Access methods vary from single output head switches to high-tech eye gaze systems. Given that many students have physical disabilities, AAC decisions must include factors such as positioning and placement of AAC systems that allow for access throughout the day. Below, I further describe two students, Sara and Tommy, whose cases will be used to illustrate practice barriers.

Sara is a third-grade student who uses a Snap™ Core First® (TobiiDynavox) speech-generating device (SGD). She has a diagnosis of cerebral palsy and requires a wheelchair for mobility. Sara can answer basic request-oriented questions, (e.g., "What do you want to eat?" or "Where should we go to read the book?"); can label familiar people and objects when provided with a target folder; and can access a quickfire folder with six to eight core words. She is currently learning to navigate to target folders. Sara's classroom staff support the use of her AAC device, but due to barriers further discussed below, she has not always used her system throughout her school day. Sara's parents do not currently use her device at home, but they have expressed a desire to participate in a parent training program. Sara's device does not leave her backpack at home, but she consistently brings it to school charged and ready for the day.

Tommy is in 10th grade and has a dual diagnosis of cerebral palsy and autism spectrum disorder. He functionally and independently uses Proloquo2Go (AssistiveWare) to request, answer and ask questions, and comment. Tommy has recently been experiencing a decline in motor control resulting in decreased dexterity. Due to these motor challenges, he has been experiencing more miss hits (i.e., accidentally activating speech output for symbols not matched to his communicative intentions) with his device. This appears to have led to some frustration and an increase in challenging behaviors at school. Tommy's family do not consider themselves to be technology savvy and report that they do not use his device often because they can understand and predict his needs in other ways.

In the sections that follow I describe practice barriers that initially impacted the successful adoption of AAC for learners such as Sara and Tommy. Strate-gies used to address specific barriers and overall case outcomes are also described. Table 6–1 provides a summary of barriers, key issues, and strategies.

Barrier 1: Practices That Lead to Limited Use of AAC in Classrooms and at Home

Ideal AAC implementation in our classrooms includes students' systems being easily accessible/charged and available for all classroom routines; students being provided with ample opportunities to communicate throughout the day; and the classroom staff regularly implementing strategies such as aided language modeling and prompting. Unfortunately, this type of implementation requires appropriate staffing and adequate time to address AAC needs, which, in some cases, may seem far-reaching given the demands placed on teachers and educational staff. Practice barriers related to limited time and adequate staffing have been further impacted by the COVID-19 pandemic. For example, in our school, even though each classroom is assigned at least one educational assistant (EA), the pandemic has resulted in frequent EA absences. The EAs play a tremendous role in successful AAC implementation as they are often the ones who ensure AAC systems are available/charged and provide communication opportunities throughout the day. The absence of EAs has placed additional expectations and demands on teachers. Additionally, with limited staffing, EAs and teachers are less likely to model and promote AAC use when they cannot prioritize efficient communication and strategy use. For instance, in Sara's case,

Table 6–1. Summary of School Case Study Barriers and Solutions

Barrier	Key Issues	Strategies
Practices that lead to limited use of AAC in classrooms and at home	Staffing and time restrictions that limit the ability to focus on AAC use throughout the day (made worse by COVID-19)	Worked with classroom staff to determine easy ways to embed AAC into existing routines
	Use of AAC systems inefficient for staff modeling and students use	Sought input from classroom staff on how to customize AAC systems for efficiency/ ease of use
	Limited allotted time for SLPs to train staff and parents	Created speech groups with students and educational assistants to embed training during speech sessions; sent home parent training videos and sought parental input via phone and email
Use of "standard" AAC approaches	Standard recommended AAC system used for most students not meeting needs for individual students	Collaborated with student's OT, PT, and teacher to adapt and customize the student's current system to better meet his needs (e.g., adding stylus to support fine motor movements)
	Insurance barriers preventing immediate adoption of more appropriate system	Created a team plan for implementing modifications
Limited time and resources to conduct evaluations and customize systems	No more than 60 minutes allotted for initial AAC evaluation	Determined interests/preferences and sought parental input prior to initial assessment; focused initial evaluation on determining next steps using familiar/ efficient tools during assessment session and continue to embed assessment into intervention sessions
	Limited access to AAC trial devices	Made use of free AAC apps and sought out loaner devices from AAC companies and state resource centers
	No allotted time to customize AAC systems	Incorporated system customization as part of speech sessions to involve student in vocabulary selection while modeling new language

the fact that she uses a different AAC system than other students in her class has resulted in classroom staff reporting difficulty in locating target words and quickly modeling keywords and phrases during the school day. With only two SLPs on staff, it is challenging to ensure classroom staff is fully trained to use each student's individual device while also balancing paperwork and managing caseload requirements for productivity standards.

In addition to these barriers limiting Sara's AAC use in school, the use of her system at home is not a standard practice. At our school, AAC systems (low- and high-tech) are sent home if the family has expressed interest/motivation to use the system at home. Unfortunately, many families have expressed the desire for their child's AAC system to stay at school, stating that they don't use it at home. We recognized that this lack of buy-in is likely impacted by the limited time we have for parent training and coaching. In Sara's case, her parents did express interest in receiving training.

Strategies to Address Barrier 1

Carryover and use of a consistent form of communication across various settings and for a variety of functions is critical for successful AAC adoption. As an SLP who pushes into classrooms for short periods of time, I try to ensure AAC can be easily incorporated into daily routines and that we target goals that are immediately beneficial to the classroom staff (e.g., they see a reduction in challenging behaviors due to communication needs being met). Additionally, I have found that looking at ways to embed AAC use or AAC preparation into already established routines reduced the stress on the teachers and EAs during the COVID-19 pandemic. For example, Sara's classroom began using the morning routine as a time to get out devices and ensure they are charged and ready for the day.

Given staffing and time constraints, to make it easier for teachers and EAs to efficiently model and encourage device use, I also follow teachers' suggestions for AAC system customization options. Often this includes the creation of schematic (activity) grids and folders with vocabulary for common classroom routines. In Sara's case, I worked with her teacher and EAs to identify ways to reduce AAC system navigation requirements that often took too much time for Sara to use or staff to model. I created more easily accessible main folders with commonly used vocabulary suggested by the classroom staff (e.g., folders with vocabulary related to daily activities, peers, feelings, and lunch choices).

I also, however, have recognized the challenges classroom staff face when they have students using several different AAC systems and applications (e.g., Proloquo2Go, Snap™ Core First®, Touch Chat®). Given the lack of time for individual training, and to increase EAs' comfort and familiarity with various AAC systems and intervention methods, my SLP colleague and I created small speech groups composed of several EAs and students with similar communication needs. During the speech group meetings, we used modeling, practice, and feedback to help the EAs learn to use different systems with the students and support peer interactions. We also included discussion time to troubleshoot any issues.

While addressing classroom use of AAC, our SLP school team has also examined ways we can adapt our practices to increase use of AAC in the home environment. First, we have found that scheduling 15- to 30-minute phone calls to conduct communication interviews with the Communication Matrix (Rowland et al., 2011), and using phone calls, texts, or emails to identify goals for the student at home generally increases family buy-in. During these exchanges, we also aim to identify current routines and communication opportunities used in the home environment. To address the barrier associated with the lack of time to conduct formal parent training, we have started sending parents videos from weekly speech therapy sessions showing successful use of AAC systems during familiar routines that parents can implement with ease (mealtimes, preferred activities, etc.). By first establishing effective strategies used in school (e.g., determining which prompts facilitate AAC use), we can then model strategies that parents will likely be able to use successfully at home without experiencing too much frustration or needing extensive training.

Barrier 2: Use of "Standard" AAC Approaches

It is not uncommon for therapists and teachers to have an AAC system they feel most comfortable using due to greater familiarity. Although matching features and individualizing systems based on client needs is critical when making AAC decisions, it is equally important to examine barriers that will prevent adoption of the system in everyday contexts. One barrier to using individualized high-tech systems in school settings is the staff's familiarity and comfort with using various systems. This may lead to the adoption of one-size-fits-all practices. In our school, for example, the previous SLP began

recommending Proloquo2Go (Assistive-Ware) for most individuals who could benefit from high-tech AAC, because most staff had experience using this system. Staff familiarity did result in more fluent use, easier modeling, and more efficient programming. Additionally, because many students use the same system, the school set up a keyword labeling system in which they use paper printouts of symbols from Proloquo2Go to label educational materials and contexts. Thus, although having a preferred or "go-to" AAC system doesn't fully enable individualization, it does allow for ease of implementation in school-based contexts.

However, in Tommy's case, the practice of having a standard AAC system created barriers to his successful AAC use. Following his decline in fine motor skills, Tommy experienced declining accuracy and increased fatigue with navigation required in Proloquo2Go. I wondered if a system that required less navigation or had a greater variety of access options would be a better fit for him, but I also had to consider whether I had the time, resources, and buy-in to train classroom staff in a new system. This decision was further complicated by insurance limitations, which will generally only pay for a new system every five years unless a formal appeal is submitted and approved.

Strategies to Address Barrier 2

As previously discussed, identifying barriers is simply one aspect of the treatment planning process. The more important aspect is identifying agreed upon strategies to mitigate the barriers. In this case, due to resistance from teachers, limited buy-in for high-tech systems from

Tommy's family, and insurance barriers, being able to immediately and successfully select and adopt a new system that would more directly meet Tommy's needs did not seem likely. Instead, I focused on how to customize and adapt his current system to better meet his needs. First, this involved working with the teaching staff to develop a quick access page of wants/needs with schematic organizations to reduce navigation on days where he was exhibiting increased fatigue or frustration. I also collaborated with the PT and OT to (a) facilitate positioning techniques that would reduce fatigue, and (b) determine access modifications we could make to increase accuracy. The PT suggested that his team ensure he is sitting in a chair with arm rests when using his device, so he doesn't fatigue from sitting up unsupported. The OT suggested we introduce a weighted stylus to support fine motor skills related to direct selection. Collaboration also allowed us to agree upon a prompting hierarchy that supports Tommy's communication while also respecting his body autonomy. Additionally, as a team, we agreed to limit the use of more challenging learning tasks during times when Tommy is fatigued.

Barrier 3: Limited Time and Resources to Conduct Evaluations and Customize Systems

When I conducted my first AAC evaluation in graduate school I had several hours to complete the assessment, and I had access to various AAC systems that I could use for dynamic assessment. With ample time and resources, I was able to develop a clear picture of the client's strengths and make recommendations regarding AAC system selection and goals. After this experience, I was shocked and overwhelmed when I was given 60 minutes to complete my first assessment as a licensed SLP. In school-based settings, it is common practice for SLPs and other therapists to have limited time to conduct assessments due to caseload productivity requirements and the intersection of insurance policy barriers (e.g., therapists only being reimbursed for up to 60-minute evaluations).

In addition to having limited time to conduct assessments, it can often be challenging for SLPs to have access to a variety of different AAC systems to use during the initial evaluation process. Though there are opportunities for SLPs to download various AAC applications for free (see resources at the end of this case study), this requires the therapist to have access to a personal iPad which may contribute to many therapists preferring a system they are more familiar with. Additionally, once a system has been identified it needs to be customized and programmed. Again, schools often do not provide SLPs with dedicated time for programming as it is typically not billable for insurance and limits the time SLPs are available to see students. In both Sara and Tommy's cases, significant customization and programming were needed to meet communication needs.

Strategies to Address Barrier 3

As a first step, I try to maximize the information I can gain from an initial evaluation with less-than-ideal circumstances (e.g., time constraints, limited resources, not familiar with client). Before the initial evaluation, I will first conduct a preference assessment to determine the student's interests and motivators and will collaborate with parents/teachers to ensure that I am using meaningful materials and activities. Often, I use the initial AAC assessment to identify the *next* best step following identification of known barriers. It is important for therapists to realize that barriers will continue to be identified since working with humans is dynamic and evolving. Based on the common profiles of students at my school, my initial evaluation process includes administering the Communication Matrix (Rowland, 2011) by gaining input from the families and teachers and directly observing how children communicate with different communication systems. The Communication Matrix helps determine how effectively a student communicates for different purposes (e.g., to request, refuse, comment) using different modalities (e.g., with unconventional and conventional gestures, picture symbols, manual sign, and natural speech). This initial assessment allows me to make recommendations to the team regarding what modalities and communication goals can be considered. However, because treatment planning is an active process, I continue to embed ongoing assessment within intervention sessions to inform future decisions regarding AAC use, implementation, and vocabulary selection. For example, the modifications we made to Sara's and Tommy's systems were implemented after observing difficulties with AAC use during speech sessions and classroom routines. After adjustments were made, we continued to

collect data to determine whether modifications are successful.

To make time to complete modifications and customizations, recently I have been looking for creative ways to spend 10 to 15 minutes of my scheduled speech therapy sessions to customize the device or certain page sets with my client, their teacher, or classroom staff. I have found that by allowing students to pick certain icons or take pictures for their system, they take more ownership and feel more involved in critical decisions. My clients do not always select the same pictures I would have considered based upon iconicity. Programming devices alongside my students also allows me to introduce and model the new vocabulary and demonstrate the navigational paths required to access the new words.

To maximize limited time for evaluation and customization, I also rely heavily on resources available to us through the state and from AAC companies. For example, I regularly access resources from the South Carolina Assistive Technology Program, Talk to Me Technologies, Lingraphica, and TobiiDynavox. Resources may include access to loaner devices, device trainings, and assistance in writing funding applications so that SLPs have more time to focus on AAC implementation. If a student receives a formal device trial process through companies such as Talk to Me Technologies or Tobii Dynavox, we are also able to use the time during the trial to continue our assessment process and customize page sets with relevant vocabulary. The companies are then able to transfer over the vocabulary set, which allows the student to resume with the same set from the trial.

Outcomes

As a school-based SLP who has limited time to work directly with students and communication partners, it has been critical for me to identify barriers that prevent AAC use in the classroom and home environments. Outcomes from Sara's case demonstrate how collaboration with classroom staff can lead to increased AAC use and changes to classroom practices. For instance, I have seen an increase in Sara's use of her device throughout her school day since customizing her device based on teacher feedback, identifying ways to incorporate AAC in existing routines, and involving EAs in collaborative groups. EAs and teachers regularly ensure Sara's device is available and create communication opportunities for her across different routines. Her teacher and EA also consult with me regarding strategies for implementation in the classroom. At one speech group meeting, one of the EAs mentioned how Sara's device often falls off her desk resulting in a keyguard becoming disconnected. The EA suggested removing the keyguard, given her ability to functionally access the device without it. This change resulted in more fluid responding from Sara and ease of modeling for the teachers and EAs. The small issue may not have been identified if it wasn't for the scheduled time for speech groups. Additionally, since sending home training videos, Sara's parents and caregivers have also identified ways to present more choices and communication opportunities during mealtime and leisure activities.

Whereas Sara's use of an AAC system that was less familiar to school staff may have created initial barriers to adoption, in Tommy's case the use of a standard program widely familiar to the staff was no longer meeting his needs. Although the AAC team will likely need to reassess long-term plans, Tommy has been experiencing fewer accuracy errors and is able to communicate more effectively when fatigued since programming new page sets with reduced navigational requirements and introducing a weighted stylus. Although he still engages in some challenging behaviors following communication breakdowns, the intensity and duration of negative reactions has reduced with his increased ability to efficiently repair breakdowns.

As a relatively new SLP, I have also found ways to conduct successful initial AAC assessments with limited time. By involving parents and teachers in completing the Communication Matrix (Rowland, 2011), and identifying student preferences and motivators, I have been able to select initial communication goals that consider client and family preferences and that are guided by students' current communication abilities and potential for learning. As evidenced by Sara and Tommy's cases, I have also found ways to continue to conduct ongoing assessments and make modifications as needed. By involving students in the vocabulary programming process, I have been able to find time to customize devices to meet student needs without sacrificing learning time.

Discussion

The barriers presented above are not unique and are likely common in school-based settings (Johnston et al., 2020). Although the cases provide examples of successful strategies for reducing practice barriers, they also demonstrate the need for ongoing assessment of barriers, and consideration of how addressing other opportunity barriers may affect changes to practice. In Sara's case, follow-up will be needed to ensure the strategies used in the home and school is maintained. Additional and ongoing vocabulary customization will also be needed as her communication develops and her interests change. As her language progresses, knowledge and skill barriers regarding how to use her system for more advanced language could also lead to a regression in the use of supportive AAC practices throughout the day. As limited time for training and staffing issues will continue to be barriers, creative and collaborative solutions (e.g., the EA and student speech groups) will still be needed. Thankfully, one of the lessons we learned from the pandemic is how to use online resources (utilize training videos, conduct training via Zoom, screen share an iPad, etc.) to support efficient learning.

For Tommy, although our solutions decreased some of his communication challenges in the short-term, if his motor abilities continue to decline, it is likely that he will need a different AAC system or access method. Unfortunately, getting buy-in to make this change will require addressing staff and parental attitudinal and knowledge barriers regarding the use of more high-tech systems. Additionally, data might be needed to support funding for a new device that would normally be restricted due to insurance policy barriers. Furthermore, although the modifications

we made have reduced some of Tommy's frustration and increased his communication, some challenging behaviors have persisted. We have recently noticed that school staff sometimes removes his device following challenging behaviors, which is never recommended. This practice suggests the need to address knowledge or attitudinal barriers regarding ethical and effective methods for managing challenging behaviors and honoring the communication bill of rights (Brady et al., 2016).

Ultimately, Sara and Tommy's cases highlight the fact that both individual students' needs and the feasibility of AAC recommendations need to be considered when creating AAC plans. Whereas AAC teams should not adopt "one-size-fits-all" approaches, they must also weigh how time and resource demands impact the selection and use of "ideal" methods for assessing, selecting, and implementing AAC systems. When the ideal is not possible, AAC team members should focus on developing efficient ways to conduct assessments, train parents and staff, and customize systems to better meet individual needs. Rather than accepting the status quo, or viewing barriers as roadblocks and dead-ends, AAC team members should view practice barriers as detours that can be addressed and managed. Although one person on an AAC team may not be able to immediately affect systemwide change on their own, by seeking input from other team members, and starting with small achievable changes to practice, they will likely see positive outcomes. In the words of an AAC consultant with complex communication needs, "barriers crumble and critics withdraw when they see a person achieve something that previously was thought to be impossible" (Hohn, 1998).

Case Example 2: Home-Based Setting Involving an Adult With Aphasia (Jennifer W. Hanson, CCC-SLP)

Individuals with acquired disorders who are introduced to AAC as adults often require the support of care partners (Beukelman & Light, 2020). Frequently, these care partners are family members of the person who relies on AAC. Thus, AAC team members working with this population must not only address the needs of the client but also meet family needs. These needs can be impacted by family dynamics, makeup, and culture. Even though AAC clinical teams can draw from their previous experiences to troubleshoot practice barriers that can impact working with families, it is prudent to be on the lookout for new challenges.

As an SLP working for an AAC company, I provide direct support and training to patients and their families. Although SLPs working for AAC companies may experience fewer organizational practice barriers, as well as fewer policy restrictions (e.g., we are not working within the confines of insurance billing), relying on the way things have always been done can still create practice barriers, especially during unpredictable times. The following case arose during the heart of the COVID-19 pandemic in 2020. Sean (a pseudonym) is a 67-year-old African American man who presented with severe, chronic expressive

aphasia secondary to stroke. He has mild receptive language deficits in both reading and listening comprehension and spends the majority of his day in his wheelchair or bed. Sean has right hemiparesis and primarily uses his left hand for activities of daily living. Because of his stroke, Sean moved in with a sister and some extended family, spanning three generations. Sean is also very close with another sister, who lives three time zones away. He had owned a business with the long-distance sister in the past, and the family reported he was very proud of his career. In this case, there were several practice barriers that impacted Sean and his family. These barriers included (a) COVID-19 practices that led to service delivery disruptions, (b) an initial training timeline that did not meet Sean's family's needs, and (c) the use of a default AAC device feature that did not meet cultural needs. These barriers and solutions are described further below and summarized in Figure 6–1.

Barrier 1: Practices in Place Due to COVID-19 Led to Service Delivery Disruptions

Prior to the start of the pandemic, Sean was receiving home health visits from an SLP, but these had terminated without any discussion of AAC. Although I am uncertain of the exact reason for his ending his prior SLP services, the discharge occurred during a time when home health therapists were experiencing high volumes of clients while being granted markedly limited visits. Although this may have been impacted by insurance policies, it is also possible that the organization providing

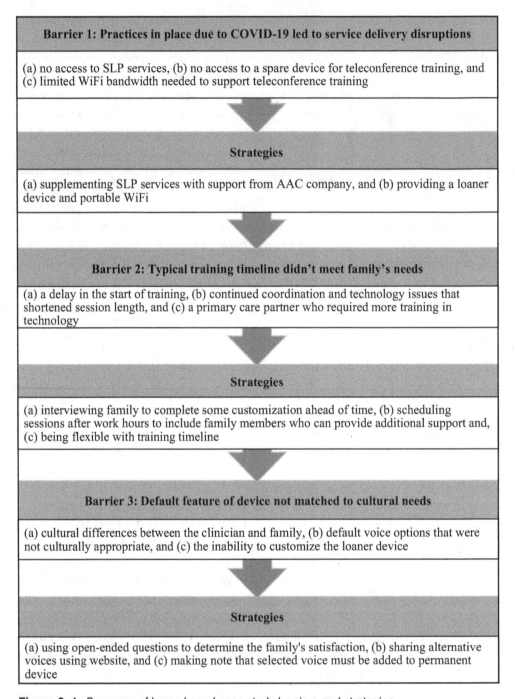

Barrier 1: Practices in place due to COVID-19 led to service delivery disruptions

(a) no access to SLP services, (b) no access to a spare device for teleconference training, and (c) limited WiFi bandwidth needed to support teleconference training

Strategies

(a) supplementing SLP services with support from AAC company, and (b) providing a loaner device and portable WiFi

Barrier 2: Typical training timeline didn't meet family's needs

(a) a delay in the start of training, (b) continued coordination and technology issues that shortened session length, and (c) a primary care partner who required more training in technology

Strategies

(a) interviewing family to complete some customization ahead of time, (b) scheduling sessions after work hours to include family members who can provide additional support and, (c) being flexible with training timeline

Barrier 3: Default feature of device not matched to cultural needs

(a) cultural differences between the clinician and family, (b) default voice options that were not culturally appropriate, and (c) the inability to customize the loaner device

Strategies

(a) using open-ended questions to determine the family's satisfaction, (b) sharing alternative voices using website, and (c) making note that selected voice must be added to permanent device

Figure 6–1. Summary of home-based case study barriers and strategies.

services implemented short-term practice guidelines to promote rapid discharge due to the pandemic. During "normal" times, a home health SLP might have identi-fied his candidacy for using an SGD and reached out to an AAC company to obtain devices to trial. This SLP might have also trialed communication apps on a tablet as part of their arsenal of therapy supplies. In this case, it did not seem likely that Sean would be receiving home-based services any time soon. There were few openings for outpatient SLP services in Sean's town. Given the additional demands on SLPs during the pandemic, outpatient providers may have changed their processes for admitting and accepting new patients. Furthermore, the few organizations that provided these services did not provide transportation (a challenge for Sean's family). Whatever the cause or combination of causes, Sean found himself without ongoing therapy despite his potential to improve his symbolic communication.

In this case, the patient's resourceful long-distance sister found out that some AAC companies lend out equipment and provide training directly to patients and families. She was inspired to give such a program a try when watching online videos of people with aphasia (PWA) using AAC to supplement their communication. I began working with Sean and his family (via Zoom) to determine an appropriate SGD to trial. After sending a loaner SGD to Sean, our next step was to begin coordinating regular teleconference meetings for training. Although the long-distance sister who kicked off the trial was familiar with Zoom, the sister living with the patient was unfamiliar with the platform. Although we knew we would have to provide training in technical skills, if we were going to conduct device trainings over Zoom, our first step was to ensure the family had access to a tablet or computer to use for teleconferencing. Due to the pandemic, the use of Zoom for work, therapy, and schooling became common practice. Unfortunately, this widespread use of online approaches became a barrier

to initiating family training, as the one computer in the house was being used for Sean's grandnephew's online school. For training and trials, the family also needed access to a strong WiFi signal so I could remotely log into the trial device, see what the user is doing in real time, and demonstrate how to make, edit, and use icons. With other family members in the multigenerational household using WiFi for other purposes, bandwidth was not adequate to support the use of an SGD and a device for teleconferencing. In summary, due to COVID-19, Sean and his family (a) had no access to SLP services, (b) did not have a spare device for teleconference training, and (c) had limited WiFi bandwidth to support teleconference training.

Strategies to Address Barrier 1

Sean's sister's decision to go directly to an AAC company was a short-term solution to overcome the COVID-19 practices that led to limited access to SLP services. AAC company device loans may serve as a bridge when practice barriers limit immediate access to a long-term device. Although it should not be a substitute for regular SLP services and a comprehensive AAC evaluation, AAC companies can also provide AAC device training. As COVID-19 practices also impacted Sean's family's access to a device that could be used for teleconferencing, our AAC company loaned out an additional unlocked device that allows users to access programs and apps other than the AAC system. In this case, the family used it to access Zoom. To address pandemic-related issues with WiFi signals (which disrupted the start of family training), through my company I was also able to request a portable

Internet hot-spot (Jetpack MyFi) to use for training sessions.

Barrier 2: Typical Training Timeline Didn't Meet Family's Needs

After resolving the initial COVID-19 practice barriers, one entire month had elapsed since the arrival of Sean's loaner SGD. For reference, at this point, I had completed many at-home trials and trainings within a one-month period. Seldom did trials exceed two months. Typically, my common practice is to conduct about four to five one-hour training sessions with families. In this case, "what I had always done" did not seem like it would meet the family's needs. For instance, on many occasions, there was a flurry of last-minute coordination issues that could leave us with only 15 solid minutes for training. This inefficiency was exacerbated by the fact that the sister with whom Sean lived was a tech novice and needed many reminders about how to connect to Zoom. In sum, the challenges we now faced focused on determining ways to maximize training time due to (a) a delay in the start of training, (b) continued coordination and technology issues that shortened session lengths, and (c) a primary care partner who required more training in technology.

Strategies to Address Barrier 2

From my experience, I know that it often takes time for families to develop customization skills. To make training more efficient, my team provides a jumpstart on customization by interviewing the family prior to starting the trial and determining personal vocabulary to add the device. For Sean, we created a starter vocabulary that included preloaded basic messages like his name, birthday, and address. Additionally, to maximize limited time for training, we met after work hours as frequently as possible to promote the participation of the patient's tech-savvy nephew. We also met at times when the patient's long-distance sister was available. This sister's strong relationship with Sean and openness to learning likely impacted the success of the training. Her particularly positive communication and attitude encouraged me to keep troubleshooting even when we had limited time. The trainings became very enjoyable, and you could witness Sean's face light up whenever he could see and communicate with his sister in a far-away state. Finally, in this case I also had to adjust my own expectations about "appropriate" training timelines. For this family, I wound up increasing the number of total sessions I provided, conducting a total of eight training sessions.

Barrier 3: Default Feature of Device Not Matched to Cultural Needs

Although I built a strong rapport with Sean and his family, I was also aware that I did not share the family's race, culture, or dialect. Additionally, I've never lived in the states where Sean has lived and am aware that I don't know much about the dialects of these states. As the trainings progressed and we had more customized messages to listen to, I wondered if the default synthesized voice on the SGD was a good fit for Sean, because it did not seem to reflect the family's dialect. Although the loaner device allowed for customization of several other culturally relevant features (e.g., changing the skin tone of symbols that depict people or using image search functions to find more culturally relevant symbols), the default voice options could not be changed on the loaner device. Challenges associated with this barrier focused on (a) cultural differences between the clinician and family, (b) default voice options that were not culturally appropriate, and (c) the inability to customize the loaner device.

Strategies to Address Barrier 3

While working with this family, I utilized the Life Participation Approach to Aphasia (Chapey et al., 2000), which focuses on determining client and family preferences and priorities for communication and participation in daily routines. Due to my training in culturally relevant practices, I also evaluated how my own perspectives or choices might differ from those of Sean and his family. With this knowledge in mind, I asked Sean and his family how they were liking the default voice and if they had interest in hearing other options. I was mindful to communicate that I did not have any assumptions or recommendations for a voice, just more options to present. It is important to note that users of AAC do not always select a voice with which they identify; sometimes they pick a voice they just happen to find pleasing. Because it is easy to share online resources when meeting on Zoom, I shared a website that presented demonstrations of

various digital voices compatible with the SGD. Through gesture and affect, Sean indicated which voice he liked. His family was supportive of his choice. I was not able to load the requested voice directly on the loaner device but made note of it for his permanent device. They seemed pleased with this solution.

Outcomes

As mentioned above, Sean's listening comprehension was a relative strength, so he learned to navigate the SGD quickly. I showed the family how to program messages that fit his communication needs and life participation goals. That is, we created messages having to do with his family, career, and favorite television shows. We also created a folder that would help his sister understand his physical symptoms and complaints. Our rapport was strong, and the family freely shared their goals for Sean with me. Sean participated in the training and once the vocabulary customization was at an adequate state, he shared TV and movie recommendations with me and told me about his career, all using the loaner SGD. It was around this time that I could see Sean and his family's confidence in using the device accelerate with each training. They were creating icons in-between sessions and reporting anecdotes of use from real-life. This uptick in device use corresponded with the start of a new calendar year which meant the patient was eligible for more speech therapy visits. His proactive sister got in touch with the primary care physician to request resumption of SLP services. When the new SLP started speech therapy visits, she encountered a patient and family who had confidence with AAC. In fact, Sean was in a good place for a comprehensive SGD evaluation, and it was not long before the SLP recommended a long-term SGD for Sean. This proactive family took a potentially frustrating barrier (a period of time without therapy services) and turned it into a positive by getting started on exploring and using an SGD with Sean.

Discussion

Prior to the pandemic, many patients who may have benefited from AAC may not have received SGD evaluations due to the reduced visibility of patients who are restricted to home environments. This issue was likely exacerbated when COVID-19 led to practice changes in how organizations decide when to initiate and terminate services. The pandemic also changed how SLP services can be delivered, and the equipment and resources families needed may have been stretched thin. In this case, by working directly with an AAC company, Sean's family was able to access a loaner SGD, a device for teleconferencing, and a portable WiFi device. Unfortunately, it might not be common practice for clinical organizations serving home-based clients to provide these same resources. To combat this issue, clinical service providers should seek to collaborate with AAC companies and create resource lists for families in need of access to loaner equipment. Resource lists may also include information about local or state level technology assistance programs. Additionally, although it is critical that patients receive comprehensive AAC

evaluations, when clinical organizations have extensive waiting lists (and referrals to other agencies or SLPs will not combat this issue), providing alternative resources might be a helpful starting point for families eager to learn more about communication options. Even as SLP practices shift back toward more in-person services, providing families with resources to hasten access to AAC systems and other useful technologies would continue to benefit patients and families.

Although changes to SLP practices during the COVID-19 pandemic created new barriers, in Sean's case I also had to evaluate how my own "typical" practices for training needed to be adjusted. In my role, I was able to adjust my practices by increasing the number of training sessions I provided to this family. Unfortunately, for private practice SLPs or clinical organizations, increasing the overall time for training might not always be a viable solution, as practices that limit family training hours may be impacted by policy barriers (e.g., insurance companies only allowing a certain number of billable training hours). Having insufficient time to work with families is a practice barrier that has long existed across a variety of settings (Johnston et al., 2020). To preemptively address limited training time, during the assessment process, SLPs should interview patients and families to determine important personalized vocabulary that can be programmed into an AAC system prior to training families on additional customization options. Furthermore, to maximize training time, clinicians will also need to utilize problem-solving, collaborative, and flexible thinking skills. When these skills are applied, telepractice approaches may, in some instances, be able to facilitate more efficient training than in-person methods. For example, in Sean's case, telepractice allowed us to schedule sessions at times most convenient for the family, include more tech-savvy family members who could support the primary care partner, and involve a long-distance family member who had a strong rapport with the patient. SLPs and other AAC team members should work with patients and families to determine priorities and goals for training, gain input regarding who should be included in trainings, and create schedules that allow for maximum family involvement when possible. As I learned in this case, SLPs may also need to deprioritize preconceived expectations about how long training should take and instead focus on determining the unique needs of a patient and their family to allow for flexibility. When clinical SLPs do face additional practice or policy barriers that prevent them from adding more training hours, they can also consider reaching out to AAC companies to determine what trainings the company may be able to provide as a supplement.

To further support families, clinicians must also skillfully and thoughtfully broach cultural and linguistic considerations with respect to AAC. Given the disparity in diversity between SLPs at large and the overall patient population they serve, clinicians can anticipate encountering cultural differences and must be prepared to address these differences (Guiberson & Vigil, 2021). Specifically, clinicians should be aware of AAC practices that may prevent cultural inclusion in home and community environments. Many AAC systems now have customization options that allow users to (a) select a synthesized voice that matches

their dialect or accent, (b) have access to bilingual or multilingual vocabulary sets, and (c) utilize icons and symbols relevant to a particular culture. Despite these customization options, in many contexts it may be common practice for clinicians to utilize default settings. Doing so may negatively impact patient and family buy-in and limit the functional usefulness of an AAC system in specific settings (e.g., at family or community events). To prevent this from occurring, clinicians should ask open-ended questions and check their personal assumptions when a patient comes from a different background than their own. Again, clinicians can work with AAC companies to better understand available options that they can pass on to their clients. For instance, some AAC companies are addressing these issues head on by offering pre-customization of loaner devices and allowing the user and family to alter device settings to fit the user's skin tone (for icons that reflect self) and language. There is more work to be done on the part of AAC companies to make it common practice to not only include these customization features in devices but make these options more transparent to both clinicians and families.

Case Example 3: Medical Setting Involving Adult With Palliative Care Needs (Stephanie M. McDougle, CCC-SLP)

In acute care settings, many barriers can limit the use of AAC (Marshall & Hurtig, 2019). Finding ways to overcome those barriers for our patients with complex communication needs can lead to the most meaningful patient care and learning opportunities. As an SLP working in a neuroscience intensive care unit (ICU) at a Level 1 trauma hospital, I have experienced both barriers and successes surrounding AAC evaluation and implementation. The following case study provides an example of how I was able to confront various practice barriers to meet a patient's communication needs. Table 6–2 provides a summary of the barriers and strategies.

Jeff (a pseudonym) was a 42-year-old male who was admitted to the ICU following a trauma that resulted in a high cervical spinal cord injury and quadriplegia. As a result of the level of the injury, he was orally intubated and dependent on a ventilator for breathing. He had been on the vent for over a week and discussions were being had with the family about potential next steps, which included a tracheostomy for long-term vent dependence and a percutaneous endoscopic gastrostomy (PEG) tube for ongoing access to nutrition and hydration.

Jeff was a rancher in a rural community on a family-run ranch. His family described him as someone who "lived to be a rancher." Outside of his daily ranch work, he worked training horses, which was his true passion in life. His family was almost certain that he would not want to get a tracheostomy and to remain on a ventilator without the ability to walk or continue working the ranch. However, "almost certain" was not enough to make this kind of decision for someone else. The discussion had turned toward moving forward with the tracheostomy and PEG tube so that he could be moved to a facility closer to home while they worked on figuring out what Jeff would want. Critical

Table 6–2. Summary of Medical Case Study Barriers and Strategies

Barrier	Strategies
Limited use of SLP consults for communication	• Educate colleagues regarding the role of an SLP and purposes of AAC. • Participate in hospital rounds to identify patients with communication needs. • Identify providers and teams open to collaboration.
Time constraints and prioritization of communication	• Embed communication evaluation or therapy into services addressing immediate medical needs. • Be flexible in scheduling of sessions to accommodate high priority medical needs. • Collaborate with professionals such as OTs and PTs on shared goals to maximize time.
Limited availability of AAC in the acute care setting	• Establish relationships with colleagues who may assist in providing short-term AAC access. • Work with organizations, such as state level assistive technology programs, charities, and AAC companies who can provide loaner devices and funding support.

care providers had employed some makeshift communication strategies (e.g., blink once for "no" and blink twice for "yes") and agreed with his family's proposed plan based on Jeff's answers. At this point, no one had consulted an SLP or discussed any type of communication outside of simple yes/no questions.

Barrier 1: Limited Use of SLP Consults for Communication

In an acute care setting, SLP services are often considered to be solely a dysphagia evaluation service. A patient who is orally intubated and likely sedated, is often not on the radar for a speech-language or AAC evaluation. In some instances, this may be because medical providers do not understand the roles and responsibilities of medical SLPs and how they can support communication. In Jeff's case, despite the medical staff and family's limited ability to communicate with the patient, contacting an SLP to conduct an evaluation was not considered by the providers or the ICU staff.

Strategies to Address Barrier 1

AAC finders is a term used to describe the individuals who can identify patients who may benefit from AAC (Beukelman & Light, 2020). To be successful, finders must understand the basic purposes of AAC, be aware of the roles of professionals who can conduct AAC evaluations, and know when and how to make AAC referrals. As an SLP in a medical setting, I have realized that colleagues often do not have such information and are unclear about my role and scope of practice. With experience, it has become apparent that the only way to address this barrier is to be proactive. Proactivity does not eliminate the barrier but can significantly reduce the role it plays in future situations.

Being proactive can be as simple as providing periodic education/in-services with providers and staff on each floor of the hospital to explain the entire scope of an SLP's job and the role we play when working with various patient populations. In this vein, I have created specific in-services for residents and attending providers to stress how important communication is for our critically ill patients. Providing concrete examples, such as Jeff's story, gives the providers something to remember when they encounter similar situations. As such, I try to use case examples specific to the service including situations in which an SLP was not consulted but could have provided intervention. These in-services have provided not only an educational opportunity for the residents and providers, but also go a long way to establishing rapport and credibility. If a provider knows you, trusts you, and respects you, you are more likely to get the referral without having to solicit it. You are also more likely to get it without pushback in the event you do have to request the consult be placed.

To help identify patients such as Jeff that can benefit from SLP involvement for communication needs, my team has also made it a priority to attend ICU rounds daily. The time spent attending rounds is considered "nonproductive time" as it is not direct patient care, however, the benefit we can provide with our input is often invaluable. This was especially true for Jeff, who we first became aware of by attending these rounds. After we learned about his case, when asked, the critical care team was more than happy to have us evaluate for better communication strategies. This was particularly relevant given the family's hesitance to finalize a plan of care and Jeff's physical limitations for participating in his own plan of care beyond a simple yes and no. At the time I met Jeff, I was not well-versed in palliative care, but have now come to realize that a great way to identify these specific patients who need rapid access to communication for end-of-life and goals of care planning, is to ensure that the palliative care team knows who you are, what you can provide, and how it can benefit their patients. This is a team that fiercely advocates for their patients' needs and understands the importance of communication. Because of this, they are often very open to collaboration.

Barrier 2: Time Constraints and Prioritization of Communication

Despite the importance of communication, when in an acute care setting, communication often takes a back seat to more immediate medical needs. For example, dysphagia resulting in no access to oral medication or nutrition/hydration will hold up a discharge to the next facility and/or complicate the overall recovery or plan of care; this makes dysphagia the priority. In fact, if you look at the mnemonic used by critical care providers across the country "FAST HUG" (feeding, analgesia, sedation, thromboembolic

prophylaxis, head-of-bed elevation, ulcer prevention, and glucose control) feeding is the number one priority in the care of critically ill patients (Vincent, 2005). Communication needs do not even make the checklist. Thus, given these priorities and the short-term nature of acute care, SLPs are often not given adequate time to evaluate patients and make communication recommendations. For instance, although more of an unspoken rule, if you are working on communication with a patient and a diagnostic test needs to be run, the providers need to do rounds (i.e., visit patients as part of a medical team to discuss current status and care plans), or a consult service needs to evaluate the patient, the communication session will likely need to be paused or postponed.

Strategies to Address Barrier 2

Although efforts to advocate and educate via in-services and attending rounds increases understanding of an SLP's role, these efforts will not make communication a bigger priority than immediate critical care needs. To combat this barrier, one strategy that I have employed is to integrate my communication evaluation or therapy into whatever immediate medical need is taking priority. It goes without saying that there will be certain instances where this is not feasible. For example, using partner-assisted scanning, a method in which a communication partner lists or "scans" through possible communication choices for the person with complex communication needs to select, will not be possible in the middle of an MRI. However, advocating to utilize ongoing patient care as part of your communication session or evaluation allows for a functional and dynamic assessment of the communication method, while also facilitating more successful communication between the patient and provider/ caregiver. By including providers in your communication sessions, especially after you have successfully achieved a reliable communication response, you are also able to "show off", how important SLP services can be for allowing patients to participate in their own care. This is a win for the patient and the provider, as well as a concrete, tangible event that providers will reference when encountering similar patients. This is one of the most effective ways to advocate for prioritizing communication in the future.

Another way to maximize time with the patient to focus on communication is to work within the schedule of the patient. SLPs must often acknowledge that there may be more critical pieces of care that need to occur and be willing to work their session around them. For instance, when working with ICU patients, I call the nurse to establish the best time to see the patient. Once in the room, I will attempt to manage time and expectations as much as possible. I hang a sign asking for no interruptions, include a time when I will be done, and respect the posted timeframe.

Collaboration with specific team members who can support communication evaluation and implementation is another way to address limited time with patients. For instance, physical PTs and OTs can help with assessing physical capabilities, positioning, and other assistive technology to aid communication access. Co-treatment with OT and PT is mutually beneficial and allows for increased imple-

mentation of communication strategies. As I mentioned previously, palliative care teams are also strong collaborators who understand the importance of communication. Often these team members will advocate for you to have the time that you need. They may also request for you to be present to facilitate more efficient communication or train them in strategies for future communication with the patient.

Barrier 3: Limited Availability of AAC in the Acute Care Setting

It is common practice that AAC implementation in the acute care setting is limited to the use of low-tech materials such as preprinted communication boards with line drawings of relevant medical needs and wants. These types of communication boards are easy, intuitive, and can often be all a patient needs to participate in their own care. However, for Jeff, the complexity of his communication needs could not be met with a generic ICU communication board. A partner-assisted scanning method was useful for novel messages; however, it was also time consuming and not as efficient as it needed to be in the time frame within which we had to work. Jeff quickly picked up the ability to use an EyeLink system, which is a transparent board with letters or symbols that is placed between a communicator and a partner so that the communicator can use eye pointing to build words or messages that are recorded by the partner. Based on his success with this low-tech system, it was obvious that he had plenty to say and wanted to participate in his own goals of care planning. However, more advanced technology was needed to improve efficiency. SGDs with eye gaze technology can be implemented when severe physical limitations for communication access exist. After I discussed my thoughts about eye gaze systems with Jeff, his family, and all the providers involved, everyone agreed that access to an eye gaze-controlled SGD would best meet Jeff's needs. The biggest roadblock was going to be obtaining a device as quickly as possible to evaluate Jeff's ability to use the device. Unfortunately, because these devices are costly and quickly become outdated, many acute settings do not have access to SGDs with eye gaze technology.

Strategies to Address Barrier 3

To address barriers related to limited access to high-tech devices, SLPs often need to build relationships with different individuals and organizations that can assist in providing loaner devices for short-term needs or provide funding assistance for more long-term needs. For instance, state level assistive technology programs typically have loaner devices as well as resources to support funding. For short-term needs, colleagues working in other hospitals, community-based settings, or at local universities may also be able to lend equipment needed for immediate use. Local chapters of charitable organizations such as the ALS Association may also be able to assist in acquiring or funding devices. Finally, AAC companies also have devices that they will lend to SLPs for evaluations or short-term needs. In Jeff's case, after reaching out to all my various contacts, within hours, a local representative from an AAC company was meeting me downstairs with an eye gaze-controlled SGD to loan the patient.

Outcomes

After Jeff and his complex communication needs were identified during rounds in the ICU, the SLP team requested to be consulted for communication. The order was put in immediately by the critical care provider and within the hour, I had met with Jeff. The OT and PT collaborated with me during this time to help me maximize his positioning to utilize a low-tech eye gaze communication method. Once I realized that Jeff was able to produce complete sentences with this method, it became apparent that he would benefit from a more efficient method of communication. I was able to obtain an eye gaze-controlled SGD (as discussed above), and with minimal instruction, Jeff was able to calibrate on the device and use it to produce a myriad of messages efficiently.

With Jeff and all of his providers and family present, we were able to quickly move forward with having a care discussion. Using his SGD, Jeff made it clear that he did not want a tracheostomy or PEG and he did not want to live without the ability to walk or breathe on his own. The palliative team offered counseling and his family asked good insightful questions. Ultimately, Jeff was able to verbally (through the SGD) confirm what his family already knew. He wanted to withdraw care. He specified that he wanted to be at home, with his family and horses on the ranch he grew up on when they took the breathing tube out.

Discussion

For many, Jeff's story might not be considered a success, but if we remove the emotion of a patient dying, we are left with a case of a patient that was able to communicate his wishes, which could then be carried out. The amazing hospital staff and patient's family made that a reality for him because he was able to tell them exactly what he wanted. There is nothing more successful than that as we are there to facilitate the communication, even when the message is tough to hear.

I learned so much from Jeff's case, but if we focus on the practice barriers that have been discussed here, there are three big lessons. First, it is necessary to educate colleagues about what SLPs can provide and how AAC can support patient communication. It may not seem like you are making much headway at the time, but it could be a random conversation about a case such as Jeff's, or a quick lunch in-service that a provider remembers and that may make the difference as to whether they become an AAC finder. Second, SLPs and other AAC team members should not be afraid to ask for what patients need. This could be a consult, time, collaboration, or equipment. It is cliche to say that the answer will always be no if you don't ask, but you will be surprised what you can get if you ask. For instance, I didn't think that an AAC representative that I had only met peripherally would let me borrow an expensive eye gaze device, but she didn't even hesitate despite knowing it wouldn't result in a sale. Finally, although communication may never meet a facility's definition of productivity, this does not make it any less important. The amount of time that I spent with Jeff over a few days left me feeling guilty that my team had to "pick up my slack" while I spent all this time on a single patient. But for Jeff and for his family, there was absolutely no better use of my time that week.

Not all of our advocacy efforts and endeavors will end in success, but when we focus on patients and learn from our experience, there is no outright failure. I have found that the successes can be so powerful that they can keep you pushing and advocating for those successes for every patient you have, no matter how small the need. The more successes you have, the easier it will be to provide a rationale for solutions to address the next practice barrier you face.

References

Beukelman, D. R., & Light, J. C. (2020). *Augmentative & Alternative Communication: Supporting children and adults with complex communication needs* (5th ed.). Paul H. Brookes.

Brady, N. C., Bruce, S., Goldman, A., Erickson, K., Mineo, B., Ogletree, B. T., . . . Wilkinson, K. (2016). Communication services and supports for individuals with severe disabilities: Guidance for assessment and intervention. *American Journal on Intellectual and Developmental Disabilities, 121*(2), 121–138.

Chapey, R., Duchan, J. F., Elman, R. J., Garcia, L. J., Kagan, A., Lyon, J. G., & Simmons Mackie, N. (2000). Life participation approach to aphasia: A statement of values for the future. *The ASHA Leader, 5*(3), 4–6.

Guiberson, M., & Vigil, D. (2021). Speech-language pathology graduate admissions:

Implications to diversify the workforce. *Communication Disorders Quarterly, 42*(3), 145–155.

Hohn, R. (1998, March). *Breaking down the barriers: A consumer perspective.* Disability Information resources. https://www.dinf .ne.jp/doc/english/Us_Eu/conf/csun_98/ csun98_072.html

Johnston, S. S., Blue, C., Gevarter, C., Ivy, S., & Stegenga, S. (2020). Opportunity barriers and promising practices for supporting individuals with complex communication needs. *Current Developmental Disorders Reports, 7,* 100–108.

Marshall, S., & Hurtig, R. R. (2019). Developing a culture of successful communication in acute care settings: Part I. Solving patient-specific issues. *Perspectives of the ASHA Special Interest Groups, 4*(5), 1028– 1036. https://doi.org/10.1044/2019_pers-sig12-2019-0015

Rowland, C. (2011). Using the communication matrix to assess expressive skills in early communicators. *Communication Disorders Quarterly, 32*(3), 190–201.

Vincent, J. L. (2005). Give your patient a fast hug (at least) once a day. *Critical Care Medicine, 33*(6), 1225–1229. https://doi .org/10.1097/01.ccm.0000165962.16682.46

Zangari, C. (2018, April). *We don't do AAC.* PrAACtical AAC. https://praacticalaac .org/praactical/we-dont-do-aac/

Section III
Understanding and Addressing Attitude Barriers

Section Overview

Attitude barriers refer to the attitudes and beliefs of others that impede the full participation of individuals who use AAC. These attitudes and beliefs may be present in individuals (e.g., clinicians, educators, employers, peers, family members), or they may be systemic in that they are held by the public as a whole or by a variety of gatekeepers. Further, attitude barriers can run along a continuum where they can be blatant (e.g., an individual using AAC being told that they cannot have a job because it takes too long to formulate a message), or more subtle (e.g., a reduced expectation by educators because a student uses AAC).

In this section, each of these different types of attitude and belief barriers will be explored in detail. Additionally, potential pathways for overcoming these barriers will be reviewed. Upon completion, readers will be able to:

- Describe the impact of attitude barriers on the lives of individuals who use AAC.
- Summarize the research on attitude barriers.
- Identify effective strategies for addressing attitude barriers.

7 Attitude Barriers: Learning From Individuals Who Use AAC and Their Families

Samuel Sennott, Lateef McLeod, Eric J. Sanders, Jay Grochala*, Kevin Williams*, and Jamie Preece*

Individuals with complex communication needs may face a range of barriers related to attitudes and beliefs. Understanding the impact of attitude barriers on the lives of individuals with complex communication needs and their families can assist people who use AAC, professionals, and family members to design effective and efficient interventions to address those barriers. Although the barriers experienced by individuals who use AAC will vary based upon their unique circumstances, the following interviews provide the reader with direct insight about attitudinal barriers from the perspective of three people who use AAC.

Kevin Williams—Individual Who Uses AAC

In the first interview, Kevin Williams, an adult male who uses AAC, shares infor-

mation about the attitude barriers that he has encountered. Kevin was selected to give the Edwin and Esther Prentke AAC Distinguished Lecture presented at the ATIA convention in 2021 and serves on the Publications and Information Committee for USAAC, a national chapter of

Figure 7–1. Kevin Williams.

---

*These authors have contributed equally to this work and share senior authorship.

the International Society for Augmentative and Alternative Communication (ISAAC) is dedicated to supporting the needs and rights of people who use AAC. In the following interview, Kevin makes several points related to attitude barriers, including the importance of person-centeredness, the need to see individuals who use AAC not as savants, but as unique language learners, and about the role of technology for the augmented communicator.

Will you tell us a little bit about yourself?

I'm a freelance web developer, adaptive sports athlete, disability advocate, and an outgoing introvert. I have cerebral palsy. I enjoy adaptive water skiing, solving problems, helping people gain independence, and learning new things.

Can you please share information about your use of AAC over the years and your current AAC system?

My use of AAC started by pointing to Blissymbols on a nonelectronic communication board when I was in preschool. As I got older and literate, Blissymbols were replaced with more text vocabulary because communication partners didn't know or care to learn Bliss. When I was 16, I received a 144 location Liberator from Prentke Romich Company (PRC) using Minspeak® Word Strategy. I'm currently on my 5th generation PRC device. With close family and friends, I use my communication device alongside my natural voice and sign language to get my point across.

What are some of the attitude barriers that you see or experience that impacts the AAC community?

The first attitude barrier that I see occurs when communicating with people who are unfamiliar with AAC and so they don't understand that an AAC user has to get points across by any means necessary. The idea of a multimodal communicator is important.

I also think that some people have the attitude that a fluent augmented communicator is the result of an inherent savant-like skill rather than a result of hard work over time. The idea of the miraculous AAC user benefits no one. Learning to use AAC takes work and time and it is important for people to know that.

> "Learning to use AAC takes work and time and it is important for people to know that."

Could you expand upon what you mean by "inherent savant-like skill rather than a result of hard work over time?"

I mean that people who don't know much about AAC look at people who use AAC devices like they are savants just by how we use the device or they think that we picked the system up quickly once we had the opportunity to get a device. I started to recognize this as a barrier because I found myself doing conferences and meetings with speech-language pathologists who asked me, "How did you learn to use your device?," and "How long did it take?" When I said it took me a week, they would say "my students can't do that." But they didn't realize that I had used AAC systems for many years before using my current system and so the transition was easy. Because I had the background experience of using other systems, I was able to adapt to new devices and systems much more efficiently.

You bring up a great point about how people who are unfamiliar with AAC may think that technology is a "quick fix," without recognizing all that goes into being an effective augmented communicator. can you please share more about that?

Yes—AAC is not all about technology, even though its product is expressed through technology. Most of the time, AAC is more about how a person expresses an idea in the most efficient way possible for another person to understand. I don't think that basic concept is applied enough to people with complex communication needs. But the important point is that the person who uses the AAC system, whatever that system entails for them, needs to be at the center.

This raises another point that I want to bring up about technology and equity. Let's say I have had my device for five years. It's working now, but what if it dies tomorrow? Is that device still available and can I get the exact same model? Or has that device been replaced with something new and so now I will need to adjust to a new device. What can we do now (before a device dies sometime in the future) so that it's not a big learning curve for me when I need to switch? To me, that is all about equity in terms of asking if we are putting people in a place to be independent.

Regarding technology and equity, do you think socioeconomic status alters one's access to SLPs and evaluations for AAC devices?

Yes, I do think socioeconomic status has a lot to do with access. I also think the attitude a speech-language pathologist has, specifically, the identification or connec-tion they have with the person plays a big role in access.

One of the ways that we can address this is through mentorship. We need to mentor others so that they shift the focus in AAC away from the speech-language pathologists and the parents and toward the individuals themselves. We are the only disability subgroup where most of the resources target people other than the person using the product. In essence, I am calling for more person-centeredness.

A pathway for SLPs and others to get around this presumption barrier is to realize that AAC is a set of skills for the client to learn and not a treatment for a SLP to apply. Also, people need to realize that the set of skills a person acquires to communicate extends beyond any one piece of technology. Technology is always finite in its use whether it's in years of durability, hours of battery life, or minutes in speaking. If the goal is to teach a person to use technology to speak rather than helping them acquire the skills to communicate, then they will always fail to adapt with change. So, teaching people how to adapt to change, can help them break down the many attitude barriers in front of them.

> "I want to have a world where people can express and interpret their ideas, in their own time with judgment on the content and not the delivery."

With that in mind, let's turn our thoughts to what world you envision for the future as it relates to attitude barriers?

I thought about that and I have a simple statement to share, in that, "I want to have a world where people can express and interpret their ideas, in their own time with judgment on the content and not the delivery."

Key Points From Kevin's Interview

Kevin's experience represents a culmination of many years of taking increasing responsibility for his AAC systems to where now, as an adult, he thinks about and is self-determined about his system at a very sophisticated level. In terms of attitude barriers specifically, Kevin emphasized the importance of professionals and communication partners realizing how much work goes into learning to use AAC, and taking a person-centered approach to intervention. Additionally, he stressed the importance of mentorship, a therapeutic focus on teaching skills as opposed to focusing on technology, and teaching AAC users more about adapting to change as AAC technology inevitably changes.

Figure 7–2. Jay Grochala.

Jay Grochala—Individual Who Uses AAC

The following interview with Jay, an individual who uses AAC, provides additional insight into the impact of attitude barriers. In this interview, he speaks about some of the ways that attitude barriers have impacted different areas of his life. He also underscores the importance of moving beyond initial assumptions of a person who communicates using AAC by increasing opportunities for visibility, and encourages others to make connections with people who use AAC.

Will you introduce yourself including your name, age, gender, and race/ ethnicity? Can you share a little bit about who you are as a person, what you're doing in your life, and what you enjoy doing?

My name is Jason (Jay). I'm 43 and a white male and I have cerebral palsy. I'm a joker. I'm easygoing. I like to have fun. I like to play poker, go out with friends, watch sports, gamble, and have a few drinks. You know . . . do fun things like a normal guy.

Can you share some information about your use of AAC over the years and your current AAC system?

When I first started school, they put me in a special school for kids with disabilities. The school was called Regional Day, where all of the kids had a disability like me. The teachers started by figuring out what was the best body part I could use to point at what I wanted to communicate. I didn't have enough hand control to point at things that I wanted, but I had good head control. So, they decided that a head stick was the best thing for me to use.

When I was 10, I got my first AAC device. It was called a Touch Talker (the first portable device from Prentke Romich Company, released in 1984). Back then, I thought that device was amazing, but thinking back about it now, it definitely wasn't as advanced as the technology today. I was still using my head stick but I could write full sentences and tell everybody what I was thinking and what I actually wanted.

Then, PRC came out with a device called the Liberator. I liked it because it had a better voice, a bigger screen, and a built-in printer. After that, PRC came out with a device called the ECO. I really liked it because it was a computer, a cell phone, and I could work everything that had a remote control. I activated it by using something called eye tracking. It was pretty amazing. Now I'm using an Accent. It's basically like an ECO, but the eye tracking is so much better than what I first used.

> "I think when people first see me, they think I'm not smart or think that I cannot hold a normal conversation. Yet, people who aren't afraid to come up to talk to me quickly realize how smart I am and that I have a sense of humor."

Could you also share what attitude barriers you see currently affecting the AAC community?

I think when people first see me, they think I'm not smart or think that I cannot hold a normal conversation. Yet, people who aren't afraid to come up to talk to me quickly realize how smart I am and that I have a sense of humor.

Also, because of attitude barriers, finding jobs is really hard. But I'm lucky. I do invoices for a local company and I organize meetings for disabled people.

As a follow-up question, could you share where you see the future is in terms of helping to overcome these attitudinal barriers?

I think this is going to be hard to change, because people don't take time to get to know people like us. And, of course, companies aren't going to want to hire us because they want people who can do the jobs faster. You have to get lucky and get a break.

Also, it isn't really about technology, it's about giving people a chance. If we could type faster and answer phones faster that would help, but that's not the problem really. Like I said, I believe companies want to hire people who can do the job easier. Maybe, I'm going to just be a professional poker player!

What do you think about programs like vocational rehabilitation that provide on-the-job training? Have they provided any support in terms of influencing attitudes or getting hired to do work that you are interested in?

I have worked with Voc Rehab and had like five coaches, but I have had only one interview in 10 years. I do regularly lead a conversation-based support group for people with intellectual disabilities and while sometimes I get a little bored, it's easy money for me. It's once a month. It's about 10 people and we talk about topics important to the group.

> "I would like it if people who use AAC could just get out there more and could show people that we can do everything that everybody else can do."

To close out our conversation, what would you like to see in the future in terms of breaking down attitude barriers?
I would like it if people who use AAC could just get out there more and could show people that we can do everything that everybody else can do. In the future, I wish more people would give us more chances to work and talk to us more to see that we're capable of holding jobs.

Key Points From Jason's Interview

Jay's interview revealed important ways that attitude barriers can impact the lives of people who use AAC. For example, he highlighted the importance of the assumptions that some people have regarding AAC users in terms of their intelligence. Additionally, he tied that to difficulties that some individuals who use AAC have regarding finding employment. To remedy these types of attitude barriers, Jay emphasized the importance of providing more opportunities for people who

use AAC to be visible in the community so that society can learn more about them as individuals.

Jamie Preece—Individual Who Uses AAC, Emma Sullivan—Partner of Jamie and Translator

Jamie Preece is a terrific example of someone who is a lifelong learner. Jamie resides in the United Kingdom and has been an enthusiastic advocate and leader in AAC. He is a husband and father who enjoys being an amateur comedian and a cycling enthusiast. Jamie has held many leadership and advocacy roles, including being a part of the ISAAC LEAD committee, which encourages and supports people who use AAC in taking a leadership role within ISAAC. Our conversation with Jamie and his wife Emma Sullivan helps us learn more about breaking attitudinal barriers and shows vivid examples of this in action.

Will you introduce yourself including your name, age, gender, and race/ethnicity?
Jamie: My name is Jamie Preece. I am a 45-year-old white male from the United Kingdom.

Emma: I am Emma Sullivan, I am a 51-year-old white female from the United Kingdom.

Jamie and I have been together quite a long time and we are pretty well practiced at communicating. For an interview like this, it could take a long time if Jamie were only to communicate using his device, so we use a combination. Jamie will get me

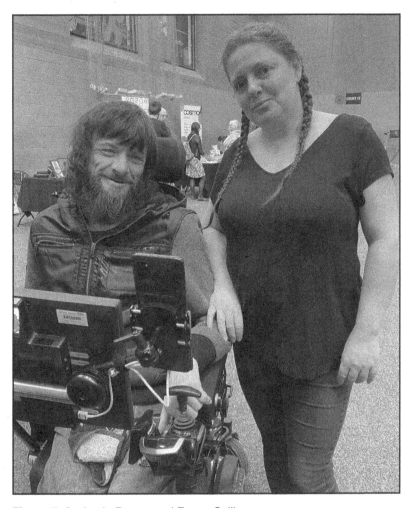

Figure 7–3. Jamie Preece and Emma Sullivan.

to translate and will add words or phrases using the device. He will approve all statements I make or get me to rephrase them so it's as authentic as possible. When you hear us talking this way it can seem as if I'm not saying the exact same thing as him but what I'm doing is rephrasing his speech into correct grammar as it is difficult for him. For this reason, I will say "Is that what you mean?" or "Is that the right way of putting it?"

Can you share a little bit about who you are as a person, what you are doing in your life, what you enjoy doing, and a bit about your AAC use over time?

Jamie: I have cerebral palsy. I use an electric wheelchair and a communication device, which gives me a lot of freedom. I also use a mobility scooter and enjoy going out for long rides. I have a partner, Emma. We have been together for 20 years and we have two children. Joe is 12 and Ruby is 10.

I like going to Sheffield Cycling 4 All, which is a disability cycling club where I am also a volunteer. I enjoy online stuff like Facebook and chatting online with many friends.

I am on the ISAAC Lead Committee and I host some of the ISAAC user chats. I am also the service user representative for Barnsley Hospital Assistive Technology Department and am involved in mentoring and peer support for other AAC users. I co-present talks for speech-therapy and occupational therapy students and recently I started writing and performing stand-up comedy using my communication device.

I did not have a communication device until I was 36 years old. Until then, I relied on my friends and family to translate my dysarthric speech. I did not learn to read and write at school and thought I was not clever enough to use AAC, but when I found out about symbol-based communication software I was amazed! Eight years on and I can't believe how much my life has changed. I can go out on my own and take the bus, train, go to the shops, etc. I can't imagine going back to not having a device.

Now, I use a Gridpad by Smartbox Assistive Technology founded here in the UK, which is a Windows tablet modified to be mounted on a wheelchair or stand. I use a stand at home and a joystick. When I am out, it fits on a wheelchair mount and I use the wheelchair joystick to control the tablet via Bluetooth®.

> "I did not have a communication device until I was 36 years old . . . Eight years on and I can't believe how much my life has changed. I can go out on my own and take the bus, train, go to the shops etc. I can't imagine going back to not having a device."

Emma: As well as being Jamie's partner and carer, and looking after our children, I support Jamie with all his tech! There's a communication device, monitor screen at home, smartphone (linked to the device), joysticks, button switches for occasional use, electric wheelchair, and mobility scooter. So, there's quite a few charging cables to manage!

I'm into photography and music, I love how having a smartphone means you have a decent camera on you at all times.

What attitude barriers do you see currently affecting the AAC community?
Jamie: Some people assume that a wheelchair user or someone who cannot use their voice to speak may be lacking in intelligence. Or they assume I am like Stephen Hawking and are disappointed when I'm just a regular guy. Other times, when I am writing something to say, a person may walk off thinking I have lost interest. They don't realize how hard it is for me to put my thoughts into words.

I once heard a mother say to her child that my device was a "sat nav" (i.e., satellite navigation system) to get me home. Another mum told her child that my device was for me to watch TV. It can be difficult to participate fully in a meeting if others don't understand my needs. These comments made me feel embarrassed because I was not able to put them straight like I could if I was able to speak clearly. But things like this make me want to increase awareness of AAC.

Another attitude barrier is when people think I'm like Lateef or Kevin (other ISAAC LEAD Committee members) who are faster at communicating. Some things can be really quick and some things tend to take a long time because I have never spelled them or the grammar isn't so easy. Eight years ago, I couldn't write my own surname.

With regard to the mother's "sat nav" story to her child, it would have been good to be able to explain it to her. Or, was she just making it up to pacify the child? You know, did she really believe what she was saying?

Could you share more about attitude barriers that you have encountered?

Jamie: Sure. Let me tell you another story. One time, I was getting on the bus and I used the joystick to control the wheelchair as well as to control my communication device through Bluetooth®. The bus driver stopped, put the ramp out, and said "Where are you going?" So, I stopped going up the ramp to say something on my device. The driver said, "Are you getting on or not?" I hadn't written where I was going. So, I said "Yes, I'm getting on" and the bus driver said "But where are you going?" So, at this point, I didn't know whether to get on or keep talking. So, I got on the bus but still hadn't told the driver where I was going. Everybody was looking at me and were wondering what was going on. What did they think? Did they think that I didn't know what I was doing? I'm very independent and like to do things on my own. I should be able to.

My new device has a screen on the back so that people can see what I'm typing. I haven't been on that bus since I got it, but when I do, I can type in where I am going and the driver can see it. The device also has the three dots (like on your cell phone when you are texting) that people can see. So, rather than interrupting me, they can give me time to write. They can then come back to me and say that it looks like you finished writing there.

> "Integration needs to start in school and carry on through life. We need to normalize other ways of speaking."

What pathways to breaking down attitudinal barriers do you see?

Jamie: Integration needs to start in school and carry on through life. We need to normalize other ways of speaking. AAC users can do so much if we are given the right support.

Emma: America seems more forward thinking than the UK. I think we need to catch up a bit with all this stuff regarding addressing attitude barriers in the UK. I think we're getting there. I would like to see more integration and more things that are led by AAC users. For example, the ISAAC AAC user chats are great because they're user led. And why shouldn't they be? You wouldn't get a bunch of doctors having a meeting, led by someone who wasn't a doctor. So, it should be the same for AAC users. It just makes sense, doesn't it? Things will be very different if there is a speaking person running the meeting and I don't think it's good. They do have some meetings in the UK and they can sometimes be not so user led, not so user focused, which is the difference. Isn't it Jamie?

> "Everybody said she didn't know anything . . . didn't understand anything, even her parents. She didn't speak at all. She was thirty. But I could see that she could understand."

Jamie: It is the difference. Let me share another story from a couple of years back, where a woman in a wheelchair was in my cycling club. Everybody said she didn't know anything... didn't understand anything, even her parents. She didn't speak at all. She was thirty. But I could see that she could understand.

After about six months, I decided to ask her "Which bike do you want to go on?" I said "Blue for my right hand and red for my other hand." She looked at the hand that represented the color that she wanted and they got the bike over. She was very happy. That led to her parents going and getting her assessed and getting a communication device. Now she lives independently and has a new life. She was thirty years old . . . she just needed to be given the chance. I was only an acquaintance; I am privileged to have been able to help.

> "Visibility is key . . . Seeing people using other ways of communicating will help change attitudes."

Thank you for sharing that pivotal moment in that woman's life. Could you help us understand that further in terms of breaking down attitude barriers?
Jamie: Visibility is key. People need to understand about AAC and they can't do that if they never see anybody using it. Seeing people using other ways of communicating will help change attitudes.

Technology will also help to break down the barriers. This will lead to more people getting help to access AAC. Also, the development of more human sounding voices will make people feel better about using computer-based AAC and improve people's perception of AAC users.

What world do you want to envision for the future in terms of attitude barriers?
Jamie: I would like to be able to go out for a coffee without people wondering what my device is for, they would just come up and chat with me like anyone else. I would like to see developing countries have access to AAC like we do, and I would love to contribute to this goal.

One project we are just setting up will involve improving the access to counseling therapy for AAC users, as this seems to be very limited right now. We are very excited about this project as we feel it's a very important area that has been neglected.

Key Points From Jamie and Emma's Interview

Jamie and Emma discussed many ways that attitude barriers have impacted their lives and provided some concrete ways to overcome these barriers. Similar to what Kevin and Jay spoke about, one of the biggest attitude barriers is related to the impressions that people have about individuals who use AAC to communicate. Jamie and Emma spoke directly about people making assumptions regarding intelligence. Additionally, they highlighted different ways that technology might aid in reducing negative attitudes. Finally, they communicated the importance of visibility. Here, having more of the general public see people using AAC to communicate could be a way to break down particular attitude barriers.

Conclusions

Each of the people interviewed in this chapter pinpointed ways that attitude barriers have impacted their lives. All of the interviewees were very clear about the fact that the impressions that others have about people who communicate using AAC can have a negative impact on a variety of aspects of their lives. Interviewees suggested pathways for overcoming attitude barriers including increasing visibility of individuals who use AAC through employment opportunities, leadership roles, or simply through encouraging others to get to know them. Additionally, the role of technology in both perpetuating and ameliorating attitude barriers were discussed. Specifically, one message was that people believe that some individuals who use AAC can just figure out how to use a communication device without recognizing all of the work that goes into developing communication skills and using an aided system. The other message was that technological advances may aid in increasing positive attitudes. While it is clear that attitude barriers impact the participation of people who use AAC, it is also clear that there are pathways that could be used to decrease these barriers. Decreasing attitude barriers is important for ensuring full participation and equity for people who use AAC.

8 Attitude Barriers: Exploring the Evidence Base

Eric J. Sanders, Samuel Sennott, and Lateef McLeod

Attitudes can be defined as showing approval or dissatisfaction when making an evaluation of an entity such as an object, person, or ideology. This evaluation occurs as an interaction of cognitive (e.g., beliefs and thoughts), affective (e.g., feelings and emotions), and behavioral (e.g., overt actions) factors (Eagly & Chaiken, 2007). These attitudes can be expressed or can be more covert (Beukelman & Light, 2020; Eagly & Chaiken, 2007). Furthermore, the evaluation that results from this interaction can be both positive and negative (Eagly & Chaiken, 2007). The attitudes of both individuals who use AAC and communication partners can impact the successful communication of an AAC user (Beukelman & Light, 2020; Light & McNaughton, 2014).

In terms of attitude as an opportunity barrier, negative attitudes of an AAC user's extended community (e.g., caregivers, peers, professionals, general public) may create obstacles to successful use of AAC (Beukelman & Light, 2020; Johnston et al., 2020). The interviews in the preceding chapter detailed some of the ways attitude barriers impact the experiences of individuals using AAC. Further, a robust research base exists that underscores the impact of attitudes on the lives of individuals with disabilities, including those who use AAC. Research has also looked at measuring attitudinal change in communication partners over time and as a result of intervention (Beck et al., 2010). In this chapter we will review how attitude barriers may impact AAC use and then provide potential solutions to address this issue.

Attitudes Toward Individuals Who Have Disabilities

According to recent estimates, there are one billion people worldwide that have some sort of disability, accounting for approximately 15% of the world's population (World Health Organization &World Bank, 2011). Unfortunately, individuals with disabilities often experience negative attitudes related to their disability (Wilson & Scior, 2014), and there are a variety of undesirable outcomes that may result from these negative attitudes. For example, experiencing these negative attitudes may result in people with disabilities to experience feelings such as powerlessness and frustration (Jahoda & Markova, 2004), and difficulties in the workplace (Snyder et al., 2010) and school (Cook et al., 2007). Research has also examined negative attitudes toward people with communication-related disabilities. For example, children who are typically developing may have negative attitudes toward peers with fluency (Guttormsen et al., 2015) and articulation impairments (Hall, 1991), as well as those with intelligibility of speech (Lee et al., 2017) and resonance (Bettens et al., 2020) impairments related to cleft-lip and/or palate. Taken together, it is clear that the attitudes toward individuals with disabilities, including those with communication impairments, can have a significant impact on various facets of life for people with disabilities.

Discrimination against individuals with disabilities, often referred to as ableism, may be related to negative attitudes (Friedman & Owen, 2017). The basis for ableism is related to the historical marginalization of people with disabilities. For example, starting in the nineteenth century in the United States, people with significant disabilities were routinely placed in institutions (Pelka, 2012). Because of this institutional practice, that lasted until the mid-twentieth century, the mainstream public was not accustomed to living amongst people with disabilities (Pelka, 2012). This, in turn, may have influenced public attitudes. However, the Disability Rights movement and the Independent Living movement that started in the late 1960s eventually led to the closing of these institutions and made it a right

for many people with disabilities to live in the community (Pelka, 2012). Coupled with that cultural change was the development of AAC systems in the late 1950s and early 1960s and the development of speech generating devices (SGDs) in the 1970s. This resulted in people with complex communication needs communicating independently and living in the community (Wendt et al., 2011). Although these changes have been positive and have potentially decreased negative attitudes toward people who use AAC, attitude barriers persist.

Attitudes and AAC

Given the impact of attitudes on individuals with disabilities, including those with communication impairments, it is predictable that researchers have investigated attitudes in relation to a variety of AAC related topics. Investigations reveal that negative attitudes toward individuals who use AAC and AAC in general may result in outcomes as diverse as lowered expectations by teachers (Popich & Alant, 1997), negative attitudes toward hiring employees who use AAC (McNaughton et al., 2002), and fewer friendships between those who use AAC and those who do not (Thierren, 2019). It is important to understand as much as possible about attitudes toward AAC as this can help identify methods to change those attitudes and the resulting behaviors that may manifest themselves (McCarthy & Light, 2005). Additionally, it is necessary to keep in mind that the attitude of individuals who use AAC themselves toward AAC also plays an important part in successful communication (Light & McNaughton, 2014), although the focus of this section is on the impact of attitude barriers of the AAC user's extended communication network. In this section, we review research literature related to attitude barriers and AAC.

The Attitudes of Children and Adolescents Toward AAC and Individuals Who Use AAC

A major line of research has investigated the attitudes of children without disabilities toward their peers that use AAC (Beck et al., 2000; Beck et al., 2002; Lilienfeld & Alant, 2002). This area of research is necessary because attitudes of peers are thought to influence the quality of communication interactions (Beck et al., 2010). In these types of studies, researchers have investigated the influence of communication partner characteristics such as age and gender, as well as the type of AAC system that is being used, toward positive or negative attitudes.

In order to address peer-based attitude barriers, it is first necessary to determine what types of attitudes exist. This research has traditionally been conducted by asking participants to watch videos of individuals communicating with AAC and asking them to make attitudinal judgments about the videos. Different tools have been used to judge the attitudes of communication partners. Two tools that were developed by Beck and colleagues have been used in many of these studies. The first is the Assessment of Attitudes Toward Augmentative Alternative Communication (AATAAC; Beck et al., 2000), which is designed for elementary school-aged children, and the second is the Assessment of Attitudes Toward Augmentative Alternative Communication–2 (AATAAC-2; Beck et al., 2010), which was developed for adolescents. Another tool that assesses the attitudes of communication partners is the Communication Aid/Device Attitudinal Questionnaire (CADAQ; Lilienfeld & Alant, 2002), which has been used in research with school-aged children. The use of tools like these are interesting because they can help identify attitudes and factors related to those attitudes that might be important for ultimately learning how to break down attitude barriers. A nonexhaustive list of tools that may be helpful in identifying attitudes and factors that influence attitudes is provided in Table 8–1.

Through using these types of tools, researchers have examined a variety of variables that may influence the attitudes of communication partners toward individuals who use AAC. In particular, Beck and colleagues' work examined the influence of both age and gender and the interaction between these for school-aged students from elementary through high school. For elementary school-aged children, there were equivocal results in terms of the influence of age on attitudes. For example, in one study, Beck et al. (2000) found that 3rd graders had more positive attitudes toward peers who use AAC than 5th graders. However, no difference was found by Beck et al. (2002) between the attitudes of 4th and 5th graders. In terms of adolescents, Beck et al. (2010) revealed a trend indicating that, as children moved from middle to high school, they may have

Table 8–1. Assessments Used to Measure Attitudes Toward AAC

Name of Instrument	Population	Sample Citation
Assessment of Attitudes Toward Augmentative Alternative Communication (AATAAC)	Children, Grades 1–5	Beck, A., Fritz, H., Keller, A., & Dennis, M. (2000). Attitudes of school-aged children toward their peers who use augmentative and alternative communication. *Augmentative and Alternative Communication, 16*(1), 13–26.
Assessment of Attitudes Toward Augmentative Alternative Communication–2 (AATAAC-2)	Adolescents, Grades 7–12	Beck, A. R., Thompson, J. R., Kosuwan, K., & Prochnow, J. M. (2010). The development and utilization of a scale to measure adolescents' attitudes toward peers who use augmentative and alternative communication (AAC) devices. *Journal of Speech, Language, and Hearing Research, 53*(3), 572–587.
Attitudes Toward Nonspeaking Persons Scale (ATNP)	College students	Gorenflo, C. W., & Gorenflo, D. W. (1991). The effects of information and augmentative communication technique on attitudes toward nonspeaking individuals. *Journal of Speech, Language, and Hearing Research, 34*(1), 19–26.
Communication Aid/Device Attitudinal Questionnaire (CADAQ)	Children, Grades 6–7 (but used in studies with similar but different aged children)	Lilienfeld, M., & Alant, E. (2002). Attitudes of children toward an unfamiliar peer using an AAC device with and without voice output. *Augmentative and Alternative Communication, 18*(2), 91–101.
Professionals' Attitudes Regarding Children Who Communicate Alternatively	Adult-aged school personnel	Beck, A. R., Thompson, J. R., Clay, S. L., Hutchins, M., Vogt, W. P., Romaniak, B., & Sokolowski, B. (2001). Preservice professionals' attitudes toward children who use augmentative/alternative communication. *Education and Training in Mental Retardation and Developmental Disabilities*, 255–271.

more negative attitudes toward AAC use. In terms of gender, the majority of studies with elementary school-aged children, adolescents, and adults have found that girls have more positive attitudes toward AAC use than boys (Beck et al., 2000; Beck et al., 2002; Beck et al., 2010; Lilienfeld & Alant, 2002) although this was not the case for 1st graders (Beck et al., 2000). This information is important and suggests that interventions designed to decrease attitude barriers among children may need to be differentiated based on age.

The impact of other factors on attitudes such as a child's familiarity with individuals with disabilities have also been explored. Across different age groups, increased level of familiarity was shown to result in more positive attitudes toward those who use AAC (Beck et al., 2000; Beck et al., 2002; Beck et al., 2010). This may also be important for the differentiation of interventions designed to improve attitudes.

Another area that has been explored is the relationship between the type of aided AAC system that is being used (e.g., low-tech vs. high-tech) and attitudes. Here, Beck et al. (2000) found no difference in attitudes based on this factor with elementary school-aged children. Similarly, Lilienfeld and Alant (2002) examined whether 11- through 13-year olds had different attitudes toward a video of a child using aided AAC with voice output versus without voice output. They found that the participants had more positive attitudes toward the video with voice output. More recent research explored whether the use of an iPad to communicate versus communication board had an impact on the attitudes of 1st graders (Hyppa-Martin, 2016). Similar to Beck et al.'s findings, no differences were found related to the type of device that was used. Additionally, with adolescents, Beck et al. (2010) found no differences based on whether the research participants were viewing an AAC communicator with a static versus dynamic display device.

This is an interesting finding when considered in relation to the comments made by Jamie in Chapter 7 regarding the relationship between their technology and the attitude barriers that stemmed from it. Specifically, Jaime spoke about the importance of how design features, such as a screen on the back of the device so that communication partners could see what was being communicated, was crucial for increasing positive attitudes. Although research investigating the relationship between technology and attitudes is equivocal, this area of investigation is important because technological advanced in AAC devices (e.g., higher quality voice output, increased functionality), may have a collateral impact on attitude barriers.

The Attitudes of Other Stakeholders Toward AAC

The Attitudes of Family Members and Other Caregivers

In addition to exploring the attitudes of children, research has investigated the attitudes of other stakeholders toward AAC, including family members. Family perceptions regarding AAC are particularly important for successful use of AAC (Baxter et al., 2012) and research suggests that attitudes of family members may be influenced by a variety of factors. For example, knowledge and frustration with technology may impact the attitudes family members may have toward aided AAC (McCord & Soto, 2004). As caregivers are particularly important in teaching individuals with CCN how to use AAC, ensuring their comfort with technology is important for its successful use (McNaughton et al., 2008).

Another important consideration is that families of individuals who use AAC may believe that the use of AAC will hinder speech development or recovery of speech for individuals who have acquired impairments (Romski & Sevcik, 2005). Research indicates that this is not the case, and that AAC can help to facilitate speech in individuals who use AAC (Romski et al., 2010; Schlosser & Wendt, 2008). It is possible that this type of attitude barrier could lead to inadequate communication solutions for children and adults who require AAC.

Caregivers may also have negative attitudes toward aided AAC. For example, Moorcroft et al. (2019) found that some caregivers believed that AAC was not necessary for communication with their child, that their child was not developmentally ready for AAC, or viewed a system as a toy (Moorcroft et al., 2019). Investigating these types of attitudes is crucial as they are examples of characteristics that may ultimately lead to device abandonment (Johnson et al., 2006; Moorcroft et al., 2019).

The Impact of Culture on Attitude

It is also important to consider cultural differences and resulting attitudes in terms of AAC. Given that communication systems should be designed to reflect the cultural and linguistic practices of the family (Soto & Yu, 2014), it is certainly possible that negative attitudes and perspectives will result if this is not considered in the assessment and implementation process (Light & Beukelman, 2020; Soto & Yu, 2014). For example, in a qualitative study examining the perspec-

tives of four Mexican-American family members of individuals who used AAC, McCord and Soto (2004) found that some participants expressed frustration with AAC devices related to the language of the device and the pronunciations of the synthesized speech. In terms of cultural differences, communication style using AAC was identified as a particular barrier because interactions with a device were not as intimate and interdependent as their preferred communication styles.

Other factors that should be considered when identifying barriers related to AAC use include understanding the impact of cultural views on disability as well as including the voices of individuals with disability in research regarding AAC (McCord & Soto, 2004). It is important to note that these types of findings are not unique to Mexican-American families and speak to the importance of cultural competence and responsiveness of professionals tasked with providing AAC intervention to (Soto, 2012). It is clear that if aspects related to cultural and linguistic diversity are not addressed, negative attitudes toward AAC by both the support network of individuals who use AAC and the user may proliferate.

The Attitudes of Educators and Health Care Professionals

In addition to families, the attitudes of educators toward AAC have been explored. This is a particularly important group to investigate because negative educator attitudes may result in low expectations, reduced opportunity to communicate, and poor academic outcomes (McCarthy & Light, 2005; Popich & Alant, 1997).

Dada (2019) investigated teacher attitudes in South Africa by administering the Teacher Attitude Scale (TAS; Dada & Alant, 2003) to teachers working at a school for students with disabilities. Here, the teachers viewed two videos, one with a child using an iPad and one with a child using a communication board. Positively, there were no statistically significant differences between the teachers' perceptions of their own ability in providing AAC-related services, the expectations that they had for the students, and the perception of the communication ability based on whether the focal student was using the communication board or the iPad. The teachers did, however, show a difference on how they viewed the devices, perceiving the communication board more positively than the iPad. This may have been due to factors such as the simplicity of a low-tech system compared to one using more technology. Importantly, the teachers had positive expectations of the focal students and their own ability to work with them, regardless of the AAC device used. This is encouraging given the importance of educators on success of AAC use in the classroom.

Related to the previous study, the attitudes of pre-service SLPs and special educators toward children who use AAC have also been explored. To accomplish this, Beck et al. (2001) developed a tool designed to evaluate the attitudes of professionals, the Professionals' Attitudes Regarding Children Who Communicate Alternatively (PARCCA). Here, pre-service undergraduate students interested in speech-language pathology and special education viewed videos of children, with different labels with regard to their disabilities (i.e., intellectual disability, physical disability, or no label), communicating using AAC and were asked to complete the tool. Similar to the previously reported studies involving children (Beck et al., 2002; Beck et al., 2010; Hyppa-Martin, 2016), there were no attitudinal differences related to the type of AAC that was used. Additionally, there were no differences based on disability label. These findings are positive as they speak to the attitudes of the pre-professionals who will later be charged with serving individuals who use AAC.

The attitudes of undergraduate college students toward those using AAC has also been examined. In one of the first studies to investigate attitudes toward AAC, Gorenflo and Gorenflo (1991) found that undergraduate students had more positive attitudes toward high-tech AAC devices that had voice output than an alphabet board, unlike the other studies that have been reviewed with different populations (Beck et al., 2001; Beck et al., 2010; Hyppa-Martin, 2016) and undergraduate students in speech-language pathology and special education (Beck et al., 2002). Although these findings are important, it is possible that the findings may be an artifact of age as exposure to AAC has become more common over the past three decades and mobile technologies, including those that use AAC applications, have become relatively ubiquitous. Additionally, Gorenflo et al. (1994) found that there was no difference in attitudes of undergraduate college students' regardless of whether a male or female synthesized voice was used. However, overall, females were found to generally have more positive attitudes than males. Further, undergraduates were found to have more positive attitudes toward individuals using AAC who they viewed as being more similar to themselves (i.e., with respect to values, activities of daily living). These findings speak to the complexity of different factors that may impact the attitudes of young adults toward those who use AAC.

In addition to attitudes related to AAC specifically, it is possible that other factors related to working with individuals who have disabilities may also be important to consider. For example, practitioners may be trained in only one type of intervention and may therefore have difficulty matching the most appropriate strategy(ies) to the person with whom they are working. Related to this, some practitioners may hold negative views in relation to expectations of individuals who use AAC. For example, some practitioners may believe that individuals with more significant delays or disabilities are not "ready" for AAC. These types of attitude barriers will clearly have an impact on the ultimate participation of an individual who requires AAC.

Attitudes Within the Workplace and Friendships

It is also important to examine the attitude barriers that adults who use AAC may experience in the workplace. Prior research has noted that a relatively small percentage of adults who use AAC are employed (McNaughton & Arnold, 2010). There are a variety of factors that may impact the employment of individuals who use AAC including effective communication, literacy skills, technology, and funding (Bryen et al., 2007; McNaughton

et al., 2002). However, one of the major barriers to employment includes the negative attitudes of co-workers (McNaughton et al., 2002; McNaughton et al., 2003). Negative attitudes of co-workers were also noted by Jay in Chapter 7 of this text when sharing his difficulties finding employment as a result of attitude barriers, and points to the importance of identifying attitude barriers in employment contexts in order to develop interventions that may ultimately reduce negative attitudes.

In a focus group consisting of eight employed adults with cerebral palsy who communicate using AAC, attitudes considered negative at the societal level, and by employers specifically, were identified as one of the major barriers to full-time employment. In the same focus group, the participants recommended that employers dispel these attitudes and provide opportunities for individuals who use AAC to show their employment-related abilities (McNaughton et al., 2002). This echoes Jay's sentiments in the previous chapter when he expressed his disappointment at not being offered chances for employment. From the employer perspective, Bryen et al. (2007) confirmed that although these types of barriers exist in the work setting, employers believe that they can be overcome through a combination of developing job-related skills in individuals who use AAC and being open to providing novel strategies and accommodations for those employees.

Another area that can be impacted by attitude barriers is the development of friendships. Individuals who use AAC may have difficulty establishing friendships (Beukelman & Light, 2020). It is plausible to assume that these friendships may be impacted, in part, by attitude barriers. Therrien (2019) used focus group methodology to ask eight individuals who used AAC about their friendships. For those that had friends who did not use AAC, attitudes and the resulting behaviors were thought to be important for the success of friendships. Studies such as this show the far-reaching impact of attitudes on the full participation of individuals who use AAC.

It is clear that attitude barriers are important to consider for the effective use of AAC and that there are a range of variables that may be impacting attitudes. Based upon prior research, it seems important to understand the developmental differences in attitudes toward AAC, the attitudes of caregivers and co-workers, and the potential impact of attitudes on the development of friendships. Further, it is necessary to promote pathways that may be used to ultimately improve these attitudes and result in fuller participation for those who use AAC.

Pathways to Overcoming Attitude Barriers

Attitude barriers may potentially impact the lives of individuals who use AAC at many different levels. As such, it is imperative that AAC teams identify ways to identify negative behaviors and influence the use of more positive actions (Beukelman & Light, 2019). There are a variety of pathways that can be used to improve attitudes. These pathways include (a) increased exposure of individuals with disabilities to those without disabilities as a means of improving relationships

and understanding (McCarthy & Light, 2005), (b) ensuring that communication partners are taught methods designed to improve communication with those who use AAC, and (c) implementing mentoring programs in order to improve overall communication skills and increase the ability to advocate. In this section we will describe the literature surrounding these pathways and provide concrete methods for decreasing attitude barriers experienced by individuals who use AAC.

Breaking Down Barriers: Increasing Opportunities for Exposure to Individuals Who Use AAC

The impact of exposure to individuals who have disabilities on the attitudes of individuals who do not have disabilities is an important area of study. At the most basic level, it is speculated that having contact with individuals with disabilities may have a positive impact on attitudes (Yuker, 1994). Here, exposure and contact can be thought of in terms of increasing levels of connectedness and proximity. For example, a more distal form of contact could be through exposure to individuals with disabilities through different forms of media, while a more proximal form of contact could be through formalized initiatives such as "Best Buddies," inclusion in schools, or programs in the workplace. Both of these forms of contact can provide avenues for increasing positive attitudes. In this section, we will review the literature, moving from studies that are more distal (e.g., exposure to someone with a disability) to those that are more proximal (e.g., the impact of inclusion). We will also provide suggestions for increasing both distal and proximal contacts.

> **Best Buddies** is an international program that serves individuals and developmental disabilities with through focusing on facilitating one-to-one friendships, integrated employment opportunities, leadership development, and inclusive living.

Distal Contact With Individuals Who Use AAC and Its Impact on Attitudes

At the most basic level, the development of this exposure can come through programs designed to increase awareness of people with disabilities. For example, De Boer et al. (2014) reported on the results of an intervention designed to improve knowledge about individuals with disabilities. Here, the researchers examined the impact of a program intended to influence attitudes toward students who had severe physical and intellectual impairments on kindergarteners and elementary school-aged children. This was done through the use of a six-week program designed to encourage positive attitudes through the use of storybooks. The program was effective in increasing the positive attitudes of kindergarteners but not elementary school-aged children. This may indicate a need to provide different types of materials based on age. This intervention's use of distal contact is important as these types of materials

and trainings could potentially be used to improve attitudes or prime children for more inclusive environments, including those who use AAC.

In terms of AAC specifically, there have been very few studies examining the impact of contact on attitudes. However, anecdotally, Krista (one of the authors of a case study in Chapter 9), talks about how she uses AAC in many different environments to increase visibility as a way to decrease negative attitudes. Earlier, we reviewed Beck and colleagues' studies indicating that familiarity with someone who had a disability may have an impact on attitudes. This type of familiarity was the focus of a study by Smucker et al. (2018). Here, a narrative about a young girl who used AAC was presented to 37 5th graders, and this group was compared to a control group that read a different narrative. Changes in attitude based on exposure to this narrative were measured using the AATAAC. Interestingly, there were no significant differences between the groups using the narrative. However, higher scores were documented for students who had previous experience with other students with disabilities. In addition to completing the AATAAC, the students answered questions about their perspectives regarding friendship with and the future of individuals who use AAC after reading the story. These qualitative findings revealed that the students saw the benefit of learning from someone who uses AAC, while also recognizing that it would be difficult to communicate with someone who used AAC. Although the findings from this study were equivocal, they do point to the potential of promoting positive attitudes by increasing distal exposure to individuals who use AAC as a first step.

More Proximal Contact With People Who Use AAC and Its Impact on Attitudes

At a closer level of exposure, the influence of the amount of contact individuals have had with individuals with disabilities on attitudes has also been explored with college-aged students. For example, Barr and Bracchitta (2015) examined the impact of disability type on attitude through the use of questionnaires designed to determine attitudes, the type of contact they had with individuals with disabilities, and related demographic information. Attitudes related to three disability groups were explored: physical impairment (a person in a wheelchair), developmental disability (intellectual impairment), and behavioral impairment (ADHD). Here, participants were found to have the most positive attitudes toward individuals with physical disabilities and the most negative attitudes toward those with developmental disabilities, indicating that there may be differential attitudes toward different disabilities. Positively, increased levels of contact resulted in reduced misconceptions, greater optimism, and more positive attitudes toward individuals with behavioral and developmental disabilities. Interestingly, the strongest predictor of positive attitudes toward all disability groups was the contact participants had with individuals with behavioral difficulties. Although this study did not investigate the relationship between contact with individuals who use AAC and attitudes, it is important because there may

be a differential impact of these attempts at contact depending on the disabilities. Individuals who use AAC tend to be heterogeneous in terms of their primary disabilities, and this may result in programs having differing levels of impact.

Similarly, the impact of contact has also been explored in the workplace. Novak and Rogan (2010) surveyed employment specialists to determine the impact of contact with individuals who have disabilities on attitudes. Indeed, contact in the workplace with individuals with disabilities was shown to have an impact on the attitudes of co-workers. It is important to note that job competence was also related to the attitudes of co-workers, especially if they relied on the job of the individual with disabilities that they worked with. They also found that the role of the supervisor was important in creating an accepting workplace environment for the social inclusion of their employees with disabilities. Again, although this study was not conducted with individuals who use AAC as the focus, it does point to the importance of inclusion in the workplace for the amelioration of negative attitudes and identifies factors that could be important in facilitating more positive attitudes. These results are also in line with the experiences that Jay shared in Chapter 7 related to the relationship between attitude barriers and employment when he noted that negative attitudes were a factor in him having difficulty finding work. Including more people with disabilities in the workplace, may have the potential to result in more positive attitudes toward those who use AAC in general.

The impact of the use of personal narratives to help establish familiarity by individuals who use AAC on the attitudes of pre-professional business students has also been explored. McCarthy et al. (2010) presented a set of four personal narratives that relayed information pertaining to various aspects of life as a user of AAC to juniors and seniors enrolled in an undergraduate business program. Here, the ATNP (Gorenflo & Gorenflo, 1991) was used to determine the impact of the narratives on the attitudes of the professionals when compared to a control group. A significant effect was found, indicating that the narratives had a role in the participants having more positive attitudes toward individuals who use AAC. The authors suggest, however, that these narratives contain information that pertains to the fit between the person who uses AAC and the business they are applying to, in order be even more effective. Similar to previous studies examining school-aged children, the use of these techniques to bring awareness and exposure may have an impact on decreasing attitude barriers. However, more work needs to be done to increase the volume of materials that are used at this level of connectedness between individuals who are typically developing and those who use AAC.

In summary, SLPs and educators should take the body of evidence pertaining both to more distal and proximal levels of contact into account when thinking of strategies to increase positive attitudes toward individuals who use AAC. It is clear that contact, even at a more distal level, could be used to improve attitudes. In schools, strategies for impacting attitudes through distal contact could include ensuring that there are age-appropriate curricular lessons and other media pre-sented to students without disabilities about students with disabilities, particularly those who use AAC. For the workplace, it is also important to increase levels of contact but also to emphasize the work that those who use AAC do in their job. Here, emphasizing the quality of the work of someone who uses AAC as well as using techniques, such as narratives told from the perspective of an AAC user may be a way to reduce attitude barriers.

The Potential Impact of Friendships on Attitude Barriers

Given the potential impact of contact on the reduction of attitude barriers, it is plausible that even closer levels of contact with individuals who use AAC may result in more positive attitudes. One of the closest types of contacts are relationship-building connections, such as friendships. As previously discussed, some individuals who use AAC may have difficulty forming close friendships with those who do not use AAC. For younger people in school, one way to help facilitate these friendships with those who do not use AAC, and thereby reduce attitude barriers, could be to include those who use AAC in inclusive settings where children who use AAC have opportunities to develop friendships with peers without disabilities due to proximity and shared activities.

These friendships can have a reciprocal, positive impact on both the person using AAC and peers not using AAC (Anderson et al., 2011). However, proximity and shared activities alone are not a guarantee that friendships will form and the friendships that do develop may look different because of the balance between being friends and the role a peer may take as a "helper" (Anderson et al., 2011). Unfortunately, children without disabilities who have friendships with children who use AAC are sometimes pressured by adults into a role that is more of a caretaker than a friend (Anderson et al., 2011). This type of relationship may shift the balance of power in the friendship to the extent that the relationship becomes more unilateral and less reciprocal.

There are some strategies that AAC teams can use to facilitate friendships that are balanced and reciprocal. For example, children without disabilities may establish friendships with children with disabilities in school due to an adult intervention, such as a buddy program, in which children with disabilities are paired with students who do not have disabilities (Anderson et al., 2011). However, it is important for AAC teams not to require peers to be "helpers," as that might reduce friendship to the role of "caretaker." Additionally, it may be important to promote opportunities for the individual using AAC to choose communication partners and teach both strategies for communication (see the future section focusing on communication-partner training). It could also be worthwhile to provide instruction to caregivers about how they can use activities and some of these techniques to promote friendships outside of school (Østvik et al., 2017).

A final strategy that may increase opportunities to develop friendships and strengthen relationships is the use of flexible grouping. Here, heterogeneous groups of students are intentionally arranged into small groups by teachers in order to sup-

port learning. Although the use of flexible grouping is most often discussed in the context of the classroom (Jameson & Johnston, in press), the concept is also applicable in community and employment settings. It is possible that these types of more intimate groups with individuals of varying levels of skills could have a positive impact on fostering the relationship between people who have disabilities, including those who use AAC, and those who do not. The use of these strategies may help bolster friendships, which could be a way to improve attitudes, as a whole, to individuals using AAC.

Breaking Down Barriers: Communication Partner Training as a Pathway for Improving Attitudes

Another potential pathway for decreasing attitude barriers is to ensure that individuals who do not use AAC are taught how to communicate with individuals who use AAC. This is important because the interactions between individuals who use AAC and those who do not are often qualitatively different than the exchanges between individuals who primarily use oral language. For example, communication exchanges between caregivers and children who use AAC often result in reduced conversational turns, not enough wait time, and the child being in a more passive communicative role as opposed to initiating conversation (Light et al., 1985). Decades of research have made it clear that effective communication with AAC requires more than just being presented with an aided communication device.

Individuals who use AAC need instruction focused on how to communicate using AAC (Kent-Walsh et al., 2015). To accomplish this, communication partners also need to be taught strategies for interacting and teaching these individuals.

Learning to communicate and enhance the interaction that occurs between people who use AAC and those who do not can be complicated. Light and McNaughton (2014) posit that in order to be competent communicators, individuals who use AAC must develop strong linguistic, operational, social, and strategic skills. It seems logical to assume that communication partners should also have strong linguistic, operational, social, and strategic skills in order to facilitate more positive and successful interactions with individuals who use AAC. Table 8–2 provides examples of how communication partners can address their own communicative competence for communicating with individuals who use AAC. Additionally, these are the types of areas that can be assessed in communications partners as part of a comprehensive AAC evaluation (Kovach, 2009).

It is plausible to posit that if communication partners learn more about techniques to facilitate communication with individuals who use AAC, there may be resulting positive impacts on attitude barriers. Specifically, it may increase the meaningfulness of the interactions themselves. Further, it is possible that through using these techniques, people who use AAC may increase their communicative competence. The combination of these two factors point to this as an important pathway for increasing positive attitudes toward individuals who use AAC.

One way that individuals communicating with individuals who use AAC have been taught to do this is through communication partner training protocols. Studies investigating communication-partner training have shown success in terms of facilitating these skills across family members, professionals, and peers (Beukelman & Light, 2020). For example, after going through a communication-partner intervention with parents, some children using AAC increased the length of utterances (Binger et al., 2008) and number of communicative turns (Nunes & Hanline, 2007; Rosa-Lugo & Kent-Walsh, 2008). In terms of teaching educational assistants, these types of techniques have also resulted in changes in the length of utterances (Binger et al., 2010). Finally, communication-partner trainings targeting peers has also impacted some children using AAC in terms of their communicative turns (Trottier et al., 2011) and communicative acts (Trembath et al., 2009).

The eight-stage instructional model developed by Kent-Walsh and McNaughton (2005) discussed in Chapter 2 may be a particularly useful strategy for training communication partners. As discussed in Chapter 2, this model has been used to teach communication partners how to implement a variety of instructional techniques, including modeling, asking wh-questions, and utilizing wait-time (Kent-Walsh & Binger, 2013); as well as using tag questions and providing written/visual choices (Ball & Lasker, 2013).

When using this type of strategy instruction, it is also necessary to consider cultural and linguistic diversity. One way to do this is ensuring that the targets and instruction are culturally responsive.

Table 8–2. Examples of Strategies for Addressing Communicative Competence in Communication Partners	
Areas of Communicative Competence	*Potential Strategies for Increasing the Communicative Competence of Communication Partners*
Linguistic competence • Understanding and expressing language through AAC	• Understanding that AAC users are receptively exposed to a different language than they are expected to express • Providing linguistic input/Modeling • Knowing where different symbols are on a communication device • Responding contingently
Operational competence • Understanding of how to use the technology of both low- and high-tech aided communication systems	• Helping to troubleshoot technology on communication devices • Knowing the features of a communication device • Understanding philosophies for device organization (both low and high-tech) (e.g., Fitzgerald Key organization, how visual scene displays are organized)
Social competence • The pragmatic and sociorelational skills of discourse using AAC	• Waiting for the AAC user to finish their message to respond • Understanding differences in the time it takes to communicate a message • Understanding the impact of a communication device on conversational turns • Teaching partner-focused questions
Strategic competence • The compensatory skills necessary if there is a breakdown in one of the other areas of competence	• Reaudization • Asking for clarification of a message • Recognizing and responding to alternate communication techniques in the event of a communication breakdown • Understanding the importance of multi-modal communication

Based on work to identify aspects of communicative competence for users of AAC by Beukelman & Light, 2020; Light, 1989; Light & McNaughton, 2014

There are a variety of ways to increase cultural responsiveness including considering the perspectives of the person who uses AAC and their support network, seeking to understand their values, and understanding how interaction styles related to culture may impact AAC intervention (Soto, 2012). Soto (2012) also recommended practices such as having training manuals in the home language of the user of AAC, providing ongoing support, allowing time to learn technology, and ensuring that there is a translator during communication partner training sessions if necessary. Implementing these types of practices is essential for communication partner training to be effective and may lead to a decrease in negative attitudes.

Communication partners can also be taught to use techniques that may decrease negative attitudes. For example, a process called reauditorization may impact attitude barriers. Here, a communication partner provides a contingent response (e.g., repeating the message but making changes such as verb tense) to a message said by an individual using a non-electronic AAC system. After watching a video of an AAC user and a communication partner who was using reauditorization, undergraduate college students had more positive attitudes toward the user of AAC (as measured by the PARCCA) (Hyppa-Martin et al., 2021). Teaching communication partners to use a strategy like reauditorization may be another pathway to decreasing attitude barriers.

In summary, communication partner training has the potential to positively impact the communication skills of both the communication partner and the person who uses AAC. This dual benefit may, in turn, lead to an increase in positive attitudes regarding AAC use. Communication partner training as a strategy for decreasing negative attitudes is discussed in additional detail in Chapter 9.

Breaking Down Barriers: The Impact of Mentoring on Attitudes

AAC mentoring involves individuals who are less experienced in using AAC learn-ing from those who are more experienced in using AAC (Ballin et al., 2009). AAC mentoring may improve AAC use in mentees (Ballin et al., 2013b) as well as help individuals who use AAC learn to cope with employment challenges, navigate the educational world resulting in greater academic success, and learn self-advocacy skills. Sociorelational skills and learning to collaboratively problem solve may also be benefits that develop from the mentoring relationship (Light et al., 2007). The skills developed through mentoring may result in mentees having increased visibility in school, community, and employment settings. This, in turn, may decrease the negative attitudes that AAC users experience. In Chapter 9, Krista details her involvement as an AAC mentor and the impact that mentoring can have on attitudes.

Studies investigating mentoring programs have taken place in a variety of physical and virtual settings. George and Warren (2012) wrote about their mentoring program designed for public schools in which co-author Warren (an AAC user) visited schools where there were individuals who used AAC to coach and encourage them to use their communication devices. In terms of virtual mentorship opportunities, Cohen and Light (2000) examined the impact of more advanced individuals using AAC mentoring young adults and adolescents through the use of e-mail and found that the more advanced AAC mentors were able to teach their mentees about age-appropriate topics such as transitioning to college and how to use different communication strategies. More recently, Grace et al. (2019) described a mentoring program for adolescent AAC users that operated through virtual platforms such as social media, e-mail, and video conferencing. Here, the participants reported that they had positive experiences throughout the time they were receiving mentoring including increases in social belonging and psychological engagement. These studies point to not only the effectiveness of mentoring programs but also the variety of ways they can be implemented.

The positive outcomes of mentoring programs may have a subsequent impact on changing negative attitudes. Ballin et al. (2013a) studied the impact of a mentoring program in which mentors and mentees had the opportunity to meet and discuss a variety of topics. Here, mentors in the program reported that they enjoyed the process, believed their mentees were communicating more effectively, and remarked that they would have liked to have had a mentor when they were younger. The impact of these programs on mentors was also documented by Cohen and Light (2000). In this case, mentors expressed satisfaction from participating in the email mentoring experience. Mentoring has even been shown to improve AAC use in mentees as measured by number of total words, number of different words used, and the number of bound morphemes (Ballin et al., 2013b). Through these types of mentorship programs, it is possible that mentors could relate their experiences with attitude barriers and help to provide solutions to help overcome these barriers. Finally, George and Warren (2012) explicitly posited that their program resulted in differences in expectations and attitudes of the people in schools toward the individuals who used AAC who connected with their mentor. This finding is unsurprising, and it is logical to assume that mentoring programs in other forums and age groups could have the same impact on the expectations and attitudes of an AAC user's extended communication network.

Table 8–3 provides examples and contact information for several mentoring programs. Although research has not been conducted demonstrating a direct link between mentoring and the decrease of attitude barriers, it is likely that inclusion in mentoring programs for both younger and older individuals who use AAC may have an indirect but positive impact on the attitudes of those who do not use AAC.

Conclusion

Attitude barriers have the potential to impact successful AAC use. However, it is important to recognize that attitude barriers do not exist within a vacuum and that the intersection of these barriers along with other opportunity barriers such as knowledge/skill, practice, and policy also have an impact on the participation of individuals who use AAC. There are a variety of factors that may impact the attitudes that individuals who do not use AAC have toward individuals who use AAC. This includes the experiences they have had with individuals who use AAC. It is also important to consider that there are other factors, such as disability type, age, and gender that may impact attitudes. Research investigating the attitudes of individuals who are typically developing toward individuals with disabilities indicates that the interaction between these factors is complex with different interactions seen between these factors (Nowicki,

Table 8–3. Resources for Establishing AAC Mentoring Programs

Resources

The Bridge School Mentorship program • https://selfdetermined.bridgeschool.org/mentorship/mentorship-and-aac/	Mentors from the Bridge School in California meet virtually with mentees through their self-determination program.
Alternatively Speaking AAC Mentors Issue June 1996 • https://www.augcominc.com/newsletters/newsletter_63.pdf	This is a link to an older newsletter that provides important information about mentoring and some good "how to" steps.
ISAAC LEAD Committee (People who use AAC) • https://isaac-online.org/english/about-isaac/activities-and-projects/people-who-use-aac-lead/	Although this is not an explicit mentoring program, it provides opportunities for individuals who use AAC to develop leadership skills within ISAAC and an opportunity to connect with other people who use AAC.
AssistiveWare webpage focusing on the development of mentoring programs • https://www.assistiveware.com/learn-aac/aac-mentors-role-models-and-experts-for-aac-users	This is a link to a web post highlighting the importance of mentoring and how to find mentors. Additionally, it includes links to blogs and websites for other AAC mentors.
Practical AAC Video of the Week: Mentoring AAC Learners • https://praacticalaac.org/uncategorized/video-of-the-week-mentoring-aac-learners/	Video links are provided on the PrAACtical AAC website regarding AAC mentoring.
Book an AAC Mentor • https://www.wespeakaac.com/book-an-aac-mentor.html	This is a website that provides links to book an AAC mentor, including Krista Howard, author of a case in Chapter 9.

Mentoring Articles Referenced in This Chapter

Ballin, L., Balandin, S., Togher, L., & Stancliffe, R. J. (2009). Learning to use augmentative and alternative communication (AAC): Is there a mentoring role for adults experienced in using AAC? *Journal of Intellectual and Developmental Disability, 34*(1), 89–91.	Perspectives article detailing the importance of mentoring programs for learning to use AAC
Ballin, L., Balandin, S., & Stancliffe, R. J. (2013a). The speech generating device (SGD) mentoring program: Supporting the development of people learning to use an SGD. *Journal of Developmental and Physical Disabilities, 25*(4), 437–459.	A description of the impact of an AAC mentoring program

Table 8–3. *continued*

Mentoring Articles Referenced in This Chapter

Ballin, L., Balandin, S., & Stancliffe, R. J. (2013b). The speech generating device (SGD) mentoring programme: An evaluation by participants. *Disability and Rehabilitation: Assistive Technology, 8*(3), 195–203.	An evaluation of the program described above by the participants
Cohen, K., & Light, J. (2000). Use of electronic communication to develop mentor-protégé relationships between adolescent and adult AAC users: Pilot study. *Augmentative and Alternative Communication, 16*(4), 227–238.	Mentoring of young adults who use ACC through email exchanges
Grace, E., Raghavendra, P., McMillan, J. M., & Gunson, J. S. (2019). Exploring participation experiences of youth who use AAC in social media settings: Impact of an e-mentoring intervention. *Augmentative and Alternative Communication, 35*(2), 132–141.	The description and evaluation of an AAC mentoring program conducted online for young individuals who use AAC
Light, J., McNaughton, D., Krezman, C., Williams, M., Gulens, M., Galskoy, A., & Umpleby, M. (2007). The AAC Mentor Project: Web-based instruction in sociorelational skills and collaborative problem solving for adults who use augmentative and alternative communication. *Augmentative and Alternative Communication, 23*(1), 56–75.	A description and evaluation of an AAC mentoring program that was web-based designed for adolescents and young adults using AAC
George, C., & Warren, F. (2012). Mentoring as a communication coach in a public school setting. *Perspectives on Augmentative and Alternative Communication, 21*(3), 115–121.	AAC mentor, coaching communication in schools with students who use AAC

2006). When attitude barriers exist, it is important to design and implement strategies to address the barriers. Although there is a need for research to determine these strategies' direct impact on attitudes, these might include: (a) increasing the level of contact that individuals who do not use AAC have with individuals who use AAC, (b) understanding how to communicate with individuals who use AAC, and (c) creating opportunities for AAC users to learn from mentors. Implementation of these types of strategies may aid in ameliorating different types of attitude barriers.

References

Anderson, K., Balandin, S., & Clendon, S. (2011). "He cares about me and I care about him." Children's experiences of friendship with peers who use AAC. *Aug-*

mentative and Alternative Communication, 27(2), 77–90.

Ball, L. J., & Lasker, J. (2013). Teaching partners to support communication for adults with acquired communication impairment. *Perspectives on Augmentative and Alternative Communication, 22*(1), 4–15.

Ballin, L., Balandin, S., & Stancliffe, R. J. (2013a). The speech generating device (SGD) mentoring programme: An evaluation by participants. *Disability and Rehabilitation: Assistive Technology, 8*(3), 195–203.

Ballin, L., Balandin, S., & Stancliffe, R. J. (2013b). The speech generating device (SGD) mentoring program: Supporting the development of people learning to use an SGD. *Journal of Developmental and Physical Disabilities, 25*(4), 437–459.

Ballin, L., Balandin, S., Togher, L., & Stancliffe, R. J. (2009). Learning to use augmentative and alternative communication (AAC): Is there a mentoring role for adults experienced in using AAC? *Journal of Intellectual and Developmental Disability, 34*(1), 89–91.

Barr, J. J., & Bracchitta, K. (2015). Attitudes toward individuals with disabilities: The effects of contact with different disability types. *Current Psychology, 34*(2), 223–238.

Baxter, S., Enderby, P., Evans, P., & Judge, S. (2012). Barriers and facilitators to the use of high-technology augmentative and alternative communication devices: A systematic review and qualitative synthesis. *International Journal of Language & Communication Disorders, 47*(2), 115–129.

Beck, A., Bock, S., Thompson, J., & Kosuwan, K. (2002). Influence of communicative competence and augmentative and alternative communication technique on children's attitudes toward a peer who uses AAC. *Augmentative and Alternative Communication, 18*(4), 217–227.

Beck, A., Fritz, H., Keller, A., & Dennis, M. (2000). Attitudes of school-aged children toward their peers who use augmentative and alternative communication. *Augmentative and Alternative Communication, 16*(1), 13–26.

Beck, A. R., Thompson, J. R., Clay, S. L., Hutchins, M., Vogt, W. P., Romaniak, B., & Sokolowski, B. (2001). Preservice professionals' attitudes toward children who use augmentative/alternative communication. *Education and Training in Mental Retardation and Developmental Disabilities,* 255–271.

Beck, A. R., Thompson, J. R., Kosuwan, K., & Prochnow, J. M. (2010). The development and utilization of a scale to measure adolescents' attitudes toward peers who use augmentative and alternative communication (AAC) devices. *Journal of Speech, Language, and Hearing Research, 53*(3), 572–587.

Bettens, K., Alighieri, C., Bruneel, L., De Meulemeester, L., & Van Lierde, K. (2020). Peer attitudes toward children with cleft (lip and) palate related to speech intelligibility, hypernasality and articulation. *Journal of Communication Disorders, 85,* 105991.

Beukelman, D., & Light, J. (2020). *Augmentative and alternative communication: Supporting children and adults with complex communication needs* (5th ed.). Paul H. Brookes.

Binger, C., Kent-Walsh, J., Berens, J., Del Campo, S., & Rivera, D. (2008). Teaching Latino parents to support the multi-symbol message productions of their children who require AAC. *Augmentative and Alternative Communication, 24*(4), 323–338.

Binger, C., Kent-Walsh, J., Ewing, C., & Taylor, S. (2010). Teaching educational assistants to facilitate the multisymbol message productions of young students who require augmentative and alternative communication. *American Journal of Speech-Language Pathology, 19,* 108–120.

Bryen, D. N., Potts, B. B., & Carey, A. C. (2007). So you want to work? What employers say about job skills, recruitment and hiring employees who rely on AAC. *Augmentative and Alternative Communication, 23*(2), 126–139.

Cohen, K., & Light, J. (2000). Use of electronic communication to develop mentor-protégé relationships between adolescent and adult AAC users: Pilot study. *Augmentative and Alternative Communication, 16*(4), 227–238.

Cook, B. G., Cameron, D. L., & Tankersley, M. (2007). Inclusive teachers' attitudinal ratings of their students with disabilities. *The Journal of Special Education, 40*(4), 230–238.

Dada, S. (2019). A comparison of special education teachers' attitudes toward various augmentative and alternative communication systems. In S. Halder & V. Argyropoulos (Eds.), *Inclusion, equity and access for individuals with disabilities* (pp. 153–178). Palgrave Macmillan, Singapore.

Dada, S., & Alant, E. (2003). A comparative study of the attitudes of teachers at special and educationally inclusive schools toward learners with little or no functional speech using communication devices. *South African Journal of Education, 22*(3), 213–219.

De Boer, A., Pijl, S. J., Minnaert, A., & Post, W. (2014). Evaluating the effectiveness of an intervention program to influence attitudes of students toward peers with disabilities. *Journal of Autism and Developmental Disorders, 44*(3), 572–583.

Eagly, A. H., & Chaiken, S. (2007). The advantages of an inclusive definition of attitude. *Social Cognition, 25*(5), 582–602.

Friedman, C., & Owen, A. L. (2017). Defining disability: Understandings of and attitudes towards ableism and disability. *Disability Studies Quarterly, 37*(1), 2.

George, C., & Warren, F. (2012). Mentoring as a communication coach in a public school setting. *Perspectives on Augmentative and Alternative Communication, 21*(3), 115–121.

Gorenflo, C. W., & Gorenflo, D. W. (1991). The effects of information and augmentative communication technique on attitudes toward nonspeaking individuals. *Journal of Speech, Language, and Hearing Research, 34*(1), 19–26.

Gorernflo, C. W., Gorernflo, D. W., & Santer, S. A. (1994). Effects of synthetic voice output on attitudes toward the augmented communicator. *Journal of Speech, Language, and Hearing Research, 37*(1), 64–68.

Grace, E., Raghavendra, P., McMillan, J. M., & Gunson, J. S. (2019). Exploring participation experiences of youth who use AAC in social media settings: Impact of an e-mentoring intervention. *Augmentative and Alternative Communication, 35*(2), 132–141.

Guttormsen, L. S., Kefalianos, E., & Næss, K. A. B. (2015). Communication attitudes in children who stutter: A meta-analytic review. *Journal of fluency disorders, 46*, 1–14.

Hall, B. J. C. (1991). Attitudes of fourth and sixth graders toward peers with mild articulation disorders. *Language, Speech, and Hearing Services in Schools, 22*(1), 334–340.

Hyppa-Martin, J., Chen, M., Janka, E., & Halverson, N. (2021). Effect of partner reauditorization on young adults' attitudes toward a child who communicated using nonelectronic augmentative and alternative communication. *Augmentative and Alternative Communication, 37*(2), 141–153.

Hyppa-Martin, J., Collins, D., Chen, M., Amundson, C., Timinski, K., & Mizuko, M. (2016). Comparing first graders' attitudes and preferences toward a peer using an iPad®-based speech-generating device and a non-electronic AAC system. *Augmentative and Alternative Communication, 32*(2), 94–104.

Jahoda, A., & Markova, I. (2004). Coping with social stigma: People with intellectual disabilities moving from institutions and family home. *Journal of Intellectual Disability Research, 48*(8), 719–729.

Jameson, J. M., & Johnston, S. (in press). Using flexible grouping. In *High leverage practices in special education*, Arlington, VA: Council for Exceptional Children & CEEDAR Center.

Johnson, J. M., Inglebret, E., Jones, C., & Ray, J. (2006). Perspectives of speech language pathologists regarding success versus abandonment of AAC. *Augmentative and Alternative Communication, 22*(2), 85–99.

Johnston, S. S., Blue, C., Gevarter, C., Ivy, S., & Stegenga, S. (2020). Opportunity barriers and promising practices for supporting individuals with complex communication needs. *Current Developmental Disorders Reports, 7*(3), 100–108.

Kent-Walsh, J., & Binger, C. (2013). Fundamentals of the ImPAACT program. *Perspectives on Augmentative and Alternative Communication, 22*(1), 51–58.

Kent-Walsh, J., & McNaughton, D. (2005). Communication partner instruction in AAC: Present practices and future directions. *Augmentative and Alternative Communication, 21*(3), 195-204.

Kent-Walsh, J., Murza, K. A., Malani, M. D., & Binger, C. (2015). Effects of communication partner instruction on the communication of individuals using AAC: A meta-analysis. *Augmentative and Alternative Communication, 31*(4), 271–284.

Kovach, T. M. (2009). *Augmentative & alternative communication profile: A continuum of learning.* LinguiSystems.

Lee, A., Gibbon, F. E., & Spivey, K. (2017). Children's attitudes toward peers with unintelligible speech associated with cleft lip and/or palate. *The Cleft Palate-Craniofacial Journal, 54*(3), 262–268.

Light, J. (1989). Toward a definition of communicative competence for individuals using augmentative and alternative communication systems. *Augmentative and Alternative Communication, 5,* 137–144.

Light, J., Collier, B., & Parnes, P. (1985). Communicative interaction between young nonspeaking physically disabled children and their primary caregivers: Part I-Discourse patterns. *Augmentative and Alternative Communication, 1*(2), 74–83.

Light, J., & McNaughton, D. (2014). Communicative competence for individuals who require augmentative and alternative communication: A new definition for a new era of communication? *Augmentative and Alternative Communication, 30*(1), 1–18.

Light, J., McNaughton, D., Krezman, C., Williams, M., Gulens, M., Galskoy, A., & Umpleby, M. (2007). The AAC Mentor Project: Web-based instruction in sociorelational skills and collaborative problem solving for adults who use augmentative and alternative communication. *Augmentative and Alternative Communication, 23*(1), 56–75.

Lilienfeld, M., & Alant, E. (2002). Attitudes of children toward an unfamiliar peer using an AAC device with and without voice output. *Augmentative and Alternative Communication, 18*(2), 91–101.

McCarthy, J. W., Donofrio-Horwitz, L. M., & Smucker, L. M. (2010). The effects of reading personal narratives written by an individual who uses AAC on the attitudes of pre-professionals in business. *Augmentative and Alternative Communication, 26*(2), 61–74.

McCarthy, J., & Light, J. (2005). Attitudes toward individuals who use augmentative and alternative communication: Research review. *Augmentative and Alternative Communication, 21*(1), 41–55.

McCord, M. S., & Soto, G. (2004). Perceptions of AAC: An ethnographic investigation of

Mexican-American families. *Augmentative and Alternative Communication, 20*(4), 209–227.

McNaughton, D., & Arnold, A. (2010). Supporting positive employment outcomes for individuals who use AAC. *Perspectives on Augmentative and Alternative Communication, 19*(2), 51–59.

McNaughton, D., Light, J., & Arnold, K. (2002). 'Getting your wheel in the door': Successful full-time employment experiences of individuals with cerebral palsy who use augmentative and alternative communication. *Augmentative and Alternative Communication, 18*(2), 59–76.

McNaughton, D., Light, J., & Gulla, S. (2003). Opening up a 'whole new world': Employer and co-worker perspectives on working with individuals who use augmentative and alternative communication. *Augmentative and Alternative Communication, 19*(4), 235–253.

McNaughton, D., Rackensperger, T., Benedek-Wood, E., Krezman, C., Williams, M. B., & Light, J. (2008). "A child needs to be given a chance to succeed": Parents of individuals who use AAC describe the benefits and challenges of learning AAC technologies. *Augmentative and Alternative Communication, 24*(1), 43–55.

Moorcroft, A., Scarinci, N., & Meyer, C. (2019). "I've had a love-hate, I mean mostly hate relationship with these PODD books": Parent perceptions of how they and their child contributed to AAC rejection and abandonment. *Disability and Rehabilitation: Assistive Technology, 16*(1), 72–82.

Novak, J. A., & Rogan, P. M. (2010). Social integration in employment settings: Application of intergroup contact theory. *Intellectual and Developmental Disabilities, 48*(1), 31–51.

Nowicki, E. A. (2006). A cross-sectional multivariate analysis of children's attitudes toward disabilities. *Journal of Intellectual Disability Research, 50*, 335–348.

Nunes, D., & Hanline, M. F. (2007). Enhancing the alternative and augmentative communication use of a child with autism through a parent-implemented naturalistic intervention. *International Journal of Disability, Development and Education, 54*(2), 177–197.

Østvik, J., Ytterhus, B., & Balandin, S. (2017). Friendship between children using augmentative and alternative communication and peers: A systematic literature review. *Journal of Intellectual & Developmental Disability, 42*(4), 403–415.

Pelka, F. (2012). *What we have done: An oral history of the disability rights movement.* University of Massachusetts Press.

Popich, E., & Alant, E. (1997). Interaction between a teacher and the non-speaking as well as speaking children in the classroom. *South African Journal of Communication Disorders, 44*(1), 31–40.

Romski, M., & Sevcik, R. A. (2005). Augmentative communication and early intervention: Myths and realities. *Infants & Young Children, 18*(3), 174–185.

Romski, M., Sevcik, R. A., Adamson, L. B., Cheslock, M., Smith, A., Barker, R. M., & Bakeman, R. (2010). Randomized comparison of augmented and nonaugmented language interventions for toddlers with developmental delays and their parents. *Journal of Speech, Language, and Hearing Research: JSLHR, 53*(2), 350–364. https://doi.org/10.1044/1092-4388(2009/08-0156)

Rosa-Lugo, L. I., & Kent-Walsh, J. (2008). Effects of parent instruction on communicative turns of Latino children using augmentative and alternative communication during storybook reading. *Communication Disorders Quarterly, 30*(1), 49–61.

Schlosser, R. W., & Wendt, O. (2008). Effects of augmentative and alternative communication intervention on speech production in children with autism: A systematic review. *American Journal of Speech-Language Pathology, 17,* 212–230.

Smucker, L. M., McCarthy, J. W., Benigno, J. P., & Boster, J. B. (2018). Personal contact through personal narratives: attitudes of fifth-grade children toward children who use augmentative and alternative communication. *Journal of Advances in Education Research, 3*(3), 148–157.

Snyder, L. A., Carmichael, J. S., Blackwell, L. V., Cleveland, J. N., & Thornton, G. C. (2010). Perceptions of discrimination and justice among employees with disabilities. *Employee Responsibilities and Rights Journal, 22*(1), 5–19.

Soto, G. (2012). Training partners in AAC in culturally diverse families. *Perspectives on Augmentative and Alternative Communication, 21*(4), 144–150.

Soto, G., & Yu, B. (2014). Considerations for the provision of services to bilingual children who use augmentative and alternative communication. *Augmentative and Alternative Communication, 30,* 83–92.

Therrien, M. C. (2019). Perspectives and experiences of adults who use AAC on making and keeping friends. *Augmentative and Alternative Communication, 35*(3), 205–216.

Trembath, D., Balandin, S., Togher, L., & Stancliffe, R. J. (2009). Peer-mediated teaching and augmentative and alternative communication for preschool-aged children with autism. *Journal of Intellectual and Developmental Disability, 34*(2), 173–186.

Trottier, N., Kamp, L., & Mirenda, P. (2011). Effects of peer-mediated instruction to teach use of speech-generating devices to students with autism in social game routines. *Augmentative and Alternative Communication, 27*(1), 26–39. https://doi.org/10.3109/07434618.2010.546810

Wendt, O., Lloyd L. L., Quist, R. W. (2011). *Assistive technology: Principles and applications for communication disorders and special education.* Emerald Group Publishing.

Wilson, M. C., & Scior, K. (2014). Attitudes towards individuals with disabilities as measured by the Implicit Association Test: A literature review. *Research in Developmental Disabilities, 35*(2), 294–321.

World Health Organization & World Bank. (2011). *World report on disability.* https://www.who.int/publications/i/item/9789241564182

Yuker, H. E. (1994). Variables that influence attitudes toward persons with disabilities: Conclusions from the data. *Journal of Social Behavior and Personality, 9*(5), 3–22.

9 Attitude Barriers: Studying Successful Case Examples

Eric J. Sanders, Lateef McLeod*, Samuel Sennott*, David J. Hajjar*,
Joanne K. Niemkiewicz*, Krista Howard*, Caroline Ramsey Musselwhite*,
and Brandi Wentland*

Introduction

This chapter will provide three case examples illustrating strategies for addressing attitude barriers. The case examples were written by two practicing SLPs and one person who uses AAC. These examples illustrate the successful use of strategies presented in the preceding chapter (e.g., increasing distal and proximal contacts, mentoring, communication partner training). They also discuss additional strategies for breaking down attitude barriers such as ensuring that AAC users have robust AAC systems and instruction, and engaging in advocacy. Each case highlights outcomes related to the strategies that were used and speaks to the impact of attitude barriers on children as well as adults who use AAC.

Case Example: Robust AAC, Literacy Instruction, and Communication Partner Training as a Way to Address Attitude Barriers (David J. Hajjar, PhD, CCC-SLP)

As a speech-language pathologist (SLP) family consultant, I frequently served as a liaison between the school team and the family. In this role, I often encountered barriers created by negative attitudes from a range of communication partners such as teachers, paraprofessionals, peers, therapists, and caregivers. In some instances, the lead teacher held these negative beliefs and other times educational support professionals or therapists promoted negative beliefs about students who used AAC.

---

*These authors have contributed equally to this work and share senior authorship.

This case example will describe Nick, a student with autism who used AAC during different periods of his educational journey. Starting when he was 5 years old, Nick used a variety of AAC systems, including dedicated devices along with multimodal communication methods such as vocalizations, gestures, and body movements. Nick's parents, and especially his mother, have always been actively involved in making decisions about communication, curriculum, and maintaining a robust AAC system that could grow and change with Nick's needs. Based on my observations and interactions with classroom staff, it was evident that some teachers held negative attitudes, while others expressed more positive attitudes about his potential learning and use of AAC.

Teachers with positive attitudes presumed competence with Nick and engaged with him as a student who was nonspeaking and who was focusing on improving his literacy skills while also learning to communicate using AAC. Individuals who promoted a positive outlook for Nick provided him with more frequent opportunities to consistently use AAC throughout the school day. Teachers who employed this type of communication approach typically engineered the classroom using visuals and structured activities to maintain a predictable routine, including independent work sessions, small groups, and adequate time for transitions. This approach to learning encouraged more independence while reducing the amount of adult directed physical and verbal cues. When communication partners in the classroom held positive beliefs related to Nick's abilities, they provided

and generated more frequent opportunities for communicative interactions.

Alternatively, some teachers were less enthusiastic about supporting communication and instead held negative attitudes about Nick's ability to effectively use AAC along with other multimodal communication methods. When partners held negative beliefs, Nick had more inconsistent use and access to his speech generating device, which made it challenging for him to be comfortable using AAC and engaging with others. In some classrooms, more frequent communication breakdowns and periods of dysregulation occurred during the school day. When partners failed to understand Nick's messages, his frustration increased, and it was more difficult for him to use AAC in these moments of communication breakdown.

Overall, it was difficult for Nick to sustain momentum with his education and make progress toward goals in language use, literacy, and AAC output. Since Nick also had self-abusive and physically aggressive actions toward others, this may have negatively influenced the attitudes of people who supported him across the school day. When Nick was dysregulated and acted physically toward a partner or peer, this created a difficult scenario for the entire classroom community.

Communication breakdowns became a common occurrence as Nick entered his teenage years. In general, classroom staff maintained low expectations and resulting negative attitudes and did not believe that Nick could become an independent communicator. Some teachers did not support Nick in using AAC and did not understand the value of focusing on literacy and teaching vocabulary across a range of categories and activities. AAC input and output were not regarded as priority learning goals and instead the primary focus was on compliance versus communication.

Strategies—The Importance of Instruction

One way we decided to address the attitude barriers of Nick's communication partners was through using a variety of instructional techniques designed to increase his communication skills. For example, over the course of Nick's education, his team of family and professionals used components of the TEACCH® Autism program (Mesibov et al., 2005) and the SCERTS® Model (Prizant et al., 2006) in their assessment and intervention plans. The TEACCH® Autism program is a structured intervention approach for individuals with autism that utilizes organizational supports, visual and written supports, and structured support designed to facilitate social communication. SCERTS® is an intervention model for individuals with autism and their families that targets social communication, emotional regulation, and transactional supports.

Nick's team completed SCERTS® questionnaires in the areas of social communication, emotional regulation, and transactional support. While the SCERTS® Model provided a structured method to collect the teams' observations and review Nick's progress, the TEACCH® Autism Program provided a foundation and inspiration for the development of visual supports, classroom engineering,

and the application of strategies to promote greater independence.

As a result of implementing these programs, Nick showed improvement in his ability to more frequently and consistently use AAC in the classroom. Nick's teachers noticed this and adjusted their negative attitudes by providing more consistent opportunities for him to become an independent communicator. Teachers became more comfortable implementing visual supports across the classroom setting, therefore reducing Nick's anxiety about upcoming or unexpected events. In addition, teachers engaged more in conversational exchanges with Nick and presented work tasks that were more complex, with higher demands relative to literacy, following directions, and expressive communication. As Nick demonstrated his skill and ability to more independently communicate and complete tasks, his teachers became more invested in his progress and provided more positive feedback about his learning and participation.

Within the framework of both the SCERTS® Model and the TEACCH® Autism Program, two specific strategies were used across settings to support AAC development, acceptance, and use: (a) a robust AAC system with a focus on systematic literacy instruction, and (b) communication partner training.

Strategies—Robust AAC and Systematic Literacy Instruction

Nick's family acquired and developed a robust AAC system and encouraged the school team to support access and use across a range of partners, settings, and functional activities. In addition to having access to robust AAC, Nick also engaged in a systematic and customized language and literacy program that was developed by his team and promoted his strengths as a visual learner within the context of meaningful and functional activities such as cooking, playing games, or having conversations with peers.

The use and development of a robust AAC system, paired with the implementation of a systematic literacy program, helped to mitigate negative attitudes from classroom staff. Because Nick had consistent access to AAC, he was able to build his expressive language skills and communicate about his needs, wants, and desires. Using his AAC system, Nick was able to engage in social reciprocity, indicate his preferences, and communicate his desire to stop or continue specific activities. Furthermore, as Nick acquired skills in reading both core and activity-based vocabulary, he used an increased repertoire of words and symbols. As teachers increasingly observed Nick's ability for new learning and acquiring vocabulary, they became more aware of his potential to become an independent communicator.

Using AAC, combined with literacy instruction, allowed Nick to have access to more vocabulary content and express a wider range of communication acts. He used his SGD to modify his daily schedule and provide feedback about preferred and nonpreferred activities. Overall, Nick engaged more in communicative interactions with his classroom teachers, which led to more frequent communication exchanges. This influenced how the teachers responded to Nick as they generated more opportunities for communicative interactions across the school day. As Nick experienced more communication success using AAC, this reduced negative attitudes from partners and increased their expectations for his learning and growth.

Strategies—Communication Partner Training

To expand Nick's use and access to AAC, it was critical to train communication partners about the importance of AAC input and output. Partner training was conducted using an approach to strategy instruction outlined by Kent-Walsh and McNaughton (2005). In this instructional approach, communication partners had opportunities to practice, role-play, and provide and receive feedback using a systematic method. In Nick's case, partner training empowered the teachers and educational support professionals to be more actively engaged and take ownership in the process of AAC instruction.

As a result of systematic partner training, classroom staff were more invested in supporting communication during the school day while also providing feedback on Nick's progress, as well as developing ideas for how to enhance engagement and participation. Generally, staff presented with more positive attitudes about Nick and his progress toward being a more independent communicator. Also, partners seemed to change in other ways. They engaged in more frequent dialogue sharing their perspectives and were more positive about supporting Nick through moments of dysregulation.

Partner training focused on increasing access and opportunity for Nick to use AAC, with a specific focus to reduce his overall dependency on prompts. Because Nick was a student who could easily become prompt dependent, it was critical to draw attention to this issue with the classroom staff. To prevent prompt dependency, a series of task analyses were conducted to better understand the individual steps required for Nick to independently complete a task. A prompt hierarchy was established so communication partners could provide support in a consistent manner and be more mindful about the impact of using physical, verbal, and gestural prompts.

As a result of investing time in training communication partners through demonstration and role play, an opportunity was provided for his classroom staff to better understand how to support Nick's independent use of AAC. Partner training provided concrete tools and strategies to classroom staff and empowered them to more effectively support Nick's use of AAC. When partners were provided specific ideas and methods to engage in communicative interactions with Nick, this also increased the overall frequency of AAC use and established more consistent expectations. Consequently, Nick's communicative success positively impacted the attitudes of communication partners who supported him. As a result of training partners and raising their awareness, they were more likely to offer opportunities for Nick to expand language beyond requesting and commenting. See Table 9–1 for a summary of the potential causes of the attitude barriers that Nick experienced and potential solutions.

Outcomes

Outcomes for measuring Nick's communication progress were based on the acquisition of new activity specific vocabulary, as well as accurate and independent use of utterance-based phrases and questions across appropriate settings and activities. Communication partners collected data relative to language and literacy acquisition during structured work sessions and functional tasks, such as cooking or playing

Table 9–1. Summary of Causes of Attitude Barriers Impacting Nick and Potential Solutions

Negative Attitudes Resulting From	Strategies
Presumptions about using AAC to communicate	Utilizing evidence-based instructional approaches targeting frequent and consistent AAC use
Presumptions about using AAC to communicate	Providing access to a robust AAC system paired with appropriate instruction
Presumptions about literacy development	Providing evidence-based literacy instruction
Presumptions about using AAC to communicate	Ensuring that communication partners are taught how to interact with individuals who use AAC

table-top games with peers. As outlined in Nick's individualized education plan (IEP), partners were trained to collect data while also being mindful of the type and amount of cues they were using during both structured and unstructured activities.

During Nick's elementary and early secondary education, he made great strides in his use and acceptance of AAC. His repertoire of vocabulary grew across a range of specific activities completed in both school and home settings. Over time, Nick become a more independent communicator and was able to use AAC with less prompting and for a wider range of purposes. Partners became more aware about providing prompts as they learned about following a hierarchy of type and frequency.

As Nick learned to complete tasks with greater independence, this also supported the development of positive attitudes among the school staff. Although, partner attitudes were not formally measured, it was evident that Nick's progress had a positive influence on the attitudes and beliefs of his teachers. Over time, classroom teachers and educational support professionals were more invested in supporting AAC use and as a result provided more feedback as they engaged in planning functional tasks for the curriculum. Teachers had higher expectations for Nick, created more opportunities for interaction, and were more persistent in supporting him through communication breakdowns or periods of dysregulation. These examples provide some evidence that having a strong focus on communication will benefit not only the student, but may positively impact the attitudes of communication partners as well.

Discussion

For many students who use AAC, some negative attitudes of communication partners have prevented opportunities for growth and learning in the classroom setting. When classroom staff hold skeptical beliefs and negative attitudes about a child's intelligence and general cognitive ability, it can be difficult to build an inclusive classroom community that truly facilitates communication across the entire school day and with a range of familiar and unfamiliar partners. Communication partners in the classroom should strive to support opportunities for interaction, which can lead to the use of more complex language and increased literacy skills. Supportive classroom environments can exist with purposeful engineering and support from AAC teams, including caregivers. These efforts can yield positive attitudes and generate a sense of renewed purpose and pride by staff and students who use AAC

AAC was an integral component during Nick's educational career and a critical tool to support his language and literacy development. Nick's communication success was due to having trained communication partners who used a systematic and structured programs for language and literacy instruction. In addition, using formal programs such as the TEACCH® Autism program and/or the SCERTS® Model, helped the team to continually assess progress and provide a foundation for sustainable learning to support functional communication, self-regulation, and independence in completing daily tasks.

Despite the negative attitudes of some communication partners, it is important to not let these attitudes interfere with an individuals' right to access and express themselves using AAC. When negative attitudes exist in a classroom, individuals who use AAC may have fewer opportunities to interact and communicate with others. Communication partners who underestimate the cognitive and communication abilities of people who use AAC may not consistently support receptive input or seek out opportunities for meaningful engagement and social interaction. To support students who use AAC, dedicated partners must recognize natural opportunities and implement key strategies to support both expressive and receptive communication across settings and with a range of partners.

In Nick's case, he had the unwavering support of his family and many professionals to guide him along his journey to becoming an independent communicator. However, he also encountered partners who expressed doubt about his skills and abilities. Partners who questioned Nick's cognitive ability and who held negative beliefs, were unable to move past their own personal views and traditional approaches to learning. These individuals were resistant to change, prioritized their own opinions and observations, and did not value the experiences or ideas of Nick's family. It is important for AAC teams to acknowledge differences in opinion, while also confronting negative attitudes that may exist. Teams should be inclusive of family members and ensure that individuals who provide support, promote a positive attitude, and remain focused on achieving collaborative goals in the areas of independence, communication, and self-regulation.

Case Example: Overcoming Negative Attitudes Toward AAC in a Rehabilitation Setting (Joanne K. Niemkiewicz, MS, CCC-SLP)

Early in my career, I had the opportunity to work in a standalone inpatient rehabilitation facility (IRF), with a large outpatient clinic right next to it. This allowed me to step away from my primary duties in the IRF and see outpatients for our Assistive Technology Program throughout the day. In both settings, I primarily worked with adults who survived different injuries (i.e., stroke, brain injury, spinal cord injury) or were living with a progressive condition (i.e., ALS, dementia). On some occasions, I also worked with adults with complex communication needs who had used AAC since their childhood or adolescence. Working with people with various complex communication needs was some of the most rewarding work I did. Although it was often challenging, any day I could help someone, even in the smallest way, communicate their own novel thoughts was an amazing one.

Although both populations were within the same age group, cases where people had been using AAC since childhood or adolescence always felt different than when I worked with people with acquired conditions. Typically, when I saw a person who grew up using an AAC system, they and people in their support network were more comfortable with and accepting of the idea of using AAC. Usually, they were just looking to update or repair their AAC device and were excited about the process. Seeing this level of comfort with and acceptance of AAC served as a stark comparison to my experience working with adults with acquired conditions. When the adults with acquired conditions (e.g., aphasia, acquired brain injury) were introduced to AAC, they often appeared very uncomfortable with the recommendation and initially pushed back, hoping for a new plan. In many cases, patients who were unfamiliar with AAC often saw compensation as "giving up" on speech recovery and feared a need for permanent and exclusive use of AAC. I also encountered attitude barriers related to acceptance of AAC. Some individuals, or people in their support network, felt that using an AAC system in place of verbal speech was less desirable than not communicating at all. These attitudes and beliefs seemed well-intentioned, but also rooted in complex feelings related to self-image, loss of self, and ableist views. In this case review, I will walk you through a day in my life as a medical speech-language pathologist (SLP) working with adults with complex communication needs and highlight how I handled these attitudinal barriers along the way.

I start my day in the IRF with a busy case load. One of the patients I have been helping with, Jayden, is an adolescent who survived a traumatic brain injury (TBI). He was standing on a sidewalk when a car hit him and drove off. Prior to his injury, Jayden attended a public high school and had no history of speech, language, or cognitive difficulties. He loved comics, videogames, and playing sports with friends afterschool. Although his motor skills were limited during his time in the hospital, the occupational therapist set him up with an adapted videogame system so that he could continue to connect with his friends and pursue his hobbies while he recovered. When I began working with him, his tracheostomy tube had recently been removed and the stoma site was closed, but he was still demonstrating difficulty initiating and sustaining his voice for speech. He also demonstrated motor speech difficulties, as it was difficult for him to read his lips. I assessed his language skills, which were relatively intact, and we trialed a letter communication board. Although he had paresis in his arms and hands, with appropriate placement, he was able to reach around the board and point to letters to spell out words. At first, this type of communication was slow, but based on some cognitive factors and personal preference, this level of access was more effective than partner assisted scanning or eye gaze. Jayden was thrilled to have a reliable communication system where he could express and confirm what he wanted to say. Prior to the communication board, he relied on facial expression and head nods to answer yes/no questions. He was happy to spend the time spelling out a word if it meant that he would be understood. Within speech therapy, he continued to work on initiating his voice for speech. He was eager to talk again and was a hard worker.

On this particular day, I walked by his room on my way to see another patient and overheard something that caught my attention. I was running behind schedule and rushing around a bit, but I knew I had to stop and investigate. When I looked in, a nurse, Emma, was holding his communication board in her hand, encouraging Jayden to use his words to tell her what he wanted. Although Jayden was usually very optimistic and happy, he looked frustrated, pointing toward his communication board. The nurse restated her intentions, saying something along the lines of: "if you keep using this board you might not talk again!" I took a deep breath and knew that I needed to implement strategies to overcome this attitude barrier.

Once I finished working in the IRF, I walked over to the outpatient clinic to consult on a patient that one of my coworkers was seeing, named Henry. Henry was an older man with a diagnosis of primary progressive aphasia (PPA). PPA is a progressive communication disorder that primarily effects language in the initial stages of the condition and other neurological functions (e.g., attention, memory, motor skills) in later stages. As the condition progresses, communication becomes more difficult, and a person with PPA may have limited to no verbal output by the end of their life. Although intensive speech therapy is expected to improve a person with classic aphasia's (e.g., acquired following a stroke) language skills, therapy for people with PPA is different. Typically, it is focused on maintaining language skills to prevent further decline and developing an appropriate and personalized AAC system to help maintain the person's communicative effectiveness, even as speech and language become more difficult. Going into the session, I knew that the patient had PPA, and I was prepared to begin assessment and trialing AAC techniques. However, when I met Henry and his wife Sandy, I quickly realized that we were not all on the same page about the therapy plan.

I began by reviewing his PPA diagnosis and providing what I thought to be a review of his prognosis, especially as it pertained to his speech, language, and communication skills. I mentioned that I would work with his primary SLP to help create an individualized plan that included restorative approaches with a goal to maintain function and slow the progression of the condition, as well as compensatory approaches to provide strategies to overcome communication breakdowns and focus on life participation outcomes. Because my consult time was limited, I explained that I would like to jump right into AAC trials to begin to develop the plan. This is where I realized the disconnect. The couple seemed shocked and very uncomfortable. I stopped what I was saying to check if they were okay with my plan, and Sandy explained that the information about his diagnosis was news to them. She was upset to hear that we would not be focusing only on his speech, and they did not want to just give up on talking. In that moment, I knew that I needed to stop and re-evaluate my plan and spend more time on education. The room felt tense and uncomfortable, and I knew I needed to handle the situation with compassion and humility to regain their trust.

Strategies—AAC Education

In order to address the attitudes barriers experienced by both Jayden and Henry, it would be necessary to provide concrete, and evidence-based information about the benefits of AAC. This was critical given that the beliefs and resulting attitude barriers could have potentially resulted in a situation where both patients, in addition to dealing with their health concerns, would not be able to communicate. With

Jayden, I quickly reflected on how I was going to win over his nurse Emma. I took another deep breath and advocated for my client. In a kind tone and manner, I reminded her that the patient has verbal expression goals in speech therapy and that it is very important that he has access to a consistently successful communication modality in the meantime. Then, in order to help develop the logic, I also explained the positive speech outcomes that people can have when they use an AAC system to repair communication breakdowns. Thankfully, it did not take much knowledge sharing to convince Emma to continue to use the letter board; however, this interaction did not come as a big surprise. I often heard these same well-intentioned, but misinformed beliefs expressed by other medical professionals, family members, and friends of AAC users.

With Henry, we figured out that his neurologist did not cover some of the details that I discussed in my earlier explanation. For example, the progressive nature of the condition was not clearly communicated. Henry and Sandy were under the impression that although his language skills may decline, speech therapy could help him improve his current language skills if they were persistent in therapy. They were not aware of the typical prognosis, which includes limited- to no-verbal output, and decline in other cognitive functions. My "review" of the information was actually the first time this couple processed this devastating information, and it completely violated their expectations for the therapy session that day. Since this case, and other similar situations, I have learned to never assume that a patient has been provided

the adequate amount of information regarding their condition. Whether they have lived with the condition for months or even years, patients and their families are always grateful for a refresher. In some cases, people may have originally been educated in an overwhelming setting (e.g., an intensive care unit in the hospital) where it was difficult to fully process what they were hearing, or they were not medically stable at the time, making it difficult to fully attend to the information. In other cases, people may not have ever received education on the condition because their original health care provider was too pressed for time and each subsequent provider assumed they already knew. To this current day, I have never had a patient, or someone in their support network, tell me that I over explained something or seem annoyed that I was reviewing information about their condition. Education on any aspect of the diagnosis, assessment, and therapy plan is a powerful tool in facilitating patient autonomy that should not be underutilized.

Similar to Jayden, my next challenge was that I needed to address some of the attitude barriers that Henry and Sandy faced about using AAC. The idea that developing an AAC plan meant that the patient would be "giving up on talking" seemed to stem from a misconception that speech and nonverbal communication are mutually exclusive. Upon reflection, I believe this attitude and the beliefs that underpin it is very similar to what motivated the inpatient nurse Emma to take away Jayden's letter board and encourage him to use his voice to communicate.

Although this all-or-nothing idea may seem in line with the learned nonuse principle, there is good evidence that adults with acquired communication disorders can still demonstrate improved natural speech when they use an AAC system (Dietz et al., 2020; Weissling & Prentice, 2010). In fact, there is even evidence to support a faster improvement in natural speech when people successfully communicate with alternative modalities (Dietz et al., 2018; Hux et al., 2010). Also, leaving a person without a reliable communication system while we wait for their natural speech to improve will certainly lead to frustration, frequent communication breakdowns, and a loss of autonomy. If, after this type of education, people are still skeptical, I like to use the analogy to remind them that physical therapists would not deny a patient a walker before they are strong enough to walk unassisted. Instead, they provide them with the tools they need to increase their mobility and independence as they regain their strength. More tangible examples from our physical and occupational therapy colleagues are often helpful to use in patient education, as the complexity of communication can be more abstract.

Table 9–2 summarizes some of the potential causes of attitude barriers that Jayden and Henry experienced and some potential solutions for remediating those attitude barriers.

Outcomes

By the end of Jayden's time in the IRF, he began to communicate verbally, in some single words; however, his speech was still slow and laborious, and the letter board was still his most efficient communication modality. As his motor skills improved, we began to trial a text-to-speech application using an iPad. With some practice, Jayden began to type longer messages and use synthesized speech output to communicate. As he transitioned back to home with outpatient therapy and continued to show improvements with this system, I wrote a funding report, and Jayden received his own high-tech, dynamic display device with text-to-speech software. At the time, his family and friends were encouraging and supportive of his AAC use. Although this was a very positive outcome, once he returned to school, I learned that his mother would not let him take his AAC device with him and was only able to use it at home and in therapy. When I asked her why, she told me that she did not

Table 9–2. Summary of Causes Attitude Barriers Impacting Jayden and Henry and Potential Solutions

Negative Attitudes Resulting From	Strategies
Jayden & Henry—Beliefs about patients becoming overly reliant on AAC	Instruction to communication partners about AAC and its relationship to oral communication
Henry—Misunderstanding of prognosis	Providing instruction to communication partners focused on the characteristics of impairments (e.g., the progressive nature of Primary Progressive Aphasia) and its relationship to AAC use

want him to only depend on the device and wanted him to talk more. This was similar to the attitude barrier that Jayden had encountered earlier with his nurse, Emma. Here, I utilized the same types of strategies I had before and explained how access to a more efficient communication system could help Jayden participate and engage in his learning and socializing in school more; however, his mother felt very strongly that he needed these periods of time without the device. Therefore, the outcome of this strategy was different from what I experienced in the IRF.

Across his entire plan of care, a long-term goal in speech therapy was to regain reliable and effective use of natural speech, and AAC strategies were targeted to provide a temporary solution to his communication challenges. Jayden was in agreement and enthusiastic about this plan; however, multiple people in his support network and medical provider team acted in ways that left Jayden without his most efficient communication modality. These actions stemmed from ableist attitudes that they had developed preferring speech over autonomous communication and fears of permanent disability and recovery plateau. This case is not out of the ordinary and is reflective of a survey study done by Fager et al. (2006) to document the use and acceptance of AAC in people with a TBI. They found that 94% of the respondents with TBI were accepting of a recommendation for a high-tech communication device and 76% reported long-term use of this system. Of the respondents who discontinued use of their device, most cited lack of support as the reason they stopped, highlighting the

importance of acceptance within the support network. This speaks to the importance of continued education to overcome the impact of this type of attitude barrier. This case also underscores how other opportunity barriers, such as knowledge barriers, may impact attitudes.

In the case of Henry, the patient with PPA, more barriers related to acceptance came up in subsequent sessions. Because I spent most of that first consult session on education, by the end of the session, Henry and his wife were emotionally drained, and we ran out of time. The use of this strategy, however, did lead to the acceptance of beginning to establish an AAC system in the next session. However, Sandy did express some concerns about looking "out of place" if her husband had to carry around an unusual device. Knowing this, I planned to trial techniques that could be easily implemented on a common smartphone or tablet and still meet the unique AAC needs of aphasia. I taught Henry and Sandy how they could take pictures of objects around the house or events in their lives and add captions onto the photos. I also showed them how they could sort pictures into different folders to stay organized and use other built-in apps to communicate things like numbers (i.e., calculator app) and locations (i.e., maps app). Although the couple did not have a lot of experience with technology, they picked up these simple programs quickly and were happy to use the new iPad they had recently purchased. Henry and Sandy created multiple folders that supported discussions about topics like their vegetable garden, grandchildren, and weekly hikes. Throughout this process, however, Henry and Sandy expressed struggles adjusting to and accepting the diagnosis. Both felt a loss of identity taking on new roles in the relationship. Before Henry began experiencing symptoms, he was the more outgoing partner, while Sandy was more reserved; however, since his communication challenges began, they noticed a shift in this dynamic. This struggle with self-image and loss of identity is common in people with acquired communication difficulties (Sandberg et al., 2021), and can lead to mental health difficulties and acceptance barriers. In these cases, the use of counseling techniques and collaboration with mental health professionals can be helpful. It is also important to meet the patient where they are in their journey and not push recommended strategies onto a person before they are ready.

Discussion

Although these cases were very different, both in the diagnosis and prognosis of natural speech recovery, similar attitudinal barriers were present in each. In both cases, misconceptions about learned nonuse and fears of permanency resulted in resistance to AAC techniques from patients and people in their support networks. Further, complex feelings of self-image and loss of identity created barriers to acceptance of their condition or the benefits of AAC use. When faced with these barriers, it is important to meet the person where they are, provide education, and advocate for the benefits of AAC as appropriate.

Case Example: How I Address Attitude Barriers (Krista Howard, AA, Caroline Ramsey Musselwhite, EdD CCC-SLP, and Brandi Wentland, MA, CCC-SLP)

My name is Krista Howard. I am in my 30s now and have used AAC since I was six. I have an Associates of Arts degree in General Education and am taking courses for my bachelor's degree. I'm planning to become an SLP Assistant (SLP-A). I was in a self-contained class and also have a learning disability, so writing is very hard for me. I am a single parent to a 10-year-old son. I have been an AAC model and mentor since I was 15 and will tell you about my experiences and the attitude barriers I have faced.

There are lots of attitude barriers that can make it hard to be a mentor for people who use AAC. I am going to talk about three barriers that I have faced and strategies for dealing with these. The first barrier is low expectations. People don't know my abilities so they have low expectations about what I can do. The same is true about the abilities of the students I mentor. The next barrier is the "spread effect" (assuming that because I have one disability, I must have other disabilities). Because I don't talk, many people think I am also stupid. That makes me feel very frustrated. The final barrier is time—time to communicate a message and time to learn a communication device. The first part of this is response time. People think that I can talk as fast as they can. They don't wait for me to communicate. People also don't understand that it takes time to become successful using a communication device. Many people think students should learn devices really fast; but it takes time to learn . . . And lots of modeling!

Strategies—Mentoring

A major strategy that I use to overcome these attitude barriers is through mentoring. I do many things to better myself in different mentoring situations. One of the ways I mentor is through leading Out and About groups. I have been doing this since I was 15. Out and About is a community group for people who use AAC, their families, friends, therapists, and teachers. One time, we were at the food court at a mall, and we were going to use our devices to order. I created a "notebook" (a tool on my device to prepare messages in advance and speak them one sentence at a time) to tell restaurant workers that we use devices to talk. Here is what the notebook said.

> Hello, I am Krista. I use a device to talk. I am with a group called Out and About. We are going to order on our devices. Some of my students are learning their devices. Please wait for them. Thank you.

The restaurant workers really understood. They communicated very well. They smiled and truly looked at us. They waited. They were very nice. The next time we visited they remembered us. They were better communication partners because they were prepared and knew what to do. Another way I help reduce attitude barriers during Out and About is to model for all of the newer and emerging communicators. Parents say I am good at modeling for their children. They say that they have higher expectations of their children because, if I can do it, they can too.

Another way I mentor is through supporting Dr. Caroline Musselwhite when she does sessions using Readtopia (a literacy curriculum for emergent to early conventional learners, http://www.myreadtopia.com) and with a small literacy group. I model using my device. For example, when they are learning core words, or word wall words, I make a full sentence with the word. So, if Caroline gives the word "play" I might say "I want to play with you." I also make comments after a video or during shared reading. For example, we watched a video about ziplining, and I modeled "I would like to go ziplining." I think that these students make better goals for themselves because they see my models. Some of the students are starting to use complete sentences. I think it is partly because of my modeling!

I also help an SLP named Brandi Wentland who works with an 11-year-old young man that I will call Arhaan who wants to go to a university someday. He does not like it when therapy or coursework is too easy. He will say "faster" or "university" to let people know he wants more challenging material that will prepare him for college. Because I have attended university, we placed a picture of me in front of a university along with the agenda for the day. This helped Arhaan and his mom to see that the day was focused on challenging material to prepare him for college and that like me, he can achieve his goals, attend college, and obtain a degree.

Another activity I led was called Dueling Devices (Musselwhite, 2000). For this activity, we raced to see who could say target phrases on our devices the fastest. This helped Arhaan to learn to use his device more, to learn phrases he can say to advocate for himself, to increase his vocabulary, and to help him become faster at finding words. The words we targeted were self-advocacy words and phrases like "I need a break." Or "This is too easy." "Stop this." And "I am bored." Advocacy is important to share your wants and needs. Arhaan had a lot of compliance-based teaching in the past. It was important that he be able to say what he needed, not just what others wanted him to say. By having me here, as an adult AAC user and mentor, it helped to show him he has the right and the power to tell people to "stop" or "I don't like this." When he learns to use this with others, it can also shift their attitudes regarding his abilities, intelligence, rights, and maybe they will learn to help him more with reading, writing and more challenging activities.

I also worked at an adult day center for almost three years. I was on the assistive technology team where I helped with staff training and mentored members who use devices. The staff didn't believe that modeling worked and didn't believe in me at first. I modeled all day. I learned their devices and modeled directly on them. For example, I modeled having a simple conversation and asked about their weekends. The members saw the power of using a device and they started to change. Some members often left their devices at home. After I started to model, they brought their devices every day. Many devices had been sitting on shelves. Staff members started to take them down and even model sometimes. Members began to practice and to use their devices. Then the staff started to believe in me—and in the power of modeling.

Strategies—Public Use of AAC

Another strategy I use to overcome attitude barriers is through using AAC everywhere. Strangers treat me differently when I use my device. Before I use my device to communicate, they sometimes act weird, like whispering about me, or ignoring me. Then, when I use my device and use a full sentence or ask a question, they see me differently. They start to talk to me and ask about me. My friend Brandi and I love to go to the spa or float in pools together. At first, strangers look at me weird, they usually do not initiate conversation. It makes me feel uncomfortable. But then, when I use a device, they see how smart I am. They start talking to me. One of these times, we were in a hot tub talking with a few college-age guys. I told them I had written a chapter in a book called *Becoming an Exceptional AAC User* (Howard, 2021). They thought that was pretty awesome and said they wanted to read the book. They seemed to change their attitude toward me when I used my device. They called their girlfriends over and introduced them to us. They sounded proud to introduce us and wanted us to tell the girls about me and the things I have accomplished.

I love coffee, I order caramel Frappuccinos and I drink them four times a week. When I go to a coffee shop, I order on my device. The baristas think differently after having met me. Many of them say I am brave. I think they are more understanding to future users of AAC after they meet me because they now have experience talking with an AAC user and now know more about AAC devices. When I go inside to order, I am not scared, I feel happy because I know how to communicate.

Last year, I went to Mexico with my family, my son, and my good friend Brandi. Brandi and I went down to the hot tub to relax. We brought my PicSeePal (http://www.picseepal.com). It is what I use to protect my light-tech AAC when I am around water or when I cannot use my high-tech device. I met a woman named Tara and her mom in the hot tub. They saw me using my light-tech device to talk with Brandi. They started talking to us. They told me Tara uses a device too. They asked about my light-tech system and said they wanted something like that for her. Then we talked about where we live. We realized we live close to each other. They asked our names. When I told them my name, they said they had heard about me from a company that provides respite services and had heard I was a good device user. We scheduled time to meet after we all got back to Arizona. Now, I provide services for them. I help Tara work on her goals and her device. Her mom wants me working with her because I am an AAC user. She sees the value in me modeling AAC for her daughter.

Strategies—
Making Presentations

Another strategy I use for overcoming attitude barriers is through making presentations. I have provided many presentations at local, state, national, and international conferences and often share about mentoring. Before my presentations, attendees don't really talk to me. However, after I present, they walk toward me, initiate conversation, and make a connection. It makes me feel very proud and motivates me. Many families and professionals have asked me to work with their students after they saw me present.

I am also an ambassador for two AAC companies, PRC-Saltillo, the company that developed the Accent 1000, my high-tech AAC device, and PicSeePal, my light-tech AAC housing. As an ambassador, I show emerging communicators and coach teachers, SLPs, and parents how I communicate. Often, a parent doesn't think their child is ready; but after I talk to them, they start to realize that their child is ready.

Oftentimes in AAC, we talk about modeling. Usually, this is in reference to modeling words on our device. Not only do I model the use of AAC on my device, I also model in one other way. I model in photographs. I think it is very important for users of AAC and people with disabilities to see people like them represented in advertising, in books, and in marketing for products they purchase; especially in advertising for AAC. I am proud and honored that I have been able to model in a book called *Learning to Work* (Musselwhite & Richardson, 2009), on the website, and in marketing for companies like Lincare AAC (http://www.lincareaac.com), PicSeePal (http://www.picseepal.com), and We Speak AAC (http://www.wespeakaac.com). I believe these photographs show people who use AAC that they are beautiful and can accomplish their goals. It also helps shift the perspectives for companies, parents, professionals, and everyday people around the world about who we are, what we can do and how we can and should be represented.

Strategies—Advocacy

Another way I combat attitude barriers is by advocating for other people who use AAC. Earlier, I told you about a time when I was in Mexico and I met a family while relaxing in a hot tub. Her mom told me that her daughter has a communication device but wasn't using it much. I told her about my services and described Out and About. After I began working with her, she started to attend the Out and About events. She got to see devices with more robust language. Because of that, she and her mom advocated for her to obtain a new AAC evaluation, and she is now going to get a better language system.

I am also advocating for a six-year-old boy who recently changed schools. Previously, he was in general education at his elementary school and was being taught literacy skills. Once he changed schools, they did not want to let him in the general education classes, and they didn't seem to expect much from him. They did not think he could do the same classwork as his peers. I wrote a letter and told them that regular classes were better for my education because I learned to read and write. I told them if I can do it, he can. Just expect more!

Strategies—Time

I am overcoming my barrier of time by practicing my AAC so that I am faster. Sometimes, I prepare an introduction before a meeting or important phone call, so I can be very clear, and not feel pressured. When I am asked to do a presentation, I use the notebook feature on my device to prepare what I will talk about so that I can share what I want to say in a more efficient and effective way. I still communicate on the fly or make comments "in the moment." But, being prepared really helps with communicating at a speed that other people are used to.

Another barrier of time is the time it takes to learn to use an AAC device. At a webinar I did for Click.Speak.Connect (http://www.clickspeakconnect.com) I told them, "I had my device for 5 years before I was really interested in using it." My therapist during that time, Tami Taylor, has told me that I used to throw things at her when she asked me to use my device. But she stuck with me. She helped me see the power of communication and why I should communicate. Many parents commented and e-mailed me to tell me how powerful this was. They realized that it could take years for their child to really learn to use their AAC system. My friend Sarah Cruz turned my quote into an infographic for me and posted it on Instagram. It blew up all over social media. People still use this quote and infographic to share with school teams, families, and therapists to help them understand that they should not give up on a child or an AAC device. I tell them to just keep modeling! When I present at conferences or to university students, I tell them that learning AAC takes time and not to give up. I tell them to be patient and to remember to model!

In Table 9–3, I present some of negative attitudes that I spoke about and ways that these can be addressed.

Table 9–3. Summary of Attitude Barriers and Potential Solutions

Negative attitudes described in the case

- Low expectations about the ability of AAC users to communicate
- "Spread effect"—negative attitudes related to presuming that AAC users have multiple disabilities
- Presumptions about the time it takes AAC users to communicate

Potential solutions to address these negative attitudes

- AAC mentoring programs
- Using AAC in public places
- Making presentations to the public while using AAC
- Advocating for AAC users
- Determining strategies to increase the speed of AAC communication

Outcomes

I have mostly had success using strategies such as mentoring others on how to communicate with AAC, using AAC everywhere, making presentations, being an ambassador, and advocating for others who use AAC to overcome attitude barriers. I have also worked to be faster when using AAC and to educate others about how long it takes to learn to use AAC. Now, more people believe in me. They know that I can model for others and be a good role model. People's attitudes can change in good ways. Now that people know I can communicate well, they also get motivated to model more and to expect more for students who use AAC. I also think that I have helped people in the community know more about AAC. I use my device in restaurants and churches, and even in the spa. Because I use AAC in many places where I go, more people understand that AAC works. I think that these types of strategies have changed the attitudes of other people toward AAC.

Discussion

I know now that the communication partner needs to change, not just the person who uses AAC. Communication partners need to learn to slow down, be patient, and give us time. They need to believe in us. It is also important to believe in yourself. Over time, the person who uses AAC can be part of the change by being a role model. We all need to try to have conversations with everyone, even strangers, to help people understand. I believe that we need to be advocates for everyone who uses AAC. I hope that sharing my experiences will help people reduce their attitude barriers.

References and Additional Resources

Dietz, A., Vannest, J., Maloney, T., Altaye, M., Holland, S., & Szaflarski, J. P. (2018). The feasibility of improving discourse in people with aphasia through AAC: Clinical and functional MRI correlates. *Aphasiology*,

32(6), 693–719. https://doi.org/10.1080/02 687038.2018.1447641

Dietz, A., Wallace, S. E., & Weissling, K. (2020). Revisiting the role of augmentative and alternative communication in aphasia rehabilitation. *American Journal of Speech-Language Pathology*, *29*(2), 909–913. https://doi.org/ 10.1044/2019_AJSLP-19-00041

Fager, S., Hux, K., Beukelman, D. R., & Karantounis, R. (2006). Augmentative and alternative communication use and acceptance by adults with traumatic brain injury. *Augmentative and Alternative Communication*, *22*(1), 37–47. https://doi.org/10.1080/07434 610500243990

Howard, K. (2021). With brave wings, she flies. In M. Chan (Ed.), *Becoming an exceptional AAC leader* (pp. 130–141). Mai Ling Chan.

Hux, K., Buechter, M., Wallace, S., & Weissling, K. (2010). Using visual scene displays to create a shared communication space for a person with aphasia. *Aphasiology*, *24*(5), 643–660. https://doi.org/10.1080/0268703 0902869299

Kent-Walsh, J., & McNaughton, D. (2005). Communication partner instruction in AAC: Present practices and future directions. *Augmentative and Alternative Communication*, *21*, 195–204. https://doi.org/10 .1080/07434610400006646

Mesibov, G. B., Shea, V., & Schopler, E. (2005). *The TEACCH approach to autism spectrum disorders*. Springer Science + Business Media.

Musselwhite, C. (November, 2000). *AAC all day long: Dueling devices and more*. [Workshop presentation]. Brisbane, Melbourne, and Sidney, Australia,.

Musselwhite, C., & Richardson, L. (2009). *Learning to work*. Verona, WI, Attainment Company.

Prizant, B., Wetherby, A. M., Rubin, E., Laurent, A., & Rydell, P. R. (2006). *The SCERTS(TM) Model: A comprehensive educational approach for children with autism spectrum disorders*. Paul H. Brookes.

Sandberg, C. W., Nadermann, K., Parker, L., Kubat, A. M., & Conyers, L. M. (2021). Counseling in aphasia: Information and strategies for speech-language pathologists. *American Journal of Speech-Language Pathology*, *30*(6), 2337–2349. https://doi .org/10.1044/2021_AJSLP-20-00312

Wagner, D., Musselwhite, C., & Odom, J. (2005). *Out and about: AAC in the community*. Download for free at: https://www .teacherspayteachers.com/Store/Caroline-Musselwhite

Weissling, K., & Prentice, C. (2010). The timing of remediation and compensation rehabilitation programs for individuals with acquired brain injuries: Opening the conversation. *Perspectives on Augmentative and Alternative Communication*, *19*(3), 87–96. https://doi.org/10.1044/ aac19.3.87

Section IV

Understanding and Addressing Policy Barriers

Section Overview

With this section, we invite you to explore another dimension of being an AAC advocate through the understanding, design, and usage of AAC policy. In Rosenberg and Beukelman's early conceptualization of the Participation Model (1987), policy, along with education, was introduced as one of two major drivers of action and change related to people with CCN. AAC policy can be thought of as a multifaceted tool kit that you can use for creating defined legislative and regulatory policies, organizational policies, and personal and family policies.

In this section, we share the idea that policy can be a democratic process of standards development, as well as an act of disability and social justice. This can be for one person to create policy in their life, and can also extend out broadly, as far as international policies, such as the landmark United Nations Convention on the Rights of Persons with Disabilities (CRPD). It is important to note that, whereas access alone does not equal participation, policy does not automatically equate to well informed and skilled practices. Rather, policy is the operating procedure and it takes knowledgeable and skilled community members to put procedural guidelines into practice.

Legislative policies can significantly impact AAC use, and legislative processes influence practices, funding, and access to interventions and supports for individuals with disabilities. In addition to being a barrier, policies can be a powerful facilitator for access, supports, and services for individuals who use AAC. This section is devoted to policy barriers with a specific focus on understanding and addressing barriers related to inclusion in education, employment, and community life. Upon completion of this section, readers will be able to:

- Describe the impact of policy barriers and facilitators on the lives of individuals who use AAC and their families.
- Describe important examples of legislative policies that impact people with CCN.
- Summarize the research on policy barriers.
- Identify effective strategies for addressing policy barriers.

Reference

Rosenberg, S., & Beukelman, D. (1987). The participation model. In C. A. Coston (Ed.), *Proceedings of the National Planners Conference on Assistive Device Service Delivery* (pp. 159–161). Washington, DC: RESNA, The Association for the Advancement of Rehabilitation Technology.

10 AAC Policy Barriers: Learning From Individuals Who Use AAC and Their Families

Lateef McLeod, Eric J. Sanders*, Samuel Sennott*, India Ochs*, and Bob Williams*

People who use AAC and their allies have a long history of advocating for dismantling AAC policy barriers, including major legislative and regulatory policy advances in the funding of speech generating devices, inclusion in school, work, and community, and in access to health care. Although progress has been made, challenges persist, and it is important to listen to the voices of people with complex communication needs who are on the front lines of policy development. In the following interviews we explore the personal experiences that two individuals with complex communication needs, Bob Williams and India Ochs, have encountered with regard to advocacy, policy, and AAC.

Bob Williams—Individual Who Uses AAC

Bob Williams is a policy advocate and nationally recognized leader. Bob co-

founded the AAC advocacy organization CommunicationFIRST in 2019 after completing a distinguished four-decade career in federal and state government and the nonprofit sector. He has served as the Director of the U.S. Independent Living

Figure 10–1. Bob Williams

---

*These authors have contributed equally to this work and share senior authorship.

Administration at the U.S. Department of Health and Human Services (HHS), Deputy Assistant Secretary of HHS for Disability, Aging, and Long-Term Care Policy, and Commissioner of the U.S. Administration of Developmental Disabilities, among many roles.

Will you introduce yourself, including your name, age, gender, race, ethnicity? Can you share a little bit about who you are as a person, and what you're doing in your life, and what you enjoy doing?

I am a 65-year-old white man with cerebral palsy. I grew up in Connecticut but moved to Washington, D.C. in the 1970s to go to George Washington University and have lived and worked here ever since. I retired in 2019 but spent four decades working for different governmental agencies and non-profit organizations. I have monitored and assisted people to move out of Forest Haven, a now-abandoned institution the U.S. Congress created for the so-called feeble-minded of the District of Columbia. I have served in a variety of positions including Deputy Assistant Secretary of HHS for Disability, Aging, and Long-Term Care Policy, Commissioner of the U.S. Administration of Developmental Disabilities, and HHS Secretary Donna Shalala's principal advisor on the Americans with Disabilities Act (ADA). I also co-led the task force that developed the U.S. government's successful arguments before the Supreme Court in the influential Olmstead *v.* LC case. My most recent governmental position was as Director of the U.S. Independent Living Administration at the U.S. Department of Health and Human Services (HHS).

Currently, I am the policy manager of CommunicationFIRST, the civil rights organization I helped co-found in 2019. We are led by and advance the full equal rights and opportunities of the estimated five million children, adolescents, working-age persons, and older adults who require AAC to effectively express ourselves, be understood, and lead our lives. In my free time, I am researching and writing a social history of Forest Haven and, most importantly, the lives of those who due to a strange brew of racism, ableism, eugenics, and other prejudices were exiled there. I live with my wife of 29 years, Helen, with our mutt, Cody, in Southwest D.C. We raised her daughter, Emily, together and delight in our grandkids.

> "My first communication board can be envisioned as shown as a piece of brown wood handprinted with the alphabet in capital letters and the numerals 0 through 9."

Bob, could you please share about your experience using AAC?

I've been using AAC in all sorts of iterations over the years. Here is how I described it in Williams (2020). My first communication board can be envisioned as shown a piece of brown wood handprinted with the alphabet in capital letters and the numerals 0 through 9.

When I was about 15, my camp counselor painted the alphabet in bold black capital letters on that piece of wood hanging on my wall. I pointed to the letters to spell out words and sentences. A year or two later that same camp counselor handed me a green board that had letters, numbers, words, and phrases on it. It was called the Hall Roe Communication Board, named for the man with cerebral palsy who helped design it, and it saw me through high school, college, dating, internships, and my first two full-time jobs. In fact, I used that board to lobby with others to gain passage of the Americans with Disabilities Act (ADA).

Just after the ADA became law, I participated in the Augmentative Communication, Empowerment, and Supports (ACES) Institute at Temple University in Philadelphia (https://disabilities.temple.edu). There with about a dozen other people who used AAC, I learned to use my first speech generating device. I have been using successive iterations of this same device throughout my life. After that my life and career took off in directions even I had never before fathomed possible.

What policy barriers currently affect the AAC community?

There are, of course, many AAC policy barriers, but the major ones revolve around human and civil rights, and defining what those fundamental rights are and must come to mean for all of us who use little or no understandable speech. When I think of how to explain that to ordinary people, I talk about the right to be free of being "incommunicado" and the right

to community. Here I am referring to "community" not simply as most shorthand it to mean: a geographic point on a map. But, rather, as a complete way of living and sharing life with those around us in ways that we are understood and valued for who we truly are. The roots of "communication" and "community" are, to borrow Dr. King's (1963) phrase, tied to "an inescapable network of mutuality, . . . a single garment of destiny" (para. 4). Both derive from the Latin, "communitas," which refers to living together and coming to know one another as equals. This for me is the essence of the ADA, and what it requires, of course, is that we communicate as equals.

We want to clarify "the right to be free of incommunicado." Is that Italian, meaning you're free of being stuck without communication?

Yes, it has Latin origins. In terms of human rights, the term, incommunicado, refers to being banished, kept silent, and barred from interacting and living-in-community with all others. When any government through its actions—and I would argue by its inactions—sentences or otherwise forces someone to live incommunicado, silent, cut off from all others even when they are "living in community" that to me is a flagrant violation of all of their human and civil rights. We must end it. We at CommunicationFIRST are working to strengthen and assure the right of every person who requires AAC to have access and use it effectively as well as to have the other support they require to live life fully. The right to be free from a constant state of silence. The right to be heard and understood rather than it blithely being presumed that you should not be afforded the opportunities, tools, and the fundamental right to express yourself—absent an individual cannot and does not have any choice and control over their everyday lives. We believe the Americans with Disabilities Act (ADA) along with other disability civil rights laws equip us with power tools we need to bring down the walls of exclusion, isolation, racism, ableism, language discrimination, and other oppression that we believe most who require AAC, especially those denied it, endure. This is work all of us must do together.

When many of us throughout the country as well as D.C. first began to draft and breath meaning into legislation that was later enacted as the ADA, we had deep conversations among ourselves to gain a common understanding of the bias and discrimination we faced and needed to eliminate. Some of the barriers and discrimination manifested themselves differently based on our specific experience of disability, but all of it was similar. Recognizing this and having those conversations strengthened our understanding and resolve over what we had to accomplish. We at CommunicationFIRST are beginning to engage in those same types of conversations because we too need to identify the bias we face and the common justice we seek.

There are over 25 low incidence disabilities and conditions that can result in someone needing AAC. So, it is understandable that we are largely disconnected from each other, but as a civil rights organizer, I know that the key to getting the public policy doing what we need it to do is pulling ourselves together. It is the key to accomplishing all we must accomplish.

When I got involved in the disability civil rights movement in the 1970s, folks used the term "attitudinal barriers." It always struck me as trying to make nice. What we face every day is more than attitude barriers. We have to say the words and call it out for exactly what it is, deep and systemic prejudice and discrimination. All of which is grounded in the still widely held notion that those of us with little to no understandable speech have little intelligence, little understanding, little to say, and little to give.

These kinds of stereotypes are driving much of what most who require AAC experience every day. Additionally, research increasingly shows black, indigenous, non-English using, and people of color needing AAC face even worse discrimination. We are working to end it all. Silence does not bring about social justice, our actions do.

What do you think people who use AAC need to do to combat this ableism? As I said, it begins with creating opportunities and venues where we can get to know one another and grapple with both what needs to change and what our role and leadership must be in bringing about that change. I truly believe that this time is pivotal and that we can in fact do the work and make progress on the kind of things I have been discussing with you all. In a way, the pandemic is making people understand, perhaps better than at any time in their lives, the human cost of isolation. They can turn that into having conversations and changing hearts and minds.

What do you see as the role of technology?

Of course, it is enormous, and both specialized assistive technology as well as the off the shelf technology will continue to free people. But what concerns me most are two things. The first is the growing digital divide. Things like e-mail, the Internet, and video conferencing (e.g., ZOOM), have given me and others using AAC entirely new lives and futures. But others are frozen out, which leads to my second concern. I believe we now see technology, and specifically speech generating devices, as the silver bullet that solves everything. However, for those for whom it is not a silver bullet, the message all too often becomes "well, too bad." In Australia, Canada, and elsewhere far more importance is placed on making certain people also have access to human communication support and not just the tools. That is needed here as well in the United States. We need to see the big picture and then go and do whatever pieces of it that can be done to make a difference. And that is why I lay it out. Not to overwhelm folks, but hopefully to enable them to be a part of the solution.

> "The promise of the ADA is that we will live as equals in our communities. To do so, we must be able to communicate, connect, and find a shared sense of respect, understanding, and belonging."

Can you please share some specific information about Communication-

FIRST's advocacy goals and some steps you have taken?

CommunicationFIRST's aim is to make certain that all who require AAC have it, and that our civil rights are recognized, respected, and enforced. In our first 18 months, we have started to lay a firm foundation for achieving our goals. In 2020, we mobilized to lessen the pandemic's harsh effects on our constituency. Concentrating our efforts on elevating COVID-19 and other health care issues unique to those of us who require AAC, CommunicationFIRST:

- Led a coalition of disability rights organizations to convince the HHS Office of Civil Rights to strongly affirm the right of such patients to receive in-person communication support in hospitals despite COVID No-Visitor Policies.
- Developed and shared a COVID-19 Communication Rights Toolkit. This toolkit: (1) explains your communication rights; (2) provides tips on advocating for them, and (3) has an accommodation request form you can bring to the hospital. The rationale for this work is that legal and civil rights to access communication supports do not go away during an emergency, in quarantine, or in the hospital.
- Issued a resource brief on the communication support rights of students with significant expressive disabilities during COVID-19.
- Joined with the National Association of the Deaf and others in petitioning the FCC to add text and video-calling options to the National Suicide Lifeline.

We have continued to build on these accomplishments and the fight for free expression and other fundamental rights. In January, for example, we were joined by 47 other organizations in issuing a Communication Equity Call to Action urging the Biden Administration to make fighting discrimination against people who use AAC or lack the required access to AAC the priority it must be.

We also joined forces with autistic nonspeaking self-advocates and others to make the film *Listen* (which can be viewed at https://communicationfirst.org/LISTEN/) to denounce the use of seclusion and restraint, and the ways in which these acts of violence are thoughtlessly legitimized in films like *Music* (Kurchack, 2021). Sia, the musician and actress in the film *Music*, publicly offered to fund CommunicationFIRST's efforts to make *Listen* as an introductory short to be shown before her movie.

The promise of the ADA is that we will live as equals in our communities. To do so, we must be able to communicate, connect, and find a shared sense of respect, understanding, and belonging. It is time to tear down the seemingly impervious walls of exclusion, isolation, and injustice. Laws like the ADA are only powerful when we make them so in our everyday lives and futures. CommunicationFIRST works to make equality the rule, not the exception for those who require AAC.

> "It is time to tear down the seemingly impervious walls of exclusion, isolation, and injustice. Laws like the ADA are only powerful when we make them so in our everyday lives and futures."

If someone wanted to get involved with policy, how would you advise them? What steps would you suggest they take? This is broad advice, but it has served me and others I know who I have either been mentored by or who I have mentored well. Find an issue you are passionate about, learn about it as much as you can, seek out others who share your passion and vision, show up to make a difference, and know change will not occur overnight. It is a journey, not a destination.

> "Find an issue you are passionate about, learn about it as much as you can, seek out others who share your passion and vision, show up to make a difference, and know change will not occur overnight. It is a journey, not a destination."

Key Points From Bob's Interview

Bob's interview highlights the detrimental impact of policy barriers as well as the positive impacts of policy development. He stressed "the right to be free of incommunicado," meaning the right to be in community and explained that being in a state of "incommunicado" is synonymous with people with complex communication needs being isolated from their wider society. Related to that point, Bob emphasized that policies must address (a) the digital divide that is experienced by people with complex communication needs by ensuring equal access to the internet and assistive technologies, and

(b) the rights of people with complex communication needs to receive appropriate medical care. Further, he illustrated the positive impact that policy can have on the lives of individuals who use AAC by recounting his experiences as a civil rights advocate, sharing his involvement in the movement to pass the American Disability Act, and discussing his recent work with CommunicationFIRST. The insights that Bob shared are important for understanding the impact of policy on the lives of individuals who use AAC.

Figure 10–2. India Ochs

India Ochs—Individual Who Uses AAC

India Ochs is a mother, attorney, author, and a lifelong AAC advocate. She is the current Chair of the Board of Directors of the new AAC advocacy organization CommunicationFIRST. Currently, she works as a compliance officer for the federal government, where she interacts with policies on a daily basis.

Will you introduce yourself, including your name, age, gender, race, ethnicity, can you share a little bit about who you are as a person, and what you're doing in your life, and what you enjoy doing?
I am India Ochs from Annapolis, Maryland. I'm an attorney, advocate, and author. But first and foremost, I'm a parent. To answer your other parts I am 46, white, she/her. I was born with an undiagnosed speech-related communication disability and have been a social justice advocate for my entire life. I have been a licensed attorney since 2002.

Can you share information about your use of AAC over the years and your current AAC system?
Sure, I recently talked about this on the *Talking With Tech* podcast (Bugaj & Maddel, 2021). As many who hear me give talks know, I did not start to use an AAC system until college because I refused to use anything with symbols. So, in 1993, I started to use the text to speech software EZ Keys produced by Words Plus, which Stephen Hawking also used. Then a few years ago, I started to use the Proloquo4Text app. But I also hand write messages when in one-on-one situations in person since that is a habit from my younger years.

Talking with Tech [audio podcast], *Episode 194: India Ochs: Lawyer, Social Justice Advocate, Mother, and AAC User.* https://www.talkingwith tech.org/episodes/india-ochs

We appreciate hearing about how you use handwritten messages back and forth when in one-on-one situations with a person. I wonder what type of responses you get when you use this type of communication?

The one thing I hate is the stereotype of an AAC user. At some AAC related conferences I get slammed for using handwriting, because I am not using the stereotypical speech generating device. I've told the story before about how an AAC professional commented that my son is so talkative because I can't talk, without understanding I am a talkative one too. I don't know if hurt is the right word, but the fact is that incident stayed with me for two years until I wrote about it. That is why I believe that there is not enough written on opportunity barriers, because not everyone thinks AAC users have the opportunities to do whatever they want, and there is so much ignorance.

When you encounter this in your daily life, how do you cope with the experience and advocate, so it never happens again?

Well, I think we have to understand that it will happen again. Maybe not by the same person, but society has a long way to go. For example, at work, I didn't plan to be a groundbreaker, but my agency had to write new policies to allow me to do my job.

Specifically, the CIA has a rule stating that no electronics are allowed in classified areas. As part of my job, I was going to a CIA training in a classified area and so the staff had to write a new policy just to let me have my iPad in the class. This also happened when I was called for jury duty. They said no electronics in courtrooms, but I needed mine to communicate so I had to convince the staff to let me into jury duty. I feel bad for the security guards, as they are just adhering to policy. (However, on a related note, my son thinks I might still be a spy after telling him I turned down a job with the Secret Service.) Even purchasing an iPad for me was a policy barrier. My agency had to rewrite policy with its disability office because no employee had a speech disability before. Now a lot of employees have iPads.

I think that it is important to recognize that policy is a huge field. There is policy specifically about AAC, policies in school, policies in workplaces, the Justice system, prisons, and travel. Also, there are relevant policies for people who use AAC about things like adoptions or getting fertility treatments to have kids.

Going back to my earlier point about opportunities, I don't want "independent living" to be an accomplishment for AAC users. And what I mean by that is, when people are listing different accomplishments when promoting something like an individual who uses AAC as a public speaker, I don't want to see "independent living" listed next to doctoral candidate, published author, business owner, poet, etc. As vital an accomplishment as it is for some to be able to live independently, it only feeds into the systemic ableism rampant within our society if we portray "independent living" as an ultimate goal of people who use AAC.

What laws or policies do you want to see change that will help the AAC community the most?

Well, first, make speech disability a "significant disability." Right now, it's secondary on any form or list. It's not considered severe. This is a huge barrier for those who don't have multiple disabilities. For example, I went to my state rehabilitation center once to get help with a laptop and was put on the waitlist because they said I didn't have a severe enough disability. As another example, there is a form that nearly every Federal agency asks employees to fill out and speech disability is on the second column of disabilities. So, I am asking, why are people with severe speech disabilities being pushed aside?

Additionally, there is a lot I could go into, but let me open up a new angle to equity and AAC and disability. Right now, I'm really concerned about the presence of resource officers in schools (i.e., police officers). School systems have policies on things like restraints and seclusion for students with disabilities, but nothing on that is connected to policies for school resource officers. Yet, data shows that kids who are disproportionately in contact with school resource officers are black or have a disability, and usually are black with a disability. Those with communication disabilities are the most vulnerable. So where is the equity there? Most kids in detention centers have disabilities.

Also, disability is a distressingly underreported hate crime category, yet people with disabilities are the most abused of any of the hate crime groups (Hall, 2017; Sherry, 2010). People don't think to report it as a hate crime, especially in schools. However, if you get attacked because of your disability that is a hate crime. These crimes need to be reported if we want such abuse to stop. A month before COVID, my county had a town hall on hate crime and every demographic was on the panel except disability and not a single disability

hate crime was reported that year. So, if they are not reported, people don't even think about the disability and hate crime, even though it's a targeted group under Federal law. If something happens at school, tell people to report it to the police and not just to the school. It might not go anywhere, but it's still on record.

Next, there is this common policy of letting kids keep their AAC devices with them going to both school and home. Yet, sometimes students are barred from bringing AAC devices home. This happens even on the weekend or at night. The question I ask is, so how can they talk to their family? School policies like this create barriers to AAC and to communication development.

What do you see as the role of technology for improving outcomes related to policy barriers?
It's not easy. The technology is there, but it's about allowing it and understanding anyone can do anything. It goes back to my jury duty experience. There is a policy in my county that lets disabled people off the hook for jury duty. I get it if physically you can't get to court, but just because you have a disability doesn't mean you don't have a responsibility. People with disabilities are equal citizens and as long as a person physically can be in the courtroom, we have a responsibility to ensure they are performing their civic duty. So, what would be the standards for people with an intellectual disability you may ask? I think that it is important to note that not all people without a disability are smart enough to understand the law either. The jury is about your peers, so why can't you be on a jury if you have Down syndrome? I don't see why not. The current policies dismiss

people with intellectual disabilities, but it is assuming a lot of layers between what people can contribute as a juror and what we expect/require from jurors.

> "You can be an advocate at the local, state, or national level, doing things like testifying on different kinds of legislation, writing op-eds supporting or opposing a policy, or helping to draft policies. It's all about your passion, and how much you want to shape the world we live in."

If someone wanted to get involved with policy, how would you advise them, what steps would you suggest they take? There are many ways to get involved in policy activities. On one hand, you can pursue it as a career, becoming a "policy wonk," government official in a policy office, or running for elected office so you are setting the policy. You can also be an advocate at the local, state, or national level, doing things like testifying on different kinds of legislation, writing op-eds supporting or opposing a policy, or helping to draft policies. It's all about your passion, and how much you want to shape the world we live in.

> "Policies surrounding AAC will only be developed, in a positive way, if those making decisions truly understand both how significant speech disability is, and how much those with speech disabilities can achieve."

Related to policy and AAC, what do you envision for the future? That's a tough one because it all depends on who is in control. Policies surrounding AAC will only be developed, in a positive way, if those making decisions truly understand both how significant speech disability is, and how much those with speech disabilities can achieve. We need to reshape how society views people who use AAC, so it's not just seen in error as some small minority that won't contribute anything to their communities. Once we stop instances like a local ACLU chapter taking the side of educators who opposed legislation to have cameras in special education classrooms (educators who are able to verbally communicate and express their freedom of speech), and have the ACLU defend the right to speech for children who are most vulnerable to not having access to communication, we can then draft polices protecting and enhancing the lives of all people who use AAC.

Key Points From India's Interview

India provided information and ideas about AAC and policy as a person who uses AAC and who is also an attorney and a parent. India emphasized the importance of people who use AAC participating in citizen duties such as jury duty and the need for policies to be adopted to ensure that these types of activities are accessible. Further, India advocated for policy changes in a number of different contexts such as schools, healthcare, and in the workplace. In addition to providing examples of the impact of policies on people who communicate with AAC, she gave recommendations for becoming active in policy making. Her insights about policy reveal the importance of ensuring that people who use AAC have a seat at the policy making table and provide an example of what it takes to be a successful advocate who uses AAC.

Conclusion

In summary, Bob and India provide insights into the policy barriers faced by individuals who use AAC. Although they emphasize that the specific policy barriers encountered may differ for different members of the AAC community, they highlight the need for people who use AAC and their allies to advocate for laws and policy that will ensure their equity as citizens. In addition to discussing barriers, both interviewees shared the positive impacts of policy work and reminded the reader that the promise of policies, such as the ADA, is that we will live as equals in our communities. They went on to provide examples of how to get involved in policy, including through advocacy, and remaining engaged civically. Additional information regarding policy barriers, and strategies for addressing those barriers, will be discussed in the chapters that follow.

References

Bugaj, C., & Madel, R. (2001) Episode 194: India Ochs: Lawyer, social justice advocate, mother, and AAC user. [Audio podcast] In *Talking with Tech*.

Hall, E. (2017). Why disability hate crimes are woefully under-reported. *The Conversation*. http://theconversation.com/why-dis ability-hate-crimes-are-woefully-under-reported-85964

King, M. (1963). *Letter from a Birmingham jail*. https://www.theatlantic.com/maga zine/archive/2018/02/letter-from-a-bir mingham-jail/552461/

Kurchack, S. (2021, February). Sia's Golden Globe-Nominated *Music* isn't just offensive. It's also bad art—and the distinction matters. *Time Magazine*. https://time.com/5942094/ sia-music-disability-representation

Sherry, M. (2010). *Disability hate crimes: Does anyone really hate disabled people?* Routledge.

11 Policy Barriers: Exploring the Evidence Base

Samuel Sennott, Lateef McLeod, and Eric J. Sanders

AAC policy barriers and supports can occur as "the result of legislative or regulatory decisions that support the communication and participation of individuals with complex communication needs" (Beukelman & Light, 2020 , p. 38). As discussed in prior chapters, the Participation Model provides a comprehensive and systematic framework for AAC assessment and intervention, including an evaluation of policy barriers (Beukelman & Light, 2020), and can be useful in identifying barriers and developing pathways to address those barriers.

In this chapter, we propose and discuss strategies for ensuring that policy barriers are fully considered and addressed for the purpose of supporting the participation and self-actualization of individuals with complex communication needs. In this context, it is important to recognize that developing policies (and identifying/ addressing AAC policy barriers) are not goals in and of themselves. Rather, they are part of the process for achieving participation and inclusion. For individuals with complex communication needs, family members, and practitioners alike, this distinction is critically important because it sets the focus on actively using and creating policy as an "opportunity intervention."

In *The Obstacle is the Way* (2014), Ryan Holiday describes the stoic philosophy that obstacles are challenges that point to solutions. In that light, the AAC policy barriers that we encounter can be viewed as signals that point to areas of need. Once the barriers and needs are identified, they can serve as guideposts toward opportunity interventions designed to address those needs. In this chapter, we explore (a) policies that impact AAC, (b) AAC policy barriers and pathways, and (c) future directions.

Policies That Impact AAC

There are a myriad of AAC policies and policy barriers, which can be categorized into (a) legislative and regulatory policies, (b) organizational policies, and (c) personal and family policies. The purpose of organizing policies into different categories in the context of this chapter is to clarify how policy works across various levels of governance; from the larger policies that govern country and state, to the organizational regulations that govern schools and workplaces, and to the house rules or personal policies that individuals and their families maintain. People with complex communication needs may experience barriers across these various types of policies and can also leverage these types of policies to create the systems of support they require in their lives.

Legislative and Regulatory Policies

Legislative and regulatory policies in AAC include the laws, rules, and statutes that govern our communities at the Federal, State, and local level. For citizens in the United States examples of federal laws and policies include the Individuals with Disabilities Education Act (IDEA) and the Americans with Disabilities Act (ADA). These examples have broad implications for people with complex communication needs and guide organization level policy setting. For instance, in the four decades of the IDEA (renamed in 1990 but first passed as PL-94-142, titled the Education for All Handicapped Children Act in 1975) the law has shaped special education service provision for generations of students with complex communication needs.

In addition to federal laws, regulatory policies also impact the lives of people with complex communication needs. There are regulations that are connected to health, education, and civic systems. For example, related to the previously discussed IDEA, regulatory policies encountered at the national level include levels of federal funding for special education. Further, a regulatory policy example related to funding speech generating devices is the 2015 National Coverage Determination regulatory guidance issued by the Centers for Medicare and Medicaid Services (CMS) (Goldman, 2016).

Recognizing the impact of federal laws and regulatory policies on other levels is critically important. For example, states and schools interpret the federal law (e.g., IDEA) and work to implement the practices and policies set forth. Individuals with complex communication needs and their families then engage with these organizations. Similarly, federal regulatory policies, such as those that regulate the funding of speech generating devices, impact organizations such as private health insurance providers who look to CMS coverage determinations when developing their own regulations. Then agencies and individuals with complex communication needs work through these systems to request funding for speech generating devices, still all too often encountering various barriers along the way (Goldman, 2016; Golinker, 2009).

Organization Policies

Organization policies are the rules and standards of an organization or agency. Oftentimes, organizational policies serve as a set of standard operating procedures, contextually fit to the requirements of the particular agency. Examples of organizational policies in schools include policies for behavioral expectations as well as policies for how the students enter and exit the school building. Broad organizational policies impact all people, including individuals with complex communication needs. However, there are also organizational policies that are specific to AAC. For instance, The ACE Centre of the United Kingdom created a resource titled, "Developing augmentative and alternative communication policies in schools: Information and guidelines" (Chinner et al., 2001) with the purpose of creating a "document [that] recommends that schools and local education authorities devise AAC policies which reflect the requirements of individual establishments" (p. 1). This resource exemplifies the process of an agency, in this case ACE, working intentionally to create discrete policy statements around AAC and supporting students with complex communication needs.

Personal and Family Policies

Personal and family policies are rules and standards in people's home and personal life that are often not documented formally (Beukelman & Light, 2020) but have strong potential to be tools for inclusion and support. For example, a family's

"house rules" might include ensuring that all family members have adequate knowledge of a member's AAC system. In Chapter 7, interviewee Kevin Williams exemplifies an augmented communicator (term he likes to use) who leverages personal and family policy as an opportunity intervention. Specifically, in conversation with Kevin, he shared that he uses personal policies extensively in his personal care to create order and predictable practices that support his life and overall experience in the world. Kevin's careful documentation of his personal policies aids in the coordination of paid staff who support him in his life. Further, his utilization of personal policies extends beyond the home. For example, when Kevin travels about his city, he incorporates the use of personal policies (e.g., in the form of calendar items and short notes) to keep him on time and organized with the resources he requires.

As we examine these three different types of AAC policies (e.g., legislative and regulatory, organizational, personal and family), we recognize the interrelationship

---

Developing augmentative and alternative communication policies in schools: Information and guidelines. Published by the ACE Center and edited by Sue Chinner, Gillian Hazell, Paul Skinner, Pat Thomas, and Gill Williams can be downloaded for free (https://ace centre.org.uk/resources/developing-aac-policies-schools). This document articulates the need for AAC policies in schools that are designed to:

- provide human rights and equal opportunities.

- provide means of communication.
- develop language skills.
- ensure access to all potential modalities of language development.
- ensure there is a community of users.
- provide models of language and communication.
- raise the status of the systems.
- safeguard access to the curriculum.
- maintain levels of training.
- maintain levels of resources.

among policies and how they can be aligned or stacked together to create opportunities. To close this section, we further explore Kevin's experiences to illustrate that alignment. Specifically, consider a situation in which Kevin experiences an opportunity barrier in finding, hiring, and coordinating care staff. This barrier may be due to policies regarding funded training for care providers, the lack of established standards for communication and coordination of care between multiple care providers, and low pay for care providers. In order to address this opportunity barrier, Kevin harnesses federal and state legislative and regulatory policies that mandate and fund support for providing personal care services. At the organizational level, Kevin works with case managers who leverage their own policies and standard operating procedures to obtain and coordinate the hiring and pay of his carers. Then, with regard to personal policy, he uses his computer and software development skills to coordinate his care through agile project management, which requires task analysis, documentation, and check-ins with carers and case managers to set priorities and maintain focus. Thus, through federal legislation, state and agency level support, and personal policy, Kevin aligns policy in support of his daily life.

AAC Policy Barriers and Pathways

As discussed previously, policy barriers can, when analyzed, serve as guideposts for what the Participation Model terms opportunity interventions (Beukelman & Light, 2020). Policy focused opportunity interventions can be used as a pathway in the systems of support for an individual or a community. In reflecting on the underlying reasons for policy barriers, we acknowledge that they connect very closely and often incorporate other opportunity barriers, including practice, skill, knowledge, and attitude (Beukelman & Light, 2020). The following sections identify frequently encountered policy barriers as well as strategies and pathways to address those barriers.

Policy Barrier: Systemic Ableism

When considering AAC policy barriers, a foundational issue is that systemic ableism permeates the systems of our communities (Hehir, 2009). The disabled scholar, Talia A. Lewis (2021) defines ableism as:

A system that places value on people's bodies and minds based on societally constructed ideas of normality, intelligence, excellence, desirability, and productivity. These constructed ideas are deeply rooted in anti-blackness, eugenics, misogyny, colonialism, imperialism, and capitalism. This form of systematic oppression leads to people and society determining who is valuable and worthy based on a person's language, appearance, religion and/or their ability to satisfactorily [re]produce, excel and behave. You don't have to be disabled to experience ableism. (p. 1)

Ableism discriminates against everyone who does not conform to society's standard for body and mind function. In section three of this text, which focused on attitude barriers, we heard directly from individuals who have experienced the impact of ableism across school, work, and community life. In this section, we extend that discussion by exploring and confronting how ableism intersects with AAC policy barriers, policy development, and policy implementation across health, education, and civic life.

First, let us consider some disturbing but compelling evidence highlighting the need to address ableism and discrimination. At the legislative and regulatory level, policies such as the IDEA governing special education and ADA governing civic life were both created because of discrimination. Specifically, in outlining the findings and purpose, section 1201 for the ADA (1990) states that,

(1) physical or mental disabilities in no way diminish a person's right to fully participate in all aspects of society, yet many people with physical or mental disabilities have been precluded from doing so because of discrimination; others who have a record of a disability or are regarded as having a disability also have been subjected to discrimination:

(2) historically, society has tended to isolate and segregate individuals with disabilities, and, despite some improvements, such forms of discrimination against individuals with disabilities continue to be a serious and pervasive social problem.

(3) discrimination against individuals with disabilities persists in such

critical areas as employment, housing, public accommodations, education, transportation, communication, recreation, institutionalization, health services, voting, and access to public services.

This broad and comprehensive barrier acknowledgment is substantive, validating the lived experience of people with complex communication needs. The law itself is not only a validation of the presence of discrimination, but also a vehicle to create protections and support for people with complex communication needs. By listening to the lived experiences of people with disabilities and acknowledging the substantive impact that ableism can have on the lives of people with complex communication needs, we find a guidepost that points us toward a pathway, using existing policy documents and guidelines to achieve goals.

Policy Pathway: Using Existing Policy Documents and Guidelines to Achieve Goals Related to AAC

For those who are employed in positions that provide advocacy and support, there is often a calling toward service and a basic charter toward social justice that is reflected in policy documents (e.g., in the oaths of medicine for health care professionals, the licensure of educators, and the national organizations of Speech-Language Pathologists (SLPs) and special educators). For many with complex communication needs and their advocates, seeking social justice is intimate and deeply personal. Listening to their direct lived experience is vital to developing a truthful understanding of needs. The word democracy comes from the Greek roots, "demos" (meaning people), and "kratos" (meaning rule). The democratic process is fundamental to understanding and progressing AAC policy issues. Listening to people with complex communication needs is important not just for people who are formally employed as policy makers, but in nearly all levels of policy development and implementation, including agency level policy makers who need to listen to the people who make up the agency such as schools and adult services organizations that specialize in education, care, and employment.

In addition to listening directly to key stakeholders, examining established policy documents and guidelines relevant to AAC policy is important given that those documents and guidelines provide a synthesis of information based upon the lived experiences of people with disabilities and their advocates. As discussed, policy documents and guidelines can be developed at the international, national, state, and local level. Examples include the United Nations Convention on the Rights of Persons with Disabilities (CRPD) (2006), the National Joint Committee for the Communication Needs of Persons with Severe Disabilities (NJC) Communication Bill of Rights (Brady et al., 2016), and Sins Invalid's Disability Justice Principles (Berne et al., 2018). Table 11–1 summarizes key elements of each of these policy documents and guidelines.

At the international level, the United Nations promotes democracy as a core value and works as an organization for human rights, development, and peace and security. The purpose of *The United Nations Convention on the Rights of Persons with Disabilities* (CRPD) (2006) is to "promote, protect and ensure the full and equal enjoyment of all human rights and fundamental freedoms by all persons with disabilities, and to promote respect for their inherent dignity." The CRPD is an international policy that was modeled after the ADA. As illustrated by Table 11–1, the guiding principles of the CRPD are focused on respect, dignity, and inclusion for people with disabilities. Globally, 184 countries have ratified the treaty as of January 2022. However, despite U.S. President Barack Obama signing the landmark international treaty, the U.S. Senate failed to approve the treaty in 2012 and therefore it is not currently ratified in the United States.

The National Joint Committee for the Communication Needs of Persons with Severe Disabilities (NJC) provides an example of an AAC policy document that was developed at the national level in the U.S. The NJC developed the *Communication Bill of Rights* in 1992 and then they were refined by Brady et al. (2016). In the *Rights*, it is stated that, "All people with a disability of any extent or severity have a basic right to affect, through communication, the conditions of their existence" (p. 123). As illustrated by Table 11–1, the focus of the Communication Bill of Rights is not only on describing standards for comprehensive communication resources made available for individuals with complex needs, but also on describing standards for communication partner behavior, which speak to organization level policy. The Communication Bill of

Table 11–1. Sample Principles and Guiding Documents Developed at the International, National, and State Level

Convention on the Rights of Persons With Disabilities (CRPD) Guiding Principles	Disability Justice Principles	Communication Bill of Rights
1. Respect for inherent dignity, individual autonomy including the freedom to make one's own choices, and independence of persons	1. Intersectionality	1. The right to interact socially, maintain social closeness, and build relationships
2. Non-discrimination	2. Leadership of Those Most Impacted	2. The right to request desired objects, actions, events, and people
3. Full and effective participation and inclusion in society	3. Anti-Capitalism	3. The right to refuse or reject undesired objects, actions, events, or choices
4. Respect for difference and acceptance of persons with disabilities as part of human diversity and humanity	4. Cross-Movement Solidarity	4. The right to express personal preferences and feelings
5. Equality of opportunity	5. Recognizing Wholeness	5. The right to make choices from meaningful alternatives
6. Accessibility	6. Sustainability	6. The right to make comments and share opinions
7. Equality between men and women	7. Cross-Disability Solidarity	7. The right to ask for and give information, including information about changes in routine and environment
8. Respect for the evolving capacities of children with disabilities and respect for the right of children with disabilities to preserve their identities	8. Interdependence	8. The right to be informed about people and events in one's life
	9. Collective Access	9. The right to access interventions and supports that improve communication
	10. Collective Liberation	10. The right to have communication acts acknowledged and responded to even when the desired outcome cannot be realized
		11. The right to have access to functioning AAC (augmentative and alternative communication) and other AT (assistive technology) services and devices at all times
		12. The right to access environmental contexts, interactions, and opportunities that promote participation as full communication partners with other people, including peers
		13. The right to be treated with dignity and addressed with respect and courtesy
		14. The right to be addressed directly and not be spoken for or talked about in the third person while present
		15. The right to have clear, meaningful, and culturally and linguistically appropriate communications

Note. Guiding principles adapted from: United Nations Enable. (2006). *Convention on the rights of persons with disabilities.* United Nations. Disability Justice Principles adapted from Berne, P., Morales, A. L., Langstaff, D., & Sins Invalid. (2018). Ten principles of disability justice. *WSQ: Women's Studies Quarterly, 46*(1), 227–230. Communication Bill of Rights adapted from Brady, N. C., Bruce, S., Goldman, A., Erickson, K., Mineo, B., Ogletree, B. T., Paul, D., Romski, M. A., Sevcik, R., Siegel, E., Schoonover, J., Snell, M., Sylvester, L., & Wilkinson, K. (2016). Communication services and supports for individuals with severe disabilities: Guidance for assessment and intervention. *American Journal on Intellectual and Developmental Disabilities, 121*(2), 121–138.

Rights is an example of an AAC policy tool that was developed collaboratively at the national level that has been used and adopted by schools and agencies to support individuals with complex communication needs.

An example of a policy document created at the local level is provided by the San Francisco, California, based Sins Invalid group. This group created "a disability justice-based performance project that incubates and celebrates artists with disabilities, centralizing artists of color and LGBTQ/gender-variant artists as communities who have been historically marginalized" (Sins Invalid, 2022). As part of this group's efforts, they created the Disability Justice Principles. As noted in Table 11–1, the Disability Justice Principles focus on mitigating the barriers that people who use AAC face, including ableism. Disability Justice is a comprehensive

philosophy of how people with disabilities will obtain equity and a sense of belonging in society. Specifically, in addressing systemic ableism, the Disability Justice principle of *recognizing wholeness* comes to mind as it relates to the importance of people with complex communication needs being recognized as three-dimensional and as whole people with a multiplicity of desires, wants, and needs, not just people who need to learn AAC.

Listening to the synthesis of lived experiences of people with disabilities that are present in the form of policy documents and guidelines provides an anchor, grounding ourselves to the needs of the people we serve. Next, we look at an example of an important set of policy barriers, early and ongoing access to AAC, and strategies to address those barriers, that are faced by people with complex communication needs.

The Disability Justice principle of *recognizing wholeness* is an important principle for SLPs and other AAC specialists to remember when interacting with people who use AAC (Berne et al., 2018). These specialists should constantly see their clients who have complex communication needs as whole people and not just people who need to learn AAC. They need to see their clients as three-dimensional with a multiplicity of desires, wants, and needs. Too often, people who have complex communication needs are dismissed as not being able to contribute to a conversation or be sociable because of their speech disability. The dominant society often deems this segment of the population as not being able to contribute. That is why recognizing wholeness for people who use AAC becomes so important. It changes the narrative of who these people are. Instead of being people who cannot interact with their community, they become family members, friends, employers, employees, and romantic partners, who have many connections with their communities. SLPs and AAC manufacturers should take this under consideration when they are developing AAC systems and teaching AAC use to people with complex communication needs.

Policy Pathway: Early and Ongoing Access to AAC

An important policy pathway is the successful advocacy efforts of the AAC community toward securing near universal funding of speech generating devices (Goldman, 2016; Golinker 2009; Navrotski, 2015; Wiles & Hill, 2015). Golinker (2001) wrote about one important milestone in funding, "January 1, 2001, marked a revolution in the way the Medicare program responds to the needs of individuals with severe communication disabilities. At the start of the year, Medicare began to provide reimbursement for AAC devices" (p. 12). Then another milestone was reached in 2015, when the Centers for Medicare and Medicaid Services updated the National Coverage Decision (NCD) for SGDs and restored the full scope of Medicare SGD coverage, allowing computer-based devices to be covered and device functions to be unlocked, with the 2016 Steve Gleason Act ending capped rentals (Sennott, Ferrari, et al., 2016). Despite this substantial progress, AAC device funding is frequently perceived as a policy barrier in the United States (Goldman, 2008, 2016). However, in reality, AAC device funding is usually available from one or multiple sources in the United States and has strong legal and regulatory precedent across health systems and education (Golinker, 2009).

As noted previously, just because the policy is in place it is not always an easy or equitable road to get to the goal. For instance, Ball et al. (2015), in their retrospective review of 64 individuals with amyotrophic lateral sclerosis (ALS) and their SGD acquisition process, described how SGDs are an important communication tool for people with ALS, and synthesized from their research that funding should be available independent of residence, access method, device dedication, and type of SGD. They cautioned about how safety, social connection, and independence can be lost when policy barriers threaten to lock-down device features. Further, even when SGDs are acquired, individuals sometimes struggle to navigate erroneous organizational level policies where, for instance, a school may not allow a child to take a device out of the therapy room or home for the summer (Goldman, 2008). Another example is the perceived policy that a school must fund SGDs to meet the requirements of IDEA, but instead an acceptable and often preferred route is that they assist families in using health-care-benefit funding for SGDs (Goldman, 2016; L. Golinker, personal communication, May 4, 2022).

Although it is impossible to identify all of the policy barriers that people with complex communication needs may face, Harris (2015) asserts that strong advocacy may be necessary to help families navigate the funding and acquisition process. Thus, in order to address barriers to early and ongoing access to AAC, the following sections will discuss how to advocate and leverage policy by reviewing the process of how someone in the United States obtains an AAC device and how to share resources around funding of speech generating devices.

The purpose of the funding process is to help individuals with complex communication needs obtain the communication prosthetic tools they require for inclusion and participation in their lives. Strong

A review of the process for obtaining funding for SGDs (Sennott, Ferrari, et al., 2016).

1. An assessment with a speech-language pathologist (SLP) in order to identify what device will be the most appropriate for the individual's needs.
2. The SLP will need to then create a report for the purposes of justifying the individual acquiring an SGD. The physician then writes a prescription and completes any necessary paperwork. The SLP will then contact the local sales representative of the company of the particular device chosen.
3. The individual's eligibility of different paying sources is assessed. This can include Medicaid, Medicare, or other health insurance.
4. A funding submission packet is provided to the device company.
5. The company submits the funding request and ensures to bill the applicable entity. The company then fulfills the device order.

advocacy (Harris, 2015) may be needed to aid families including families from a range of diverse and multicultural backgrounds, in order to ensure that all communities obtain collective access to communication support in the form of AAC devices such as SGDs.

As a field, we have made considerable progress toward collective access to AAC devices for people with complex communication needs. Despite that progress, early and ongoing access to AAC systems may take considerable effort from those with knowledge of the process. Table 11–2 contains useful AAC funding resources to support the process.

Policy Barrier: The IDEA Demands More in Supporting Inclusive Participation

All people who serve individuals with complex communication needs in school settings can benefit from an understanding of the fundamental aspects of the Supreme Court case Endrew F. *v.* Douglas County School District, 580 U. S. (2017). In summary, Endrew, a child with autism and complex communication needs, was being passed along through each IEP reporting period, making little meaningful progress. Because of access, as well as opportunity barriers, school staff were not able to change this destructive trajectory. As a result, Endrew's parents withdrew him from the public school and chose to enroll him in a private program, where his school performance pattern changed for the positive. The legal arguments between the family and the school revolved around the interpretation of what is required by IDEA (2004) in regard to a free, appropriate, and public education (FAPE). This quote from the Supreme Court ruling (Endrew F. *v.* Douglas County School District, 2017) helps summarize the finding that the message of IDEA is one of high

Table 11–2. AAC Funding Resources	
AAC Funding Resource	**Description**
https://www.aacfundinghelp.com	AAC funding guide, funding program information, report coach template, and general resources
https://www.asha.org/njc/funding-for-services	ASHA hosted NJC funding for communication supports webpage
https://www.ussaac.org/aac-info/funding	United States Society of Augmentative and Alternative Communication (USAAC) funding page
https://www.ataporg.org	Association of Assistive Technology Act Programs (ATAP) facilitates coordination of state AT Programs nationally
Public school students: Who can pay for SGDs? https://www.aac-learning-center.psu.edu/2018/07/13/public-school-students-who-can-pay-for-sgds	Video presentation by Lew Golinker, legal and regulatory funding expert with the Assistive Technology Law Center, sponsored by the AAC-RERC
Medicaid SGD Funding Update: Current Developments and Issues, youtu.be/b55U92VIfvE	USAAC sponsored presentation by Lew Golinker
AAC Funding Quick Reference Guide aacfunding.com/assets/uploads/Funding-Quick-Reference_120821.pdf	Funding Quick Reference Guide Medicaid, Medicare, Private Insurance, and/or Tricare from AACFunding.com

expectations for students receiving special education services.

When all is said and done, a student offered an educational program providing "merely more than de minimis" progress from year to year can hardly be said to have been offered an education at all. For children with disabilities, receiving instruction that aims so low would be tantamount to "sitting idly . . . awaiting the time when they were old enough to 'drop out.'" (Rowley, 458 U. S., at 179). The IDEA demands more. It requires that an educational program be reasonably calculated to enable a child to make progress appropriate in light of the child's circumstances. (p. 14)

In essence, similar to the previously shared section of the ADA, which highlights the destructive impact of discrimination and ableism on the lives of people with disabilities, the Endrew F. Supreme Court opinion highlights the opportunity barriers students with complex communication needs and their families face in seeking FAPE. The barrier of low expectations includes barriers to inclusion in pivotal areas such as general education, communication devices and support, friendship, and literacy instruction (Beukelman & Light, 2020; Brady et al., 2016;

Erickson & Koppenhaver, 2020; Johnston et al., 2020; Østvik et al., 2017). The IDEA demands more than "de minimis" and the Endrew F. opinion is a call to action for a FAPE to be "reasonably calculated." This includes ensuring that resources are available to staff schools with practitioners who are capable of the dynamic assessments necessary for creating educational programs that enable students with complex needs to make progress.

The implications of Endrew F. are concerning and suggest that, for students with complex communication needs, some schools may be out of compliance with federal policy. This is a significant policy barrier. The good news is that high expectations in education is (a) both chartered through IDEA and included in that policy, and (b) contains the fundamentals for creating those high expectations, including the tools for using careful reasoning to create a uniquely individualized program fit to the student's context. Figure 11–1 summarizes the purpose of IDEA.

IDEA's statement of purpose outlines FAPE and emphasizes meeting unique needs through a FAPE that prepares individuals with disabilities for next steps in education, employment, and independent living. Yet, as illustrated by the landmark Endrew F. opinion, barriers are present. Leveraging existing policies is one strategy for addressing those barriers.

Policy Pathway: Leverage Policy to Address Barriers

A key aspect of the IDEA policy, outlined in Section 1400 under purposes, mandates a learning system "to assess and ensure the effectiveness of efforts to educate children with disabilities" (Section 1400), which speaks to a dynamic measurement system. The implications for leveraging IDEA for individuals who use AAC are substantial and are operationalized, in part, via the *Individualized Family Service Plan* (IFSP) and the *Individualized Education Plan* (IEP). The IEP and IFSP are designed to support children with disabilities and their families in the planning and implementation of services

Visiting the Bridge School by Samuel Sennott

"I am thankful to have been able to visit or co-create a few educational or therapeutic spaces that have had elements of what I experienced at the Bridge School. No, I am not talking about the communication systems they have for every child or the innovations in visual supports present all around the classrooms or even the highly skilled assistants, teachers, and therapists who serve at the Bridge School. What really impressed me was this overwhelming feeling of how much the people cared about the students, who all have complex communication needs, and additionally how much they believe in the students. This is the mandate of IDEA and is practically speaking, to me what I hope for in the disposition of teachers or therapists we educate. The Endrew F. Supreme Court guidance calls us toward this positive disposition and away from 'de minimis.'"

IDEA Sec. 300.1 Purposes

The purposes of this part are—

(a) To ensure that all children with disabilities have available to them a free appropriate public education that emphasizes special education and related services designed to meet their unique needs and prepare them for further education, employment, and independent living;

(b) To ensure that the rights of children with disabilities and their parents are protected;

(c) To assist States, localities, educational service agencies, and Federal agencies to provide for the education of all children with disabilities; and

(d) To assess and ensure the effectiveness of efforts to educate children with disabilities

---

Note. Adapted from Individuals with Disabilities Education Act, 20 U.S.C. § 1400 (2004).

Figure 11–1. IDEA Sec. 300.1 Purposes.

and supports. For children with complex communication needs, early intervention in teaching the use of AAC opens doors to participation in the myriad of activities of early childhood (Cress & Marvin, 2003; Light & Drager, 2007; Romski & Sevcik, 2005; Romski et al., 2015; Solomon-Rice & Soto, 2014). And more generally, there

Visiting the Cerebral Palsy Education Center in Melbourne Australia
by Samuel Sennott

"Upon entering the early childhood therapy center, you realize that something is different about how they operate here. When you enter the main activity spaces, you cannot tell who is a therapist, let alone which discipline someone is from. Seeing families and therapists, in a transdisciplinary model, co-treat so naturally was an inspiring experience to me, bringing to life the ideals of intervention textbooks and demonstrating what a family-centered practice looks like. After hearing about this center in Gayle Porter's Pragmati- cally Organized Dynamic Display (PODD) workshops for years, it was a privilege to see how, through implementation of organizational policy, a committed group of therapist leaders co-created a space where AAC is fluently modeled across all people participating and social, educational, and therapeutic activities are engaged in vigorously and supported by all participants. This seamless coordination of policy to specific goals to implementation changed the way I look at AAC intervention and what is possible."

is a consistent evidence base supporting the communication and language benefits from a quality early language environment for children (Romski et al., 2015; Sennott, Light, et al., 2016). Thus, the IEP and IFSP are important tools embedded within policy that can be used to connect to family centered practices (Coburn et al., 2021; Mandak et al., 2017), functional goal writing and implementation (García-Grau et al., 2022; Rowland et al., 2012), delineation of important resources such as early and ongoing access to AAC (Light & Drager, 2007), and carryover across providers and home (Lorang et al., 2022). Using what we have called activation cards for AAC is an ecological momentary assessment format for capturing data in real contexts and can be used to create dynamic assessment of IFSP or IEP goals (Sennott et. al., 2017). Figures 11–2 and 11–3 provide an example of a digital activation card for AAC form.

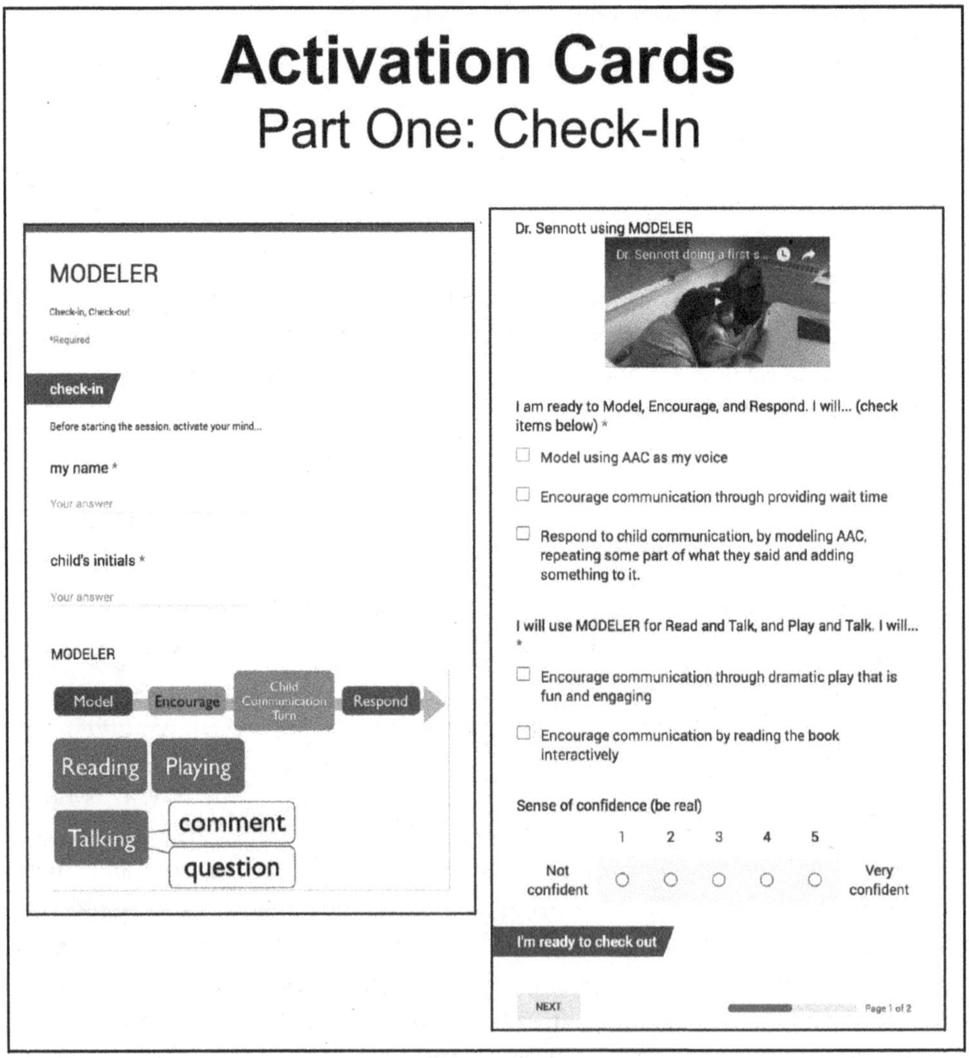

Figure 11–2. Activation Cards, Part One: Check-In.

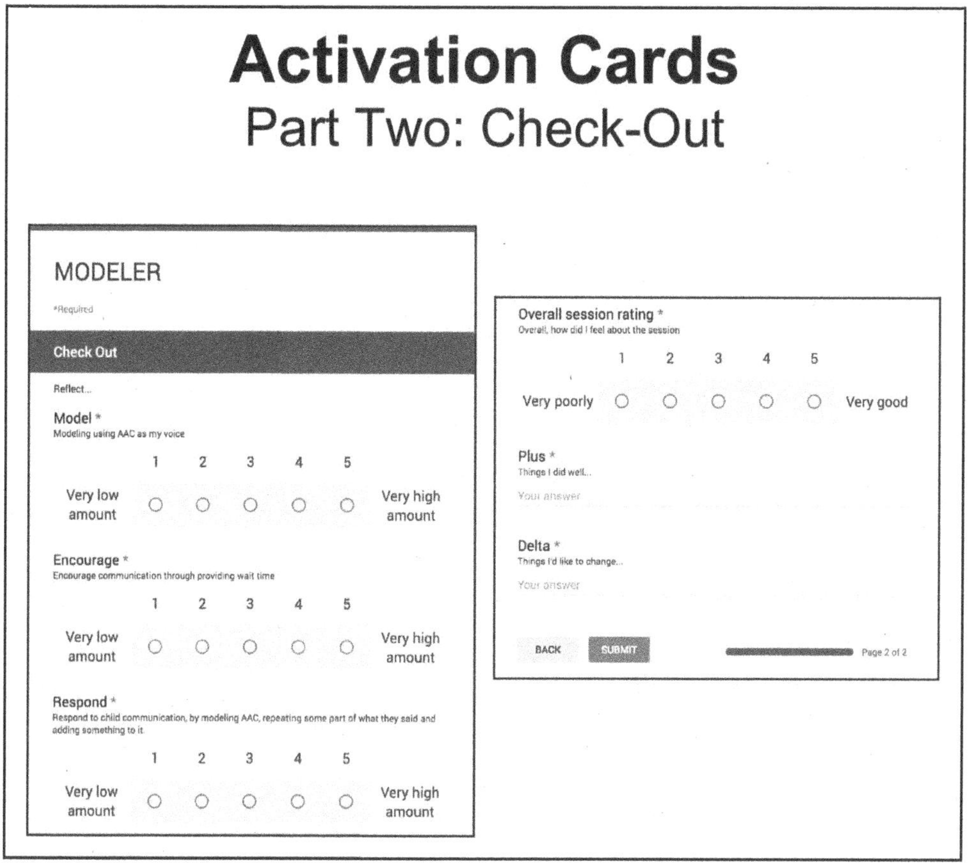

Activation Cards
Part Two: Check-Out

MODELER

*Required

Check Out

Reflect...

Model *
Modeling using AAC as my voice

	1	2	3	4	5	
Very low amount	○	○	○	○	○	Very high amount

Encourage *
Encourage communication through providing wait time

	1	2	3	4	5	
Very low amount	○	○	○	○	○	Very high amount

Respond *
Respond to child communication, by modeling AAC, repeating some part of what they said and adding something to it.

	1	2	3	4	5	
Very low amount	○	○	○	○	○	Very high amount

Overall session rating *
Overall, how did I feel about the session

	1	2	3	4	5	
Very poorly	○	○	○	○	○	Very good

Plus *
Things I did well...

Your answer

Delta *
Things I'd like to change...

Your answer

BACK   SUBMIT   Page 2 of 2

Figure 11–3. Activation Cards, Part Two: Check-Out.

Future Directions

Future research and actions are needed to help ensure inclusion in all areas of life for people with complex communication needs, with a particular emphasis on shared governance, equitable access, and representation.

Future Research on Equitable Access and Shared Governance

Additional research and policies are needed to ensure equitable access and shared governance. For example, artificial intelligence tools continue to hold great potential for individuals with complex communication needs, but the creation and use of these tools raise important policy questions around data governance, ethical use, and the roles of people and computers (Sennott et al., 2019). Further, virtual reality (VR) appears to be making another comeback and this time is being led by the large technology companies (Bryant et al., 2019; Carreon et al., 2022). However, equitable access to virtual tools and virtual worlds will require careful thought toward overall design, accessibility, and governance. In addition to researching new innovations, research is needed examining the efficiency and effectiveness of existing policies related to FAPE, funding of AAC devices, and policies and services that span across school, work, healthcare, and community life.

Regardless of the focus, future research can benefit from following the Disability Justice Principle of *leadership of the most impacted* and the disability rights motto of "nothing about us, without us." In the context of AAC, this means that AAC policies and technology must be developed based upon the advice and insight of people who rely on AAC (Berne et al., 2018; Williams et al., 2008).

Future Directions Toward Inclusion in All Areas of Life

In listening to the lived experience of people with complex communication needs, we are reminded that seeking collective access to opportunity and support is an ongoing process for both individuals and for communities. For example, in earlier sections of this book we empathized with the attitude barriers experienced by Jay Grochala when he spoke about his experiences with ableism in the form of people assuming that he lacked the cognitive skills needed for work. Further, we can only imagine what Toña Rivera must have felt when first getting consistent access to a bilingual AAC system at 33 so that she could speak Spanish with her father. At times we heard about struggles, such as those in Chapter 13 that Siddharth and his mother Daya describe in seeking AAC intervention in India. In addition, we

learned of the challenges that Cas McNamara experienced and worked through as she encountered knowledge/skill barriers that impacted her son's use of AAC.

These personal accounts of opportunity barriers support the need for progress across a wide range of important life areas such as community integration (Beukelman & Light, 2020; Hamm & Mirenda, 2006; McNaughton & Bryen, 2007), work (McNaughton et al., 2002; McNaughton et al., 2010; Richardson et al., 2019), health care (DePew & Thistle, 2022; Blackstone & Pressman, 2016; Downey & Happ, 2013; Hemsley & Balandin 2014), recreation (Datillo et al., 2008; Hajjar et al., 2016; Logan et al., 2014), relationships, gender, and sexuality (Sellwood et al., 2022), and transitions (Douglas et al., 2022; McNaughton & Beukelman, 2010).

Recognizing the scale of the challenges that individuals with complex communication needs face can be overwhelming. However, person-centered planning frameworks such as the Participation Model (Beukelman & Light, 2020), and a range of person-centered planning tool sets (Schwartz et al., 2000; Shogren et al., 2017), have been used to help navigate opportunity barriers and create service designs for people with complex communication needs. By maintaining a person-centered focus, progress toward participation and quality of life is possible and often intersects with policy (Beukelman & Light, 2020; Hamm & Mirenda, 2006; Williams et al., 2008). For example, due in part to organizational and personal policies, an emphasis on patient centeredness appears to be increasing in health care, with recent steps forward in AAC in the area of patient-provider communication (Blackstone & Pressman, 2016; Hemsley & Balandin, 2014). Another example can be seen in the domain of recreation, which has been identified as important to people with complex communication needs and as providing a range of benefits from enjoyment to social opportunities (Datillo et al., 2008). Inclusive policies around recreation have the potential to impact not just the person with a disability, but the whole community (Hajjar et al., 2016). One such program demonstrates what the community can do to support inclusive recreation in the community. The community-based maker group called Go Baby Go (Logan et al., 2014) modifies electric ride-on cars so that young children with mobility challenges can drive them and experience powered mobility through play. This initiative has been supported through inclusive recreation policies at the local organization level, including multiple parks and recreation agencies.

Conclusion

For individuals who use AAC and their allies, policy can be used as a powerful tool for addressing opportunity barriers. With the lens of AAC policy barriers being guideposts that point to solutions, this chapter explored three types of policies (legislative and regulatory, organizational, and personal and family). In exploring policy barriers and pathways, we are daunted by systemic ableism and its broad implications, but are encouraged by the laws, policy documents, and guidelines we have to inspire and inform practice and policy. By leveraging legal and regulatory, organizational, and personal and family policy through careful person-centered planning, we can engage in the hard work of helping people with complex communication needs engage in society fully.

References

Americans With Disabilities Act of 1990, Pub. L. No. 101-336, § 1, 104 Stat. 328. (1990).

Ball, L. J., Pattee, G. L., Golinker, L., & Beukelman, D. R. (2015). Speech-generating device funding and patterns of acquisition for persons with amyotrophic lateral sclerosis. *Perspectives on Augmentative and Alternative Communication, 24*(4), 155–160.

Blackstone, S. W., & Pressman, H. (2016). Patient communication in health care settings: New opportunities for augmentative and alternative communication. *Augmentative and Alternative Communication, 32*(1), 69–79.

Berne, P., Morales, A. L., Langstaff, D., & Sins Invalid. (2018). Ten principles of disability justice. *WSQ: Women's Studies Quarterly, 46*(1), 227–230.

Beukelman, D. R., & Light, J. C. (2020). *Augmentative & alternative communication: Supporting children and adults with complex communication needs* (5th ed.). Brookes Publishing.

Brady, N. C., Bruce, S., Goldman, A., Erickson, K., Mineo, B., Ogletree, B. T., . . . Wilkinson, K. (2016). Communication services and supports for individuals with severe disabilities: Guidance for assessment and intervention. *American Journal on Intellectual and Developmental Disabilities, 121*(2), 121–138.

Bryant, L., Brunner, M., & Hemsley, B. (2019). A review of virtual reality technologies in the field of communication disability: Implications for practice and research. *Disability and Rehabilitation: Assistive Technology, 15*, 1–8.

Carreon, A., Smith, S. J., Mosher, M., Rao, K., & Rowland, A. (2022). A review of virtual reality intervention research for students with disabilities in k–12 settings. *Journal of Special Education Technology, 37*(1), 82–99.

Chinner, S., Hazell, G., Skinner, P., Thomas, P. & Williams, G. (Eds.). (2001) *Developing augmentative and alternative communication policies in schools.* ACE Centre.

Coburn, K. L., Jung, S., Ousley, C. L., Sowers, D. J., Wendelken, M., & Wilkinson, K. M. (2021). Centering the family in their system: A framework to promote family-centered AAC services. *Augmentative and Alternative Communication, 37*(4), 229–240.

Cress, C. J., & Marvin, C. A. (2003). Common questions about AAC services in early intervention. *Augmentative and Alternative Communication, 19*(4), 254–272.

Dattilo, J., Estrella, G., Estrella, L. J., Light, J., McNaughton, D., & Seabury, M. (2008). "I have chosen to live life abundantly": Perceptions of leisure by adults who use augmentative and alternative communication. *Augmentative and Alternative Communication, 24*(1), 16–28.

DePew, S. C., & Thistle, J. J. (2022). Supporting communication between individuals with disabilities and first responders: A preliminary case-based interview study. *Perspectives of the ASHA Special Interest Groups, 7*(1), 115–122.

Douglas, S. N., Meadan, H., & Schultheiss, H. (2022). A meta-synthesis of caregivers' experiences transitioning from early intervention to early childhood special educa-

tion. *Early Childhood Education Journal, 50*(3), 371–383.

Downey, D., & Happ, M. B. (2013). The need for nurse training to promote improved patient-provider communication for patients with complex communication needs. *Perspectives on Augmentative and Alternative Communication, 22*(2), 112–119.

Endrew F. v. Douglas County School District, 580 U. S. (2017). https://www.supremecourt.gov/opinions/16pdf/15-827_0pm1.pdf

Erickson, K. A., & Koppenhaver, D. A. (2020). *Comprehensive literacy for all: Teaching students with significant disabilities to read and write.* Brookes Publishing.

García-Grau, P., McWilliam, R. A., Bull, K., & Foster, J. (2022). Good goals matter: Functional child goals, family goals, and parent perceptions of difference in performance. *Infants & Young Children, 35*(2), 106–119.

Goldman, A. (2008). Funding AAC. *Perspectives on Augmentative and Alternative Communication, 17*(1), 33–35.

Goldman, A. (2016). Ten funding myths demystified! *Perspectives of the ASHA Special Interest Groups, 1*(12), 6–9.

Golinker, L. (2001). Medicare now covers AAC devices. *Perspectives on Augmentative and Alternative Communication, 10*(1), 12–14.

Golinker, L. (2009). Speech generating device funding for children. *Exceptional Parent, 39*(9), 64–65.

Hajjar, D. J., McCarthy, J. W., Benigno, J. P., & Chabot, J. (2016). "You get more than you give": Experiences of community partners in facilitating active recreation with individuals who have complex communication needs. *Augmentative and Alternative Communication, 32*(2), 131–142.

Hamm, B., & Mirenda, P. (2006). Post-school quality of life for individuals with developmental disabilities who use AAC. *Aug-*

mentative and Alternative Communication, 22(2), 134–147.

Harris, O. (2015). A cultural bases to develop strong advocates for client and family involvement in the speech-generated device evaluation and funding process. *Perspectives on Augmentative and Alternative Communication, 24*(4), 142–146.

Hehir, T. (2009). Eliminating ableism in education. *Harvard Educational Review, 72*(1), 1–33.

Hemsley, B., & Balandin, S. (2014). A meta-synthesis of patient-provider communication in hospital for patients with severe communication disabilities: Informing new translational research. *Augmentative and Alternative Communication, 30*(4), 329–343.

Holiday, R. (2014). *The obstacle is the way: The timeless art of turning trials into triumph.* Penguin.

Individuals with Disabilities Education Act, 20 U.S.C. § 1400. (2004).

Johnston, S. S., Blue, C., Gevarter, C., Ivy, S., & Stegenga, S. (2020). Opportunity barriers and promising practices for supporting individuals with complex communication needs. *Current Developmental Disorders Reports, 7*(3), 100–108.

Lewis, T. A. (2021). January 2021 Working definition of ableism. *Talia A. Lewis Blog.* https://www.talilalewis.com/blog/january-2021-working-definition-of-ableism.

Light, J., & Drager, K. (2007). AAC technologies for young children with complex communication needs: State of the science and future research directions. *Augmentative and Alternative Communication, 23*(3), 204–216.

Logan, S. W., Huang, H.-H., Stahlin, K., & Galloway, J. C. (2014). Modified ride-on car for mobility and socialization: Single-case study of an infant with Down syndrome. *Pediatric Physical Therapy, 26*(4), 418–426.

Lorang, E., Maltman, N., Venker, C., Eith, A., & Sterling, A. (2022). Speech-language pathologists' practices in augmentative and alternative communication during early intervention. *Augmentative and Alternative Communication,* 1–12.

Mandak, K., O'Neill, T., Light, J., & Fosco, G. M. (2017). Bridging the gap from values to actions: A family systems framework for family-centered AAC services. *Augmentative and Alternative Communication, 33*(1), 32–41.

McNaughton, D., Arnold, A., Sennott, S., & Serpentine, E. (2010). Developing skills, "making a match," and obtaining needed supports: Successful employment for individuals who use AAC. In D. B. McNaughton & D. R. Beukelman (Eds.), *Transition strategies for adolescents and young adults who use augmentative and alternative communication* (pp. 111–129). Brookes Publishing.

McNaughton, D. B., & Beukelman, D. R. (Eds.). (2010). *Transition strategies for adolescents and young adults who use AAC.* Brookes Publishing.

McNaughton, D., & Bryen, D. N. (2007). AAC technologies to enhance participation and access to meaningful societal roles for adolescents and adults with developmental disabilities who require AAC. *Augmentative and Alternative Communication, 23*(3), 217–229.

McNaughton, D., Light, J., & Arnold, K. (2002). 'Getting your wheel in the door': Successful full-time employment experiences of individuals with cerebral palsy who use augmentative and alternative communication. *Augmentative and Alternative Communication, 18*(2), 59–76.

Navrotski, D. (2015). Role and responsibilities of AAC manufacturers' consultants in the SGD funding process. *Perspectives on Augmentative and Alternative Communication, 24*(4), 147–154.

Østvik, J., Ytterhus, B., & Balandin, S. (2017). Friendship between children using augmentative and alternative communication and peers: A systematic literature review. *Journal of Intellectual & Developmental Disability, 42*(4), 403–415.

Richardson, L., McCoy, A., & McNaughton, D. (2019). "He's worth the extra work": The employment experiences of adults with ASD who use augmentative and alternative communication (AAC) as reported by adults with ASD, family members, and employers. *Work, 62*(2), 205–219.

Romski, M., & Sevcik, R. A. (2005). Augmentative communication and early intervention: Myths and realities. *Infants & Young Children, 18*(3), 174–185.

Romski, M., Sevcik, R. A., Barton-Hulsey, A., & Whitmore, A. S. (2015). Early intervention and AAC: What a difference 30 years makes. *Augmentative and Alternative Communication, 31*(3), 181–202.

Rowland, C., Fried-Oken, M., Steiner, S. A. M., Lollar, D., Phelps, R., Simeonsson, R. J., & Granlund, M. (2012). Developing the ICF-CY for AAC profile and code set for children who rely on AAC. *Augmentative and Alternative Communication, 28*(1), 21–32.

Schwartz, A. A., Holburn, S. C., & Jacobson, J. W. (2000). Defining person centeredness: results of two consensus methods. *Education and Training in Mental Retardation and Developmental Disabilities, 35*(3), 235–249.

Sellwood, D., Raghavendra, P., & Walker, R. (2022). Facilitators and barriers to developing romantic and sexual relationships: Lived experiences of people with complex communication needs. *Augmentative and Alternative Communication*, 1–14.

Sennott, S. C., Akagi, L., Lee, M., & Rhodes, A. (2019). AAC and artificial intelligence (AI). *Topics in Language Disorders, 39*(4), 389–403.

Sennott, S. C., Ferarri, R., Crest, C., Fogarty, J. L., & Hix-Small, H. (2017). MODELER AAC intervention during shared reading and play in early childhood. *Journal on Technology & Persons with Disabilities, 5*, 270–285.

Sennott, S. C., Ferrari, R., McLernon, G., & Lesher, D. (2016). The three definitions of application for AAC intervention. *Perspectives of the ASHA Special Interest Groups, 1*(12), 99–107.

Sennott, S. C., Light, J. C., & McNaughton, D. (2016). AAC modeling intervention research review. *Research and Practice for Persons with Severe Disabilities, 41*, 101–115.

Shogren, K. A., Wehmeyer, M. L., & Thompson, J. R. (2017). Person-centered and student directed planning. In M. L. Wehmeyer & K. A. Shogren (Eds.), *Handbook of research based practices for educating students with intellectual disability* (pp. 167–182). Routledge.

Sins Invalid. (2022). *Our Mission.* https://www.sinsinvalid.org/mission

Solomon-Rice, P. L., & Soto, G. (2014). Facilitating vocabulary in toddlers using AAC: A preliminary study comparing focused stimulation and augmented input. *Communication Disorders Quarterly, 35*(4), 204–215.

United Nations Enable. (2006). *Convention on the rights of persons with disabilities.* United Nations.

Wiles, H. C., & Hill, K. (2015). Five SGD funding rules of commitment. *Perspectives on Augmentative and Alternative Communication, 24*(4), 129–134.

Williams, M. B., Krezman, C., & McNaughton, D. (2008). "Reach for the stars": Five principles for the next 25 years of AAC. *Augmentative and Alternative Communication, 24*(3), 194.

12 Policy Barriers: Studying Successful Case Examples

Eric J. Sanders, Samuel Sennott*, Lateef McLeod*, Christina Royster*, Gretchen Hanser*, Caroline Ramsey Musselwhite*, and Monica Kaniamattam*

Introduction

In this chapter, three cases that focus on policy barriers are presented. The first case highlights the impact of school policies on service provision for an eight-year-old child with intellectual disabilities. The second case focuses on the impact of policies on emergent writing provision for students with complex communication needs. The final case presents the story of a mother and young adult in India and the impact of policies on services for individuals with complex communication needs in low and low-middle income countries. Throughout the cases, strategies for breaking down policy barriers and the impact of other barriers on policy will be shared.

Case Example: Addressing Policy Barriers to AAC Service Delivery in Schools (Christina Royster, EdD, CCC-SLP)

In this case, I will share an experience I had as an Assistive Technology Speech-Language Pathologist (AT-SLP) in a public school in the Washington D.C. area. The student I worked with was named Tobi and he was an eight-year-old African American child. He lived at home with his mother and father and had several family members that lived nearby. Tobi was diagnosed with epilepsy, an intellectual disability, and had fine motor challenges. He enjoyed listening to music, playing catch, and helping his family

---

*These authors have contributed equally to this work and share senior authorship.

cook. Tobi was a social child who liked slapstick humor. For example, he laughed incessantly when someone pretended to trip or bump their head. Further, like many children his age, he loved "gross" humor, including burps and farts! Tobi's language skills were delayed relative to peers his age. When using verbal speech, he often spoke in single word utterances or short, scripted sentences from online videos.

At home, Tobi used a dynamic speech-generating device (SGD) with communication software based on motor planning. He used a layout with 84 cells and his device had a keyguard to support his accuracy when selecting buttons. With the SGD, Tobi often produced longer sentences of 3 to 4 words, but sometimes needed verbal or gestural cues. He could navigate to pages to find familiar vocabulary but required help to search for items when he did not know where they were. Tobi could identify the first letter of words and sight words. He did well when a communication partner modeled on a separate device or when asked for permission to model on his SGD.

Although Tobi was fairly proficient in his use of AAC with communication partners in the home environment, he did not like to use his SGD at school. As his class returned to school following virtual learning in spring 2020, his teachers and therapists reported that he refused to use the SGD in the classroom. When they encouraged him to take it out of his backpack, he shouted, "NO!" and quickly stuffed it back in. Tobi even became aggressive when his school-based speech language pathologist (SLP) took the SGD out and brought it to the back of the classroom so it could be charged. Tobi raised his hand to hit the SLP, but she moved out of the way to avoid being struck. The SLP told Tobi that she would put the "talker" back and try again later. Staff attempted several more times in the following weeks of school, but this resulted in the same behaviors.

Due to these difficulties, the school team reached out to the district's assistive technology (AT) team for support. Tobi's case manager and school-based SLP worked together to complete the form to request support. As the SLP from the AT team, I responded quickly to this request and visited Tobi's school to conduct multiple observations. I witnessed the same behaviors and felt that Tobi and his school team would benefit from additional resources and ongoing support. The entire educational team held an Individualized Education Program (IEP) meeting with the Tobi's family to discuss ideas.

The Impact of Policy Barriers on Tobi's Use of AAC

During the IEP meeting, I suggested using an alternative device for modeling to increase Tobi's exposure to using AAC in the classroom environment, but also to reduce the pressure of using his personal device. I described that this would be documented on the IEP as a consultative support. Tobi's parents asked why AT would not be documented as a weekly service, like his speech therapy or occupational therapy. I explained that the policy in the state and school-district was that assistive technology is not considered a related service provided exclusively by an AT consultant. Rather, AT services are provided daily by several educators, not just the consultant. I shared the written state AT guide which defined AT services as, "... direct or indirect support provided by IEP team members that promote the selection, acquisition, and use of AT devices." In addition, I explained that the guide specifies that

> effective AT Services rely on shared responsibility for implementation by multiple team members, with guidance and training as needed from an individual with expertise in selecting and adapting AT tools and devices. The AT specialist (as needed) and other team members collaborate to support implementation that builds the student's ability to use the AT solution as independently as possible in all relevant environments. (Maryland State Assistive Technology Steering Committee & MSDE, 2021)

Even though Tobi's parents were not satisfied with having consult support from the AT team instead of weekly services, they understood that this was a policy that had been in place for several years. The team documented the family's concerns in the IEP, and then concluded the meeting.

The following week after the IEP meeting, I returned to Tobi's school with a dynamic SGD from the AT department. I sat in Tobi's proximity so that he could see the device. While Tobi's teacher went through morning meeting activities reviewing calendar concepts, the weather, class attendance, and checking in with everyone's feelings, I responded to questions and initiated comments using the device. A paraeducator in the classroom

later noted that Tobi watched me intently. When asked if he wanted to take his SGD out, he paused and then refused. I continued to use the separate device for the rest of the morning meeting and during the reading lesson that followed. Tobi continued to watch but did not attempt to access his personal SGD. At the end of my visit, the school team discussed next steps. Due to Tobi showing interest, they decided it was worth it for me to come back and attempt again as soon as possible.

The next day, I e-mailed Tobi's parents to let them know how the visit went. The family said that this was promising and wanted to know when I would return. Due to AT support being consultative, they were concerned that it would take weeks before any follow up would occur. I assured Tobi's family that I would return the next week. At this next visit, Tobi continued to watch me. This time, however, he allowed his teacher to take his SGD out and keep it on the desk next to him. This progress was exciting, so Tobi's teacher inquired about getting an SGD to keep in the classroom for modeling purposes. I put in a request to sign out the SGD for the classroom.

The Interaction of Policy and Practice Barriers

Despite the progress that Tobi continued to make with being more comfortable with his SGD in the classroom, the process to obtain a classroom SGD for staff to use was slow. The district had a limited supply of devices due to various factors such as an increase in requests throughout the district, an increase of broken devices due to students adjusting to in-person learning, and a delay in shipping devices that had been ordered. The devices that the district had were prioritized to students who had no equipment at all. Because Tobi did have an SGD, an "extra" classroom SGD was not considered as pressing. Unlike the experience with me as the AT-SLP, this was more of a practice barrier in that there was not a written policy in place related to the prioritization of SGDs.

I continued to bring an SGD to model as much as possible, but the device I was using was dedicated for consultative support and could not remain at the school. Tobi was starting to use his talker almost daily to communicate during morning meetings. The team took data each morning, keeping track of what Tobi used his talker to say, the type of communication (i.e., request, greet, respond to a question, protest), and the approximate number of models that were provided to him on the SGD. The data showed steady progress, but the IEP team firmly believed that Tobi could make more progress with increased support. Between AT being a consult instead of weekly service and the limited availability of SGDs, these barriers were negatively impacting Tobi's academic performance and communication development.

Strategies

While the team waited for a classroom SGD, strategies were put in place to address the policy and practice barriers. For example, to address the policy barrier, I dedicated time to coaching and teaching the classroom personnel about modeling AAC use. This was to ensure that, although I was unable to be there for direct services, everyone in the classroom was "on the same page" in terms of how to best provide services. To address the related practice barrier, I suggested a software program that allowed for the same communication software that Tobi used to be displayed on the classroom whiteboard. The paraeducator in the classroom also used a paper-based version of the software that was printed and laminated in a binder. The paraeducator became familiar with how to model responses in the binder, and Tobi's teacher also provided aided language input with the whiteboard display. In the five weeks that the team waited for an SGD, they were able to implement a communication partner program that supported Tobi as well as his classmates. In addition to Tobi beginning to use his talker with more independence, other students also benefited from the additional visual supports.

Outcomes

The approach that Tobi's team took to address the policy barrier and related practice barrier had a positive impact on his AAC use. When the classroom SGD arrived, Tobi's teachers and providers made sure that it was always available for communication partners to use. They also continued using the paper-based binder and whiteboard display. Tobi began to use multimodal communication that included verbal speech, his talker, and the whiteboard. The team continued to take data on Tobi's use of his talker and the supports that were provided to him. The team compared Tobi's performance at the end of the quarter with his present level sections from the last IEP, and this demonstrated a strong growth in his ability to demonstrate his understanding of academic material. Further, Tobi took advantage of opportunities to joke with his teachers by using his SGD to direct them in funny actions, and other students in the classroom were able to communicate more effectively as well.

Discussion

Tobi, like all students, has the right to a free and appropriate education. This includes the right to AT that will allow him to access the curriculum and to participate in the academic environment. While Tobi had his own SGD that was appropriate for him and supported his communication, he was not using it, and this was having a negative impact on his progress in school. Tobi's school team contacted the district AT team to get the support that was needed, but due to district/state policies and limited resources, the team experienced barriers. In response to policy barriers preventing the provision of direct AT services and practice barriers preventing access to a classroom SGD, I collaborated with the school team to establish a communication partner system with aided language input, modeling, and universal support for all students, even before a classroom device arrived. Data revealed that these strategies were effective and, although progress may have been slower as a result of the policy and practice barriers at hand, it was not halted.

> In response to policy barriers preventing the provision of direct AT services and practice barriers preventing access to a classroom SGD, I collaborated with the school team to establish a communication partner system with aided language input, modeling, and universal support for all students, even before a classroom device arrived.

A major lesson learned is that school teams must be flexible. Policies are slow to alter and it can be difficult for individuals to change policies when they are simultaneously trying to navigate the everyday demands that exist. Tobi's team learned that the commitment of individuals and collaboration between school-based staff, district level professionals, and families can result in successful outcomes. This is not to suggest that individuals should not enact policy changes, but rather to highlight the importance navigating through barriers instead of accepting them as is.

The final lesson learned is that, while supporting one student, we may also end up supporting an entire class. The strategies and tools that were implemented in Tobi's class resulted in success for Tobi as well as his classmates. However, it is important to note that, even if Tobi's team had been able to obtain a classroom device immediately, the technology alone would not have been sufficient. The success came from the team making adaptations in their instruction and being intentional about incorporating all forms of communication into the school day. This is central to how we create change.

Case Example: Change the "Policy, Change the Practice: Emergent Writing for ALL Students (Gretchen Hanser, PhD, MS, OTR/L & Caroline Ramsey Musselwhite, EdD, CCC-SLP)

In the United States, there are a variety of federal education laws and policies designed to support individuals with disabilities, including individuals with complex communication needs. Among these federal laws and policies are the Individuals with Disabilities Education Act (IDEA) of 2004 (PL 108-446) which stipulates that students with disabilities must have access to a free and appropriate public education designed to meet their unique needs, and the Every Student Succeeds Act (ESSA) of 2015 which holds states accountable for how students learn and achieve. In order to implement federal policies at the local level, additional micro-level policies are often adopted. For PreK–12 education, these micro-level policies may be written by the state, district, or school.

In some situations, barriers are experienced when attempting to implement federal, state, district, and school policies. This case summarizes our collaborative efforts with two educational settings (one large public school district and one private school for students with brain injuries) that experienced barriers in policy implementation. Specifically, both educational settings struggled to ensure that students with complex communication needs and significant disabilities received access to high quality emergent writing instruction that was in line with what was required by policy. It is important to note that although policies (or a lack of policies) can serve as direct barriers in some cases, additional opportunity barriers impact the effective implementation of supportive policies. Here, we will focus on those barriers and their impact on implementation. In terms of policy, this case example will (a) identify the barriers that were encountered in policy implementation, (b) describe how these barriers were addressed, and (c) discuss how identifying and addressing these barriers led to positive outcomes for students, as well as better implementation of existing policies.

Barriers Encountered When Implementing Existing Policies

Several barriers were encountered as the public school district and the private school engaged in policy implementation. These included knowledge/skill barriers, attitude barriers, and practice barriers related to emergent writing for students who use AAC.

Both school settings encountered knowledge/skill barriers. Specifically, conversations and observations revealed that many school faculty did not recognize that (a) there was a part of literacy development that was termed emergent literacy and that it was different from conventional literacy, (b) emergent writing development and opportunities are crucial components of the acquisition of later conventional literacy skills for individuals who use AAC, (c) emergent writing includes the behaviors and understandings that develop into conventional writing, and (d) the progression of emergent writing often involves moving from drawings that represent writing, to scribbles, to letter-like forms, and then to early conventional writing (Clay, 1975; Morrow, 2001).

Further, the school personnel had limited awareness of emergent literacy in general. Although most of the school faculty did recognize the positive impact of providing young children without disabilities multiple opportunities to use and experiment with different writing tools (e.g., pencils, keyboards) and surfaces (e.g., paper, dry-erase boards), this recognition did not extend to learners with more complex instructional needs. It is important to note that school faculty, including teachers, paraeducators, and clinicians, were extremely caring, interested, and open to learning new ways to teach their students to engage in emergent writing. However, knowledge/skill barriers precluded them from doing so. As a result, many of their students with complex communication needs and significant disabilities had not had early emergent writing experiences and would, therefore, need to learn what writers do and why writing is valuable.

In addition to knowledge/skill barriers, a variety of attitude barriers related to the concept of "readiness" were identified in the school district and private school. Specifically, some faculty believed that their students with disabilities were not "ready" for writing. However, as Karen Erickson and David Koppenhaver eloquently stated, the only prerequisites for emergent writing are "something to write with and something to write on" (Koppenhaver & Erickson, 2020, p. 69). Whether due to erroneous beliefs about students not having the cognitive skills or not being able to spell, these types of

readiness assumptions result in little or no opportunities for students to write. This may produce a perpetuating cycle in which students do not have multiple chances to write with instruction and feedback, and as a result they do not make progress.

Not surprisingly, there were also a series of practice barriers related to emergent writing instruction in both environments. Some of these practice barriers were related to the physical and visual impairments that many learners who use AAC experience. For example, it was not uncommon to observe the students with physical and visual impairments engaging in early "writing" by using a multiple-choice format with sentences that were predetermined by the adults. This format limits students' ability to learn that writing starts with developing their own ideas. It also restricts opportunities to generate writing using the individual letters of the alphabet. The same is true with other practices where instructors were observed using hand over hand techniques to help students to write and providing students with access to the alphabet and asking them to copy letters. This is important as these activities do not allow for the crucial opportunity for students who use AAC to generate their own text.

Another practice barrier that was observed was the lack of access to appropriate writing tools. Physical impairments may prevent students who use AAC from using traditional writing implements such as crayons, pencils, and keyboards. Because of this, they may not have the same opportunity to participate in this important developmental activity. There are, however, different tools (that we refer to as alternative pencils) that can provide students with access to the alphabet that they would not have if only traditional writing tools were provided. There are a range of alternative pencils that provide students access to the alphabet through methods such as direct selection, head pointing, eye gaze, partner assisted scanning, dedicated scanning, and auditory scanning (Hanser, 2006; Hanser et al., in progress; Center for Literacy and Disability Studies; Erickson & Koppenhaver, 2020). Professionals need to consider each student's unique physical and visual skills in order to identify the most appropriate alternative pencil. Alternative pencils, combined with robust instruction, can help to ensure that all learners have emergent writing experiences.

Finally, another practice barrier we observed in both settings was related to concomitant vision impairments, including Cortical Visual Impairment (CVI), which may impact students' ability to see and interpret print. Here, the practice barrier that we observed was related to a lack of collaboration between teachers and educational team members, such as Teachers of the Visually Impaired (TVI), who can play a valuable role on the team by providing information on how to visually adapt materials. A range of adaptations can be made to alternative pencils to meet students' visual needs, such as simplifying the visual complexity by using simple fonts and presenting text on black background, simplifying the array by presenting fewer letters at a time, and using neon-colored fonts based on students' color preferences. Additionally, professionals should recognize that students do not need to see the alphabet in order

to learn it and that learning the alphabet can be done through auditory channels. Visual impairments, similar to physical disabilities, should not be a gatekeeper to learning or to having emergent literacy experiences.

Strategies to Address Barriers That Were Interfering With Policy Implementation

After the barriers interfering with policy implementation were identified, our next step was to design and implement strategies to address those barriers. In both settings, a key strategy was to engage in professional development with both large group presentations and smaller, more personalized training sessions. This professional development included: an overview of literacy development (including differentiation between emergent and early conventional literacy); training in alternative pencils and physical access methods; identification of the appropriate alternative pencil for each student; coaching to support the use of instructional strategies for teaching emergent writing for students who use alternative pencils; and showing successful examples of growth in emergent writing through case examples and videos. As a result of these professional development activities, faculty at both schools forged a sense of community and developed a strong understanding of the importance of emergent writing.

Related to this, faculty in the large school district and the private school were encouraged to "share the bright spots"

(Heath & Heath, 2010) by highlighting successes that they experienced as a result of creating early emergent writing experiences. Teachers, therapists, and paraeducators shared stories of success during team meetings, e-mails, and at training sessions. Participants reported that 'sharing the bright spots' was very effective. They noted that it was extremely helpful to see a struggling student begin to make clear progress or observe the colleague next door posting emergent writing samples outside her classroom.

Although professional development through webinars, in-person training, and readings were successful in addressing many knowledge/skill and attitude barriers, changing practice required a more hands-on approach. Collaboration proved to be essential, and teams indicated that it was empowering to work together to create alternative pencils, brainstorm times to model them, think of opportunities for students to use them, and find ways to celebrate growth. The SLPs and AT team in the large school district led the effort to create and share alternative pencils, with support from OTs and TVIs. At the self-contained school, the OT department took the lead as they recognized the important role that OTs play in supporting writing. For each group 'smoothing the path' (Heath D. & Heath C., 2010) by having a range of alternative pencils readily available helped teachers and aides begin to consistently use alternative pencils in every classroom.

Another key strategy for combating barriers was ensuring buy-in from other stakeholders, including school administrators. Both educational settings had administrators who believed that writing was crucial for ALL students. Further, they supported professional development, purchased needed supplies, and allotted time for coaching and creating alternative pencils. Administrators showed interest and support by asking to look at the alternative pencils and writing samples. Administrators also established new policies such as (a) ensuring that "on-boarding" was provided for all new faculty and associated personnel that specifically included strategies for supporting emergent writing for students with significant disabilities, and (b) requiring the use of teacher reflection checklists to encourage implementation of strategies.

Outcomes

Identifying and addressing barriers to policy implementation had a powerful impact on students in both educational settings. To demonstrate the impact of these changes, we will share the strategies used and progress observed for one student, Ethan, who attended the private school. Ethan was an 8-year-old boy with spastic cerebral palsy and CVI who used switches to access his AAC device, the academic curriculum, and leisure activities. Ethan was scored at Phase II on the CVI Range, meaning that he was learning to integrate vision with function and to interpret what he sees (Roman-Lantzy, 2018). Because of this, collaboration and critical input from the TVI was necessary. At the time that the emergent writing instruction began, the school staff constructed an alternative pencil that was a light tech print flip chart accessed via 2 switch auditory partner assisted scanning. Ethan's print flip chart was carefully designed to support his CVI with a simplified array and neon letters on a black background, while also giving him access to the full alphabet. Additionally, because Ethan was working on establishing reliable movements for activating switches; engaging in emergent writing was the ideal way to work on this skill as emergent writing is about experimentation and not accuracy.

As a result of addressing knowledge/skill, attitude, and practice barriers, instructors who worked with Ethan learned how to provide comprehensive emergent literacy instruction that included alphabet and sound awareness instruction, shared reading, shared writing, and opportunities for independent reading (Erickson, 2017) and were ready to move forward with supporting Ethan's emergent writing.

In the beginning, the emphasis was on teaching Ethan both the purpose and the process of writing. During writing time, Ethan used the flip chart and worked on developing and refining his switch skills via partner assisted scanning. Writing using the flip chart with partner assisted scanning had an interactive quality that Ethan enjoyed and that helped facilitate his learning. As a result of these activities, Ethan began to love writing and sharing his work, especially with his teacher who posted students' writing samples, and his family who celebrated his writing. He was also introduced to the AAC app, TalkSuite (https://talk-suite.com/), and had an onscreen keyboard that was customized to mirror his light tech print flip chart alternative pencil.

In addition to learning the purpose and process of writing, the quality and content of Ethan's writing also changed. In the beginning, his writing consisted of random strings of repeated letters and then progressed to experimentation with spaces and punctuation. At the time of writing this case, Ethan was making more deliberate selections—including some that were relevant to the topic, such as choosing a letter that was part of a key word connected to the topic. Figure 12–1 illustrates the changes in his writing across time. It is important to recognize that although Ethan was not yet creating readable text, his alphabet exploration showed notable progress and is consistent with the normal developmental process of writing.

Discussion

Existing policies such as IDEA and ESSA are important for ensuring that students who have complex learning needs are provided a free and appropriate public education that meets their unique needs. However, these policies are often challenging to implement. As outlined in this case, it is necessary to identify barriers that impede policy implementation and then employ strategies to address those barriers. Identifying and addressing barriers to policy implementation can result in positive student outcomes as well as move educational practices in a direction where ALL students reap the benefits of these important policies.

Purpose/ Topic / Context	Ethan's Writing (Adult gave no suggestions about what to write)	Observations & Informal Assessment
12/2019 - Journal Entry Being sick at home	**bbbbbbbbcddfff** **ff bbbbbbccee**	Enjoyed repeatedly activating switches and had many unintended activations. Choosing random letters in the order that they appear on the flip chart. Very engaged in acting out writing.
11/2020 Thank You Note to Brother Sentence Starter: The present was _____	**a_ _b.h_ _.**	Began using group scanning which included a "Special Keys" page. Very interested in the page with space, period, !, ? Spent more time with punctuation than with letters. Put period at the end of his writing to indicate end of sentence.
2/2021 Valentine to Dad (To and From were written by the adult)	**To: _ _ _ a_** **From: fgqp**	Very focused on the Special Keys page with "space." Cycled through the alphabet multiple times and deliberately went back to the Special Keys page. When signing his name, cycled around a number of times before choosing letters. Was very deliberate.
5/2021 Sign for Bedroom Door: Please Knock	**kmmo**	Very selective. Cycled through the alphabet multiple times before choosing letters.
10/2021—Classroom Rules Poster Assisting Gretchen in signing poster	**g** (modeled) **r** (Ale chose)	Target letter was r. While scanning through alphabet-anticipated the r. Activated the switch right *before* the audio prompt was given for r. Is memorizing the order of the letters.

Figure 12–1. Ethan's changes in writing across time.

Case Example: The Impact of Policies on AAC Service Provision in India (Monica Kaniamattam, PhD, CCC-SLP)

Policies that impact service provision for children who use AAC exist across the world. The following case will review relevant policy barriers, provide strategies for how to address these barriers, and describe the outcomes of those strategies in developing countries, with a specific focus on India. This case centers around Siddharth, a 21-year-old individual living in India. I met Siddharth's mother, Daya, as part of a research project aimed at exploring the lived experiences of parents of children with complex communication needs in rural India. Siddharth had severe seizures from birth until the age of 2 and was diagnosed with cerebral palsy and intellectual disability. At the time of our involvement, he communicated through vocalizations and gestures. It is important to note that until this point, Siddharth had not been introduced to AAC. Siddharth was able to walk with support but had severe motor weakness and motor coordination deficits. His primary communication partner was his mother who described their communicative interaction in the following way: "*It is through this action that I will know that he is upset. . . . If I start wearing a saree, he will understand that I am getting ready to leave. At that point, he will bite his hand to express his anger.*" Siddharth is also a music enthusiast who enjoys listening to melodic tunes. In the words of his mother, "*He enjoys listening to devotional songs. He listens to the same songs over and over. If he doesn't like the music, he will beat his hands and try to show that he is not enjoying that song.*"

At the age of 20, Siddharth and Daya moved 200 miles away from his family home in order to obtain rehabilitation. Daya reports a typical day in his life in the following way: "*He will wake up in the morning. Then I have to do everything for him: brush, bathe, give him breakfast, and bring him to the center by 9 a.m. I return later to give him lunch. After the morning physiotherapy session, I take him to his class. Even though he doesn't always attend to what happens in class, I make him sit in the school, hoping that he will at least gain something. He will pass urine and defecate in the classroom sometimes. When we get home in the evening, he will watch TV. He*

will understand when the power goes out and when we turn it off." Daya is currently considering ending rehabilitation and returning home because she is discouraged by Siddharth's lack of progress.

Severe Communication Impairments and Related Policies in India

The story of Siddharth is an unfortunate case where the right to communication and social interaction which could have been achieved through efficient AAC provision and intervention was denied due to multiple barriers, including barriers related to policy and policy implementation. This is a reality for many children with complex communication needs in low resource contexts in India and other Low and Low Middle-Income Countries (LMIC) (Goldbart & Sen, 2013; World Health Organization, 2011). The fact that 80% of children with disabilities worldwide live in LMICs (World Health Organization, 2011) underscores the significance of understanding and acknowledging the impact of this lack of access to services and supports.

The provision of educational and rehabilitation services and supports is crucial for individuals like Siddharth. The Global Burden of Diseases, Injuries, and Risk Factors Study of 2016 estimated that 95% of the 52.9 million children with Developmental Disabilities globally live in LMICs, with India having the highest number of affected children (Olusanya et al., 2018). In India's most recent census, approximately 1,998,692 people were identified as having a disability in "speech" and 1,505,964 were identified as having a disability in "mental retardation" (Ministry of Statistics and Programme Implementation, 2016). However, Wylie et al. (2013) have suggested that India's disability estimates might be a significant underestimate and there are no current estimates in the country regarding children with complex communication needs. Research into developmental disabilities in general, and associated communication disorders in particular, is extremely limited in LMICs, despite the adverse impact of developmental disabilities on child development, family life, and the economy (Ertem & World Health Organization, 2012).

The United Nations Convention on the Rights of Persons with Disabilities (UNCRPD) and the United Nations Convention on the Rights of the Child (UNCRC) are two international human rights treaties that specifically focus on protecting the rights of children with disabilities. India ratified the former in 2007 and the latter in 1992. The Rights of Persons with Disabilities Act of 2016 is the current disability law adopted by the Indian Government as part of its commitment to the UNCRPD. Other laws and policies like the Rehabilitation Council of India Act of 1992, the Persons with Disabilities (Equal Opportunities, Protection of Rights and Full Participation) Act of 1995, and the National Trust for Welfare of Persons with Autism, Cerebral Palsy, Mental Retardation, and Multiple Disabilities Act of 1999 also exist to protect and promote the active participation of children with disabilities.

According to Article 23 (Children with disabilities) of the United Nations Convention on the rights of the child (CRC), children who have any kind of disability have the right to special care and support that is "designed to ensure that the disabled child has effective access to and receives education, training, health care services, rehabilitation services, preparation for employment and recreation opportunities in a manner conducive to the child's achieving the fullest possible social integration and individual development." This unfortunately is not the case for many children with developmental disabilities (Bornstein et al., 2021) and complex communication needs in India (Kaniamattam & Oxley, 2021). Although there are several policies in place, their implementation is inadequate.

Strategies for Overcoming Barriers to Policy Implementation

The development of children with complex communication needs is a dynamic, interactive process that can be either fostered or undermined by multiple factors in the family, community, and the broader social-environmental context in which a child grows (Bronfenbrenner, 1986; Hoff, 2006). For a child with complex communication needs to succeed as a communicator, it is important that they are provided with appropriate communication options, receive communication facilitation, and have an affable and conducive environment for communication development (Bruner, 1983; Nelson, 2009).

Some key factors needed to foster the optimal development of a child with complex communication needs include increasing access to early identification and intervention, availability of habilitation services and AAC options, family willingness and resources for supporting the child, and social and communicative participation opportunities (Ertem & World Health Organization, 2012). In the next section we will explore how policies, and policy implementation may impact communication development for children growing up in low resource contexts like Siddharth. Here we will present a description of a strategies designed to ameliorate some of the policy barriers mentioned previously and provide key recommendations for implementation of these strategies in order to help people like Siddharth have support to help him participate in a variety of contexts more fully.

Strategies—Increasing Access to Early Identification and Intervention

As noted previously, Siddharth had severe disabilities from birth. Although he received physical therapy services to improve his motor skills on an infrequent basis, no other services were provided despite policies dictating that he should have been served by a multidisciplinary rehabilitation team. Daya's words reveal that they were unaware of such policies and were unable to get access to services, *"We just had physio (physical therapy) in our place. We didn't have speech therapy or psychotherapy. If we had also been given that, probably our child would have been better.*

No doctors told us that there were therapies like this."

Lack of knowledge related to policies and services for individuals with disabilities, such as Siddharth, contributes to delays in seeking care, impedes timely diagnosis and early intervention, serves as an impediment to the child's development, and ultimately reduces the opportunity for fuller participation in life. Late identification of disabilities and delayed provision of habilitation (Smythe et al., 2021) pose a serious challenge in India and other LMICs. The lack of awareness at the level of the general public (Ramachandran, 2020) and primary health care providers, inferior quality and availability of health care (Younger, 2016), and social stigma and discrimination (Edwardraj et al., 2010) further contribute to this problem (see Bright et al., 2018 and Hashemi et al., 2020 for a comprehensive account of obstacles to providing rehabilitation services in India and other LMICs). To address barriers in policy implementation as they relate to access to services, the following recommendations could be implemented:

1. Ensure that all children with disabilities are identified in a timely manner by implementing government initiatives, such as campaigns to raise awareness among the public (Ertem & World Health Organization, 2012) and primary care providers (Kaniamattam & Oxley, 2021) are crucial.

2. Develop and implement policies to provide early and appropriate habilitation support for all children suspected of having developmental

delays (Ertem & World Health Organization, 2012).

Strategies—Increasing Availability of Habilitation Services and AAC Options

Siddharth did not receive appropriate communication intervention because of limited awareness and the scarcity of rehabilitation centers near their hometown. As Daya painfully shared, since they *"never knew that there was such a (speech) therapy and that there is a school like this,"* they were able to provide Siddharth with speech therapy only around age 20. As mentioned earlier, Daya and Siddharth had to travel more than 200 miles to reach the center for services. The lack of accessible public transportation made travel more expensive, as described by Daya, *"we came here (rehabilitation center) by Taxi paying 6–7 thousand (Indian) rupees. He is heavy, right, so we cannot lift him and travel by train."* Siddharth's prognosis is limited due to the extreme delay in communication intervention. For this reason, giving Daya realistic support when she shared, *"I pray he will start saying at least something so I can answer those who keep blaming me (for providing him services)"* was challenging.

In India, there are a number of barriers impacting the implementation of policies designed to ensure the availability, accessibility, and utilization of communication intervention services for children with DD, especially in rural areas. Access to AAC services is even more limited. Barriers to policy implementation include scarce and unequally available rehabilita-

tion services like speech-language pathology (Goldbart & Sen, 2013), a limited number of rehabilitation centers, and a lack of funding support. Further, like many other LMICs, India faces a shortage of SLPs. The estimated ratio of SLPs/audiologists to the Indian population is 1 per 0.46 million. This estimate is based on India's current population of 1.38 billion (World Bank, 2020) and the number of SLPs/audiologists ($n = 2986$) registered in the Indian Speech-Language and Hearing Association (Indian Speech-Language and Hearing Association, n.d.). Although India has some excellent rehabilitation centers and clinics that provide AAC services that are concentrated in large cities, they are not sufficient to meet the country's vast needs for communication intervention. In recent years, much effort has been invested in improving the education and rehabilitation provision for children with disabilities (Chennat, 2019), however, more needs to be done, especially in rural areas. To address barriers in policy implementation as they relate to access to services, the following recommendations could be implemented:

1. Develop initiatives and policies to ensure families of children with disabilities are given access to clear and precise information about the habilitation process in their native language.
2. Develop tools and resources to increase public awareness about available communication intervention services (Goldbart & Sen, 2013).
3. Provide training to primary health care providers and pediatricians

regarding communication intervention options, such as AAC, for children with complex communication needs.

4. Advocate for subsidized internet access in high-need areas, such as rural communities and poor urban neighborhoods, to support teletherapy (World Bank, 2021).

5. Provide appropriate resources, such as financial assistance for communications intervention and AAC provision through insurance coverage.

6. Provide educators with the support and training they need to ensure all students with disabilities receive assistive technology support, including AAC.

7. Advocate for policymakers to promote more rehabilitation-related research in LMICs (Tomlinson et al., 2014), learn about local realities, make informed policy and practice decisions, and increase the political commitment required for stronger health systems that facilitate communication intervention.

Strategies—Increasing Family Willingness and Resources to Support Children With Complex Needs

Daya is the primary caregiver for Siddharth. They moved to a rented apartment near the rehabilitation center for the convenience of Siddharth's intervention. Siddharth's extended family lacks awareness regarding the benefit of rehabilitation, as reflected in Daya's words, "*We are*

a joint family. We are 'tharavadis' (refers to a higher status family, mostly caste-wise). In our family, my husband's older sister also had a son like this. They never took that child for any services. They keep telling us what is the use of giving services and that there is just no cure for this. Even now they say that. They don't like the fact that I have come here (the rehabilitation center) to give him treatment."

Caregiving and providing habilitation for a child with disabilities in LMICs is challenging due to several factors including, but not limited to, barriers to policy implementation. These factors include limited resources and a lack of professional guidance regarding habilitation, stigma, a lack of social support, financial burdens, and the requirement to take on nontraditional roles to navigate rehabilitative services. In addition to serving as barriers, these factors place a significant strain on caregivers. Further, there is a strong link between disability and poverty in LMICs because of the limited financial support and the absence of insurance coverage (Banks et al., 2017). Parent-clinician collaboration and communication partner training for parents is vital in low-resource settings because parents represent a valuable untapped resource. Working collaboratively with parents enables professionals to be responsive to the needs of underserved people with communication disorders in ways that will influence change to improve policies, services, practices, and promote equity (Goldbart & Sen, 2013).

The following policies and strategies could address barriers related to support for families:

1. Introduce the role of a service coordinator or case manager to support and guide the family on the type of services needed for a child with complex communication needs (Raver & Childress, 2015).

2. Provide or promote access to appropriate formal and informal support to parents as they pass through the various stages of accepting their children's diagnoses and evolving rehabilitation needs (Sen & Goldbart, 2005).

3. Establish online support groups through messaging platforms such as WhatsApp so parents can connect, receive social support, and learn from like-minded parents.

Strategies—Increasing Social and Communicative Participation Opportunities

Because of his limited mobility, Siddharth was left indoors with little chance to attend school, play with other children, and accompany his family outside the home. Daya was his primary and only communication partner, and his social network was limited. Daya's words reflect the limited interaction opportunities Siddharth has had in his life and what his future entails if they have to stop schooling and services, "*He just was sitting by himself all these years and so he lacks attention very much. . . . If I take him back home, my child will go back to the old situation. Sitting all alone.*"

Social and communicative participation is crucial for the communication

development, well-being, and quality of life of children with complex communication needs (Eadie et al., 2006). However, owing in part to widespread stigma and negative attitudes, parents and their children with disabilities are often isolated or even self-select isolation from the family and society (Edwardraj et al., 2010). Numerous studies have demonstrated that when children's interactions are restricted, their language capacity is hampered, including their vocabulary, syntax, and discourse (von Tetzchner et al., 2018; Westby & Washington, 2017). Based on the multiple barriers at the level of the child, parents, family, and the larger society (Bronfenbrenner, 1986), it is clear that current supports are inadequate for children such as Siddharth. Some suggestions for change include:

1. Support and train rehabilitation providers and educators to apply the WHO's International Classification of Functioning, Disability, and Health (ICF) (WHO, 2001) in their everyday practice. The ICF framework that conceptualizes a person's level of functioning as a dynamic interaction between their health conditions, environmental factors, and personal factors will help uncover barriers and opportunities for the social and communicative participation of children with disabilities (Adolfsson et al., 2011; Raghavendra et al., 2007).

2. Promote inclusive and community-based rehabilitation as a strategy for combating stigmas and reducing isolation (Khasnabis et al., 2010).

Strategies—Increasing Educational and Vocational Opportunities

Barriers to access to educational and vocational opportunities can be addressed, in part, through the development and implementation of policies. When asked about Siddharth's educational opportunities, Daya replied, "*No, we didn't try sending him to school before. I told you my husband works as a low-level hired help. Then we had to change two buses to reach the nearest school and he has difficulty climbing stairs. So, the school was very far. So, we didn't take him to school so much. Then even when I asked everybody used to avoid me and never paid attention. They were always like why to go to school. Even now when I send him to school here, do you know what all they talk about? They ask me what the use of coming and staying here for 1 year was, other than that we used a lot of money.*"

Despite its benefits (Hehir et al., 2016), inclusive education remains a distant dream for many children with severe disabilities in India (Singal, 2019) and there is a lack of special education options for children with disabilities (Kalyanpur, 2008). Children with autism and cerebral palsy are the least represented among the school-going population of India (Singal, 2016). There are also few opportunities for older children with developmental disabilities to engage in meaningful learning or vocational training.

To address policy implementation barriers related to access to education and vocational opportunities, the following could be implemented:

1. Increase awareness of educational systems about the legal foundations supporting inclusion for all children (Singal, 2019).
2. Increase public understanding of the science that supports meaningful inclusion of children with disabilities, from the earliest ages (Singal, 2019).
3. Provide training to all educators regarding how to best support and educate children with developmental disabilities (Singal, 2019).
4. Expand the use of information technology for the education of children with disabilities (World Bank, 2021).

Discussion

Through this case study, we have illustrated how the various levels in the ecological system can act as a promoter or barriers to a child's development as a communicator. Additionally, we reviewed a variety of ways that barriers can be addressed through the development of policies or through the implementation of strategies to support policy implementation.

In the recent past, the Government of India has made significant strides in improving the quality of life for individuals with disabilities, including individuals with complex communication needs. A conscious effort has been made to break the cycle of poverty, disability, segregation, powerlessness, and charity, which have led to the denial of opportunity for individuals with disabilities. However, much more needs to be done. A key aspect needed to ensure better policy development and implementation is the involvement of people with disabilities at all levels. This involvement is not an option, but rather an obligation. Finally, research is essential for increasing public understanding about disability issues, informing disability policy and programs, and efficiently allocating resources. Important areas of research that can inform policy and support policy implementation include examining barriers to quality of life and well-being of people with disabilities; barriers to mainstream and specific services, and what works in overcoming them in different contexts; and accessibility and universal design programs appropriate for low-income settings.

> A key aspect needed to ensure better policy development and implementation is the involvement of people with disabilities at all levels. This involvement is not an option, but rather an obligation.

As a final note, Article 23 of UN CRC, states that

parties shall promote, in the spirit of international cooperation, exchange of appropriate information in the field of preventive health care . . . and functional treatment of disabled children, including dissemination of and access to information concerning methods of rehabilitation . . . with the aim of enabling states parties to improve their capabilities and skills and to widen their experience in these areas.

To this end, we urge all current and future professionals in speech-language pathology to work toward ensuring communication is a right for every child and adult around the world. This would be our way to contribute to the WHO's Rehabilitation 2030 initiative to tackle the challenges associated with delayed and insufficient interventions for children with disabilities and complex communication needs in LMICs. (World Health Organization, 2019)

References and Additional Resources

Acts and Policies. (2022, May 2). [Government website]. National Institute for the Empowerment of Persons with Intellectual Disabilities. https://niepid.nic.in/acts-and-policies.php

Adolfsson, M., Malmqvist, J., Pless, M., & Granuld, M. (2011). Identifying child functioning from an ICF-CY perspective: Everyday life situations explored in measures of participation. *Disability and Rehabilitation, 33*(13–14), 1230–1244. https://doi.org/10.3109/09638288.2010.526163

Banks, L. M., Kuper, H., & Polack, S. (2017). Poverty and disability in low- and middle-income countries: A systematic review. *PLoS ONE, 12*(12), e0189996. https://doi.org/10.1371/journal.pone.0189996

Bornstein, M. H., Rothenberg, W. A., Lansford, J. E., Bradley, R. H., Deater-Deckard, K., Bizzego, A., & Esposito, G. (2021). Child development in low- and middle-income countries. *Pediatrics, 148*(5), e2021053180. https://doi.org/10.1542/peds.2021-053180

Bright, T., Wallace, S., & Kuper, H. (2018). A systematic review of access to rehabilitation for people with disabilities in low- and middle-income countries. *International Journal of Environmental Research and Public Health, 15*(10), 2165. https://doi.org/10.3390/ijerph15102165

Bronfenbrenner, U. (1986). Ecology of the family as a context for human development: Research perspectives. *Developmental Psychology, 22*(6), 723–742. https://doi.org/10.1037/0012-1649.22.6.723

Bruner, J. S. (1983). *Child's talk: Learning to use language.* W. W. Norton.

Buzolich, M. J. (n.d.). *The AAC classroom: Creating an educational environment to support unity users.* The Bridge School. San Francisco, CA.

Center for Literacy and Disability Studies. (n.d.-a). *Deaf-blind model classroom.* https://www.med.unc.edu/ahs/clds/projects/deaf-blind-model-classroom/

Center for Literacy and Disability Studies. (n.d.-b). *Writing with Alternative Pencils.* https://www.med.unc.edu/ahs/clds/alternative-pencils/

Chennat, S. (2019). Disability studies: The context. In S. Chennat (Ed.), *Disability inclusion and inclusive education* (pp. 1–19). Springer Singapore. https://doi.org/10.1007/978-981-15-0524-9_1

Clay, M. M. (1975). *What did I write? Beginning writing behaviour.* Heinemann.

Eadie, T. L., Yorkston, K. M., Klasner, E. R., Dudgeon, B. J., Deitz, J. C., Baylor, C. R., . . . Amtmann, D. (2006). Measuring communicative participation: A review of self-report instruments in speech-language pathology. *American Journal of Speech-Language Pathology, 15*(4), 307–320. https://doi.org/10.1044/1058-0360(2006/030)

Edwardraj, S., Mumtaj, K., Prasad, J. H., Kuruvilla, A., & Jacob, K. S. (2010). Perceptions about intellectual disability: A qualitative study from Vellore, South India: Perceptions about intellectual disability. *Journal of Intellectual Disability Research, 54*(8), 736–748. https://doi.org/10.1111/j.1365-2788.2010.01301.x

Erickson, K. A. (2017). Comprehensive literacy instruction, interprofessional collaborative practice, and students with severe disabilities. *American Journal of Speech-Language Pathology, 26,* 193–205.

Erickson, K. & Koppenhaver, D. (2020). *Comprehensive literacy for all: Teaching students with significant disabilities to read and write.* Brookes Publishing.

Ertem, I. O. & World Health Organization. (2012). *Developmental difficulties in early childhood: Prevention, early identification, assessment and intervention in low- and middle-income countries: A review.* World Health Organization. https://apps.who.int/iris/handle/10665/97942

Goldbart, J., & Sen, R. (2013). The world report on disability and communication disability: Some considerations from an Indian context. *International Journal of Speech-Language Pathology, 15*(1), 21–26. https://doi.org/10.3109/17549507.2012.727472

Hanser, G. (2006). Promoting emergent writing for students with significant disabilities. *OT Practice, 11*(9), 1–8. https://www.aota.org/media/Corporate/Files/Practice/Children/emergent-literacy-for-children-withdisabilities.pdf

Hanser, G., Musselwhite, C., & Wagner, D. *Alternative pencils: An overview* (Manuscript in preparation).

Hashemi, G., Wickenden, M., Bright, T., & Kuper, H. (2020). Barriers to accessing primary healthcare services for people with disabilities in low and middle-income countries, a Meta-synthesis of qualitative studies. *Disability and Rehabilitation 44*(8), 1–14. https://doi.org/10.1080/09638288.2020.1817984

Heath, D., & Heath, C. (2010). *Switch: How to change things when change is hard.* Crown Publishing Group.

Hehir, T., Gridal, T., Freeman, B., Lamoreau, R., Borquaye, Y., & Burke, S. (2016*). A summary of the evidence on inclusive education.* Alana Institute. https://alana.org.br/wp-content/uploads/2016/12/A_Summary_of_the_evidence_on_inclusive_education.pdf

Hoff, E. (2006). How social contexts support and shape language development. *Developmental Review, 26*(1), 55–88. https://doi.org/10.1016/j.dr.2005.11.002

Kalyanpur, M. (2008). The paradox of majority underrepresentation in special education in India: Constructions of difference in a developing country. *The Journal of Special Education, 42*(1), 55–64. https://doi.org/10.1177/0022466907313610

Kaniamattam, M., & Oxley, J. (2021). Parenting individuals with intellectual and developmental disabilities in South India. *Research in Developmental Disabilities, 111*, 103888. https://doi.org/10.1016/j.ridd.2021.103888

Khasnabis, C., Heinicke Motsch, K., Achu, K., Al Jubah, K., Brodtkorb, S., Chervin, P., . . . Lander, T. (Eds.). (2010). *Community-based rehabilitation: CBR guidelines.* World Health Organization. http://www.ncbi.nlm.nih.gov/books/NBK310940/

Maryland State Assistive Technology Steering Committee & MSDE. (2021). *The Maryland assistive technology guide.* https://www.marylandlearninglinks.org/the-maryland-assistive-technology-guide/

Ministry of Statistics and Programme Implementation. (2016*). Disabled persons in India: A statistical profile 2016.* Social Statistics Division, Ministry of Statistics and Programme Implementation, Government of India. http://mospi.nic.in/sites/default/files/publication_reports/Disabled_persons_in_India_2016.pdf

Morrow, L. M. (2001). *Literacy development in the early years: Helping children read and write* (4th ed.). Allyn & Bacon.

Nelson, K. A. (2009). Young minds in social worlds: Experience, meaning, and memory (Harvard Univ. Press paperback ed.). Harvard Univ. Press.

Olusanya, B. O., Davis, A. C., Wertlieb, D., Boo, N.-Y., Nair, M. K. C., Halpern, R., . . . Kassebaum, N. J. (2018). Developmental disabilities among children younger than 5 years in 195 countries and territories, 1990–2016: A systematic analysis for the global burden of disease study 2016. *The Lancet Global Health, 6*(10), e1100–e1121. https://doi.org/10.1016/S2214-109X(18)30309-7

Project Core. (n.d.). *Independent writing self-reflection and observation form.* http://www.project-core.com/instructional-planning-and-reflection/

Raghavendra, P., Bornman, J., Granlund, M., & Björck-Åkesson, E. (2007). The World Health Organization's International Classification of Functioning, Disability and Health: Implications for clinical and research practice in the field of augmentative and alternative communication. *Augmentative and Alternative Communication, 23*(4), 349–361. https://doi.org/10.1080/07434610701650928

Ramachandran, R. (2020). A qualitative study on perspective of parents of children with autism on the nature of parent–professional relationship in Kerala, India. *Autism, 24*(6), 1521–1530. https://doi.org/10.1177/1362361320912156

Raver, S. A., & Childress, D. C. (2015). *Collaboration and Teamwork with families and professionals.* (pp. 31–52).

Roman-Lantzy, C. (2018*). Cortical vision impairment: An approach to assessment and intervention.* American Printing House for the Blind.

Sen, R., & Goldbart, J. (2005). Partnership in Action: Introducing family-based intervention for children with disability in urban slums of Kolkata, India. *Interna-*

tional Journal of Disability, Development and Education, 52(4), 275–311.

Singal, N. (2016). Education of children with disabilities in India and Pakistan: Critical analysis of developments in the last 15 years. *Prospects, 46*(1), 171–183. https://doi.org/10.1007/s11125-016-9383-4

Singal, N. (2019). Challenges and opportunities in efforts towards inclusive education: Reflections from India. *International Journal of Inclusive Education, 23*(7–8), 827–840. https://doi.org/10.1080/13603116.2019.1624845

Smythe, T., Zuurmond, M., Tann, C. J., Gladstone, M., & Kuper, H. (2021). Early intervention for children with developmental disabilities in low and middle-income countries—the case for action. *International Health, 13*(3), 222–231. https://doi.org/10.1093/inthealth/ihaa044

The World Bank Group. (2022, May 2). *The World Bank in India.* https://www.worldbank.org/en/country/india

Tomlinson, M., Yasamy, M. T., Emerson, E., Officer, A., Richler, D., & Saxena, S. (2014). Setting global research priorities for developmental disabilities, including intellectual disabilities and autism: Setting research priorities for developmental disabilities. *Journal of Intellectual Disability Research, 58*(12), 1121–1130. https://doi.org/10.1111/jir.12106

United Nations. (1989). *Convention on the Rights of the Child.* https://www.unicef.org/child-rights-convention/convention-text#

United Nations. (2006). *UN Convention on the Rights of Persons with Disabilities (CRPD).* https://www.un.org/disabilities/documents/convention/convoptprot-e.pdf

von Tetzchner, S., Launonen, K., Batorowicz, B., Nunes, L. R. d'Oliveira de P., Walter, C. C. de F., . . . Deliberato, D. (2018). Communication aid provision and use among children and adolescents developing aided communication: An international survey. *Augmentative and Alternative Communication, 34*(1), 79–91. https://doi.org/10.1080/07434618.2017.1422019

Westby, C., & Washington, K. N. (2017). Using the international classification of functioning, disability and health in assessment and intervention of school-aged children with language impairments. *Language, Speech, and Hearing Services in Schools, 48*(3), 137–152. https://doi.org/10.1044/2017_LSHSS-16-0037

World Bank. (2020). *Population, total—India.* https://data.worldbank.org/indicator/SP.POP.TOTL?locations=IN

World Bank. (2021). *World development report 2021: Data for better lives.* The World Bank. https://doi.org/10.1596/978-1-4648-1600-0

World Health Organization. (2001). *International Classification of Functioning, Disability and Health: ICF.*

World Health Organization. (2007). *International Classification of Functioning, Disability, and Health: Children & Youth Version: ICF-CY..*

World Health Organization (Ed.). (2011). *World report on disability.*

World Health Organization. (2019). *Rehabilitation in health systems: Guide for action.* https://apps.who.int/iris/handle/10665/325607

Wylie, K., McAllister, L., Davidson, B., & Marshall, J. (2013). Changing practice: Implications of the world report on disability for responding to communication disability in under-served populations. *International Journal of Speech-Language Pathology, 15*(1), 1–13. https://doi.org/10.3109/17549507.2012.745164

Younger, D. S. (2016). Health care in India. *Neurologic Clinics, 34*(4), 1103–1114. https://doi.org/10.1016/j.ncl.2016.06.005

Conclusion

13 Individualizing the Approach to Breaking Down Barriers

Susan S. Johnston

Thus far, this book has featured sections focused on opportunity barriers related to knowledge/skills, practices, attitudes, and policies. Within each section, readers have: (a) developed a deeper understanding of the impact of opportunity barriers through the eyes of individuals who use AAC or their families, (b) acquired knowledge based on current research and recommended practices related to addressing barriers, and (c) learned how professionals have successfully addressed opportunity barriers via case examples.

It is important to note that, although a wide range of opportunity barriers and strategies to address those barriers were presented, it was not possible to address all potential barriers and strategies in the preceding sections. This is because barriers are uniquely influenced by the contexts in which they occur. For example, consider a situation where the communicative success of two different individuals who use AAC (a three-year-old child with cerebral palsy who attends an inclusive preschool classroom and an adult with a progressive degenerative condition who works in a law firm) is being impacted by barriers related to their communication partners' knowledge of aided AAC systems. Although the barrier is the same in both situations, the context in which the barrier is occurring concerning the setting, background/experiences of the communication partners, the skills/abilities of the individuals who use AAC, and so forth, is not the same. These differences will impact the design and implementation of strategies to address these barriers. Therefore, the purpose of this final chapter is to support readers as they go "beyond the book" in breaking down the highly individualized and unique barriers that they encounter.

To individualize strategies for addressing the unique opportunity barriers encountered, professionals must examine contextual fit. Contextual fit refers to the compatibility between the strategy and a variety of variables, such as the characteristics of the person for whom the strategy was developed, the characteristics of the individuals who will implement the strategy, and the features of the environment in which the strategy will be implemented (Albin et al., 1996). Albin et al. (1996)

emphasize the importance of considering contextual fit and posit that a strategy "may be theoretically well designed and solidly grounded in both behavior theory and documented practice, and yet still not be a good fit for the people and the environments involved" (p. 83). The importance of contextual fit has been discussed and examined in relation to supporting parents of children with disabilities in home settings (McLaughlin et al., 2012; Mildon et al., 2008) as well as addressing the behavior support needs of individuals with disabilities in school settings (Monzalve & Horner, 2021). It seems plausible that contextual fit is equally important when developing strategies to address barriers experienced by individuals who use AAC (Johnston et al., 2004).

When considering the contextual fit of strategies designed to break down opportunity barriers, a strategy may lack strong contextual fit for various reasons. These reasons include the fact that the strategy may (a) be too cumbersome or time-consuming to design and implement, (b) conflict with existing priorities, or (c) fail to meet the needs of all involved. Group problem-solving may be an effective approach for developing strategies for breaking down barriers and attending to variables related to contextual fit. Group problem-solving entails bringing together stakeholders to identify problems and develop solutions and is particularly useful for addressing issues that are complex or that involve multiple constituents. Further, the use of groups in problem-solving may result in high levels of ownership for a problem as a result of the process, which involves: clearly defining the problem or situation, determining causes, brainstorming solutions, assessing the advantages and disadvantages of possible solutions, and developing an action plan (Adams & Galanes, 2009; Linabary, 2013). The following case example will be used throughout this chapter in order to illustrate the use of a group problem solving process to address opportunity barriers.

Cathy (an SLP) and Devin (a special education teacher) are employed by a public school district. They are currently working with a six-year-old boy, Matt, who is diagnosed with autism spectrum disorder and attends an inclusive first-grade classroom. When Cathy and Devin first started working with Matt three years ago, he attended an inclusive preschool classroom and communicated using natural gestures and a limited number of signs (e.g., "more," "all done," "eat"). Matt now uses a speech-generating device (SGD) to communicate. Cathy has collected data during one-on-one speech-language therapy sessions revealing that Matt understands and uses 36 different symbols and can navigate across several pages on his device. However, despite Matt's progress, Cathy and Devin note that his use of the SGD at school and home is minimal.

Cathy and Devin are aware of the potential negative impact of opportunity barriers on the communicative success of individuals who use AAC. Both suspect that Matt is encountering opportunity barriers. They decide to use a group problem-solving process to better understand and address the opportunity barriers that Matt is experiencing.

Define the Barrier

An essential first step in group problem solving involves defining the problem (Adams & Galanes, 2009; Linabary, 2013). During this part of the process, group members share what they know about the barrier without proposing solutions or evaluating it.

As discussed previously, the Participation Model provides a comprehensive and systematic framework for AAC assessment and intervention, including an evaluation of barriers related to access and opportunity (Beukelman & Light, 2020). The use of interview questions similar to the ones used in Chapters 1, 4, 7, and 10 of this text (Figure 13–1) may be constructive in furthering an understanding of the opportunity barriers encountered by an individual who uses AAC. For the purpose of this text, the interview questions were posed specifically to individuals who use AAC or their families. However, when using this strategy as part of a comprehensive and systematic process to understand the opportunity barriers and supports that are present for a given individual, it may be helpful to speak with a broader range of people (professionals and communication partners; Beukelman & Light, 2020).

To support group problem-solving, group members can use the assessment data to engage in conversations regarding the barrier(s) encountered. In the context of these conversations, the group facilitator may ask several questions (Rai-son et al., 2015). Based upon Raison and colleagues' (2015) work, Figure 13–2 includes sample questions that a facilitator might use to support group problem-solving discussions that relate specifically to opportunity barriers. After the discussion regarding defining the barrier, the group should compose a single sentence that summarizes the problem called a problem statement. Examples of problem statements written by groups addressing opportunity barriers include: "Team members do not know how to create meaningful opportunities for communication," and "Peers have negative attitudes regarding the skills/abilities of the individual who uses AAC."

Cathy and Devin use the Participation Model as a framework for their AAC assessments and interventions, which includes an evaluation of opportunity barriers. As part of their ongoing assessment process, they interview Matt's parents and other professionals and communication partners who interact with Matt. Based upon the outcomes of these interviews, Cathy and Devin discover that Matt is encountering opportunity barriers related to knowledge/skills, practice, and attitudes.

Cathy and Devin summarize the assessment information with the group and use the questions listed in Figure 13–2 to facilitate a group discussion and develop a problem statement. Based on this discussion, the group prioritized the identified barriers. They then created the following problem statement for a barrier they placed as the highest priority: "There are limited opportunities for interprofessional collaboration."

Opportunity Barriers and Supports Interview

Sometimes, an individual who uses AAC encounters barriers to communication that are not related to their current capabilities or the communication system they use. We call these opportunity barriers which include limitations based upon policies, practices, knowledge/skills of professionals and communication partners, and attitudes.

The purpose of this interview is to gain information regarding the specific opportunity barriers that are present for the individual who uses AAC by interviewing relevant constituents. These constituents may include the individual who uses AAC, their family members, professionals who support them, and other communication partners.

Knowledge/Skill Barriers

Knowledge barriers refer to deficits in understanding how to best address the communication needs of AAC users. In contrast, skill barriers occur when professionals and communication partners do not have the skills to support these individuals, despite having adequate knowledge.

- Are you currently experiencing any barriers related to the knowledge/skills of professionals and communication partners? If yes, please describe.
- Are you currently experiencing any supports related to the knowledge/skills of professionals and communication partners? If yes, please describe.
- Do you have any ideas for addressing the knowledge/skill barriers you are encountering?
- Do you have any ideas for expanding upon the knowledge/skill supports that you are encountering?

Practice Barriers

Practice barriers involve common practices of organizations, schools, businesses, or communities that are accepted in that context while not formally written as policy.

- Are you currently experiencing any barriers related to practice? If yes, please describe.
- Are you currently experiencing any supports related to practice? If yes, please describe.
- Do you have any ideas for addressing the practice barriers you are encountering? If yes, please describe.
- Do you have any ideas for expanding upon the practice supports you are encountering? If yes, please describe.

Figure 13–1. Opportunity barriers and supports interview. *continues*

Attitude Barriers

Negative attitudes held by family members, professionals, and peers can present obstacles to realizing the full benefit of AAC.

- Are you currently experiencing any barriers related to attitudes? If yes, please describe.
- Are you currently experiencing any supports related to attitudes? If yes, please describe.
- Do you have any ideas for addressing the attitude barriers you are encountering? If yes, please describe.
- Do you have any ideas for expanding upon the attitude supports you are encountering? If yes, please describe.

Policy Barriers

Legislative policies can significantly impact AAC use, and legislative processes influence practices, funding, and access to interventions and supports for individuals with disabilities.

- Are you currently experiencing any barriers related to policy? If yes, please describe.
- Are you currently experiencing any supports related to policy? If yes, please describe.
- Do you have any ideas for addressing the policy barriers you are encountering? If yes, please describe.
- Do you have any ideas for expanding upon the policy supports you are encountering? If yes, please describe.

Conclusion

- Are there any barriers or supports that you are encountering that you have not yet mentioned? If yes, please describe.
- Of the barriers that you have discussed, which one(s) do you feel should be addressed first?

Figure 13–1. *continued*

Questions to Facilitate the Group Problem-Solving Discussion

<u>Define the Barrier</u>

- What are the current barriers?

- What are the effects of these barriers?

- Why is it important to address these barriers?

- What aspects of these barriers require clarification (if any)?

- Which barrier(s) should be addressed first?

- What is our problem statement?

<u>Analyze the Barrier</u>

- Why does this barrier exist?

- What needs to be changed in the immediate future to address this barrier?

- What needs to be changed in the long term to address this barrier?

- Can this barrier be addressed using internal resources? If not, do we need outside/expert assistance, or do we need to involve others in this problem-solving discussion?

<u>Brainstorm Possible Solutions</u>

- What goal(s) are we trying to achieve?

- What steps could we take to address the barrier?

- What do we need to tackle first?

Figure 13–2. Questions to facilitate the group problem-solving discussion. *continues*

<u>Assess the Advantages and Disadvantages of Possible Solutions</u>

- Who or what will be affected by each solution?

- What are the possible immediate side effects of each solution?

- What are the possible long-term side effects of each solution?

- What would be the likely consequences of each solution?

- What would be the reaction of the people involved in each solution? Who would complain? Who would be glad? Why?

<u>Develop an Action Plan</u>

- What is our time frame for completion?

- Who are the members of the task force?

- What are the critical steps for implementing the strategy?

- Who will be involved and make decisions?

- What resources are needed?

- What information and assistance are needed to begin implementation?

- How will we know when we have successfully addressed the barrier?

- What difficulties do we anticipate, and how will we deal with them?

- How will we deal with unanticipated difficulties?

- Who do we need to contact or partner with that may also be working on this issue?

Figure 13–2. *continued*

Analyze the Barrier

After creating a problem statement, the next step in the group problem-solving process is to analyze the barrier (Adams & Galanes, 2009; Linabary, 2013). This step aims to identify the cause(s) of the barrier. Whereas the first step (defining the barrier) focuses on identifying "what" the barrier is, this step focuses on "why" the barrier is occurring. To thoroughly analyze a barrier, the group needs to explore the full range of variables contributing to the problem. To support this exploration, the group can discuss and respond to the questions posed in Figure 13–2. Sometimes, this discussion will result in additional questions that the group will want to explore. For example, when discussing a barrier related to attitudes, the group might ask: Do other programs/settings similar to ours experience this barrier? If yes, have those programs/settings developed successful ways to address this barrier? Other times, this discussion may result in the identification of different or additional barriers. For example, after discussion, what was initially identified as an attitude barrier related to supporting individuals with complex communication needs in an inclusive work environment may actually be determined to be due to a knowledge/skill barrier regarding the use of aided AAC systems.

During a group problem-solving meeting, Cathy and Devin used the questions listed in Figure 13–2 to analyze the prioritized barrier of limited opportunities for interprofessional collaboration. Although the group recognized that limited opportunities for collaboration is primarily a *practice barrier, they carefully considered whether there were other barriers that might be having an impact (e.g., policy barriers related to insurance limitations on reimbursement for group meetings, attitude barriers related to negative attitudes about the roles of other professions in AAC planning). As a result of this discussion, the group identified several reasons "why" this barrier existed. These included the fact that many members of Matt's team were not physically present at the school for large amounts of time because they (a) supported students across four to five different schools (e.g., Cathy, the OT), or (b) were not employed by the district (i.e., Matt's parents, Matt's after school daycare provider). And, even when several of the team members were physically present at the school at the same time, they rarely saw each other given the physical layout of their school and their busy schedules. Further, when interprofessional collaboration meetings were scheduled, the group noted that Matt's general education teachers and paraeducators were often unable to attend due to their other work-related responsibilities.*

Brainstorm Solutions

Upon completion of the process of identifying and analyzing the barrier, the next step is to brainstorm possible solutions (Adams & Galanes, 2009; Linabary, 2013). Studies support the use of brainstorming to generate new ideas (Kim, 2017; Korde & Paulus, 2017) and research suggests that groups that include members with diverse experiences and various areas of expertise generate more novel ideas (Haiba et al.,

2017). Four basic rules of brainstorming for group problem-solving are to (a) generate as many ideas as possible (emphasizing quantity over quality will encourage divergent thinking), (b) never criticize an idea, (c) encourage wild ideas (although many will not be feasible, ones that are might be genuinely innovative and impactful), and (d) combine ideas or improve on each other's ideas throughout the process (Besant, 2016).

To support a brainstorming discussion related to opportunity barriers, groups can start by responding to the questions posed in Figure 13–2. Brainstorming methods can include face-to-face techniques where group members verbally interact in a group session (Al-Samarraie & Hurmuzan, 2018) and paper-pencil techniques where group members generate and share ideas written on paper or sticky notes without talking (Korde & Paulus, 2017). Combining these techniques so that group members start by generating and sharing ideas written on paper or sticky notes, without talking, before engaging in a verbal discussion may significantly enhance the generation of novel ideas (Korde & Paulus, 2017).

To facilitate a group brainstorming session, Cathy and Devin used the questions listed in Figure 13–2. The brainstorming started with group members individually (and anonymously) responding to each question by writing thoughts/ideas on sticky notes, which were gathered and grouped into "themes" on a large whiteboard. Once this was complete, the group then engaged in a verbal discussion around the questions. The group adhered to the four basic rules of brainstorming, which resulted in several ideas for addressing the problem of limited opportunities for interprofessional collabo-

ration. The team discussed these ideas and developed a list of possible solutions. This list included (a) creating a shared drive where team members can upload information and collaborate on written documents, (b) organizing a group chat where team members can send short written/audio/video texts to quickly share information, (c) using ZOOM for team meetings to accommodate team members who were physically not present at the school, and (d) creating a district-wide infrastructure for supporting interprofessional collaboration for ALL relevant team members (including general education teachers and paraeducators).

Assess the Advantages and Disadvantages of Possible Solutions

Solutions generated as a result of brainstorming may not all be equal in terms of relative advantages and disadvantages. Therefore, problem-solving groups must critically evaluate the pros and cons of each solution (Adams & Galanes, 2009; Linabary, 2013). The questions listed in Figure 13–2 are designed to facilitate a discussion of the potential merits and challenges of proposed solutions.

Using the questions posed in Figure 13–2, Cathy and Devin facilitate a lively discussion regarding each strategy's relative pros and cons. For example, although the group saw many advantages related to using a group chat and ZOOM for team meetings, they also expressed concerns that, while technology is an excellent tool for communication among group members, there are times when face-to-face communication is necessary and more appropriate. Further, although everyone agreed that creating a district-wide infrastructure to better support interprofessional collaboration was advantageous, they also recognized that implementing this solution was complex and would require the involvement of many people beyond their problem-solving group.

Develop an Action Plan

After assessing the relative advantages and disadvantages of possible strategies, the problem-solving group decides which strategy(ies) they will implement and develops an action plan (Adams & Galanes, 2009; Linabary, 2013). An action plan is a tool that allows the group to identify the steps that need to be taken to implement the strategy. Figure 13–2 provides a list of questions that may facilitate the creation of an action plan and Figure 13–3 provides an example of a worksheet to use when making action plan decisions. As illustrated by Figure 13–3, completing an action plan involves making decisions regarding (a) action steps, (b) who will be responsible for each step, and (c) the start date and due date for each step.

In addition to completing the action plan worksheet, the group may find it helpful to speak individually with the people who will be involved in implementing the strategy (including individuals from outside of the problem-solving group) and ask them to complete a self-assessment checklist to examine contextual fit (Figure 13–4). The checklist, adapted from the tool developed by Horner et al. (2003) to focus on opportunity barriers, explores the match between the proposed strategy and several contextual fit features.

Action Plan for Addressing Opportunity Barriers

Problem Statement:

_____

_____

Strategy(ies) to Address Problem:

_____

_____

Action Step	Person(s) Responsible	Start Date	Due Date

Figure 13–3. Action plan worksheet for addressing opportunity barriers.

Self-Assessment of Contextual Fit for Strategies
Designed to Address Opportunity Barriers

The purpose of this self-assessment is to examine the extent to which the elements of the strategy (ies) to address an identified opportunity barrier fit the contextual features of your environment.

The self-assessment asks you to rate (a) your knowledge of the elements of the strategy, (b) your perception of the extent to which the elements of the strategy are consistent with your values and skills, and (c) the ability of your setting (i.e., school, workplace, home, community) to support the implementation of the strategy.

Name: _____   Role: _____

Knowledge of elements in the strategy

1. I am aware of the elements of this strategy.

1	2	3	4	5	6
Strongly Disagree	Moderately Disagree	Barely Disagree	Barely Agree	Moderately Agree	Strongly Agree

2. I know what I am expected to do to implement this strategy.

1	2	3	4	5	6
Strongly Disagree	Moderately Disagree	Barely Disagree	Barely Agree	Moderately Agree	Strongly Agree

Skills needed to implement the strategy

3. I have the skills needed to implement this strategy.

1	2	3	4	5	6
Strongly Disagree	Moderately Disagree	Barely Disagree	Barely Agree	Moderately Agree	Strongly Agree

4. I have received any training that I need to implement this strategy. Please initial here if no training is necessary: _____

1	2	3	4	5	6
Strongly Disagree	Moderately Disagree	Barely Disagree	Barely Agree	Moderately Agree	Strongly Agree

Values are consistent with elements of the strategy.

5. I am comfortable implementing the elements of this strategy.

1	2	3	4	5	6
Strongly Disagree	Moderately Disagree	Barely Disagree	Barely Agree	Moderately Agree	Strongly Agree

Figure 13–4. Self-assessment of contextual fit for strategies designed to address opportunity barriers. *continues*

6. The elements of this strategy are consistent with the way I believe individuals who use AAC should be supported.

1	2	3	4	5	6
Strongly Disagree	Moderately Disagree	Barely Disagree	Barely Agree	Moderately Agree	Strongly Agree

Resources available to implement the strategy

7. My setting (e.g., school, workplace, home, community) provides the time needed to implement this strategy.

1	2	3	4	5	6
Strongly Disagree	Moderately Disagree	Barely Disagree	Barely Agree	Moderately Agree	Strongly Agree

8. My setting (e.g., school, workplace, home, community) provides the funding, materials, and space needed to implement this strategy.

1	2	3	4	5	6
Strongly Disagree	Moderately Disagree	Barely Disagree	Barely Agree	Moderately Agree	Strongly Agree

Administrative Support

9. My setting (e.g., school, clinic, home, community) provides the supervision support needed to implementthis strategy effectively.

1	2	3	4	5	6
Strongly Disagree	Moderately Disagree	Barely Disagree	Barely Agree	Moderately Agree	Strongly Agree

10. My setting (e.g., school, clinic, home, community) is committed to investing in effective design and implementation of strategies to address opportunity barriers experienced by individuals who use AAC.

1	2	3	4	5	6
Strongly Disagree	Moderately Disagree	Barely Disagree	Barely Agree	Moderately Agree	Strongly Agree

Effectiveness of Strategy

11. I believe the strategy will be effective in achieving targeted outcomes.

1	2	3	4	5	6
Strongly Disagree	Moderately Disagree	Barely Disagree	Barely Agree	Moderately Agree	Strongly Agree

12. I believe the strategy will help prevent future occurrences of this opportunity barrier for the individual who uses AAC.

1	2	3	4	5	6
Strongly Disagree	Moderately Disagree	Barely Disagree	Barely Agree	Moderately Agree	Strongly Agree

Figure 13–4. *continues*

The strategy is in the best interest of the individual who uses AAC.

13. I believe this strategy is in the best interest of the individual who uses AAC.

1	2	3	4	5	6
Strongly Disagree	Moderately Disagree	Barely Disagree	Barely Agree	Moderately Agree	Strongly Agree

14. This strategy is likely to assist the individual who uses AAC experience more communicative success.

1	2	3	4	5	6
Strongly Disagree	Moderately Disagree	Barely Disagree	Barely Agree	Moderately Agree	Strongly Agree

The strategy is efficient to implement

15. Implementing this strategy will not be stressful.

1	2	3	4	5	6
Strongly Disagree	Moderately Disagree	Barely Disagree	Barely Agree	Moderately Agree	Strongly Agree

16. The amount of time, money, and energy needed to implement this strategy are reasonable.

1	2	3	4	5	6
Strongly Disagree	Moderately Disagree	Barely Disagree	Barely Agree	Moderately Agree	Strongly Agree

Scoring the Self-Assessment of Contextual Fit

This instrument can be used to build a summary score and sub-scale scores that may be helpful both for researchers and for individuals developing strategies to address opportunity barriers experienced by AAC users. To obtain a total score, calculate the mean score per subscale and then build a total score by calculating the mean of the subscale scores.

Contextual Fit Subscale	Score on the first question	Score on the second question	Mean equals Subscale Score
Knowledge of strategy			
Skills to implement strategy			
Values consistent with the strategy			
Resources to implement strategy			
Administrative Support			
Anticipated Effectiveness			
Strategy is in the best interest of the individual			
Strategy is efficient to implement			
Contextual Fit Total Score			Mean =

Adapted from *"Self-Assessment of Contextual Fit in Schools"* by R.H. Horner, S. Salentine, and R.W. Albin, 2003, Copyright 2003 by the University of Oregon.

Figure 13–4. *continued*

Gathering information by speaking with individuals and asking them to complete the self-assessment checklist will provide important insight into contextual fit from the perspective of all involved parties and may significantly impact the success (or lack thereof) of the strategy. This insight can then be used to modify the strategy or provide instruction and support to involved parties.

The problem-solving group used the questions in Figure 13–2 and the worksheet in Figure 13–3 to develop and record their action plan. The group combined three of the strategies mentioned above (shared drive for documents, group chat, and use of ZOOM) into a broad strategy related to using technology to support efficient and effective communication and then broke that strategy into action steps. Action steps included working with the district IT team and formulating guidelines on when to use (and when not to use) specific technology (e.g., group chat is for sharing information but not making decisions, etc.). Finally, based upon strengths and preferences, individual group members volunteered to take responsibility for each step and identified the start date and completion date.

Concerning the need for a district-wide infrastructure to better support interprofessional collaboration, the team developed an action plan that involved forming a new problem-solving group (that included some of the current group members but also other individuals, such as school administrators). This new group would then meet and engage in the problem-solving process of clearly defining the problem or situation, determining causes, brainstorming solutions, assessing the advantages and disadvantages of possible solutions, and developing an action plan.

Conclusion

In summary, barriers are uniquely influenced by the contexts in which they occur. Group problem-solving strategies may be helpful in developing strategies and ensuring the contextual fit of strategies designed to break down barriers. It is important to recognize that barriers are often interrelated, and, therefore, strategies designed to address one barrier may have a collateral impact on other barriers. For example, increasing a communication partner's knowledge/skills in interacting with an individual who uses AAC may increase the number and quality of interactions. Increasing the number and quality of interactions may, in turn, result in a decrease in barriers related to attitude. Similarly, changes to practices pertaining to opportunities for professionals to collaborate may result in increased opportunities to share information. Increasing opportunities to share information may, in turn, reduce knowledge/skill barriers. In addition, changes to contextual variables (e.g., the skills/abilities of the person who uses AAC, the features of the environment, etc.) may influence barriers and the strategies designed to address those barriers. Given that barriers are often interrelated and the likelihood of changes to contextual variables over time, it is essential to engage in ongoing assessment and progress monitoring to ensure an accurate understanding of barriers.

As stated previously, although it is widely accepted that AAC can increase communicative efficiency and effectiveness for a variety of individuals with complex communication needs, many individuals who use AAC are experiencing barriers. As a result, it is essential to consider both access and opportunity barriers when supporting individuals who use AAC. Addressing barriers is a significant but necessary undertaking, and addressing opportunity barriers presents a unique set of challenges. However, we can overcome these challenges by (a) developing a deeper understanding of the impact of opportunity barriers through the eyes of individuals who use AAC or their families, (b) acquiring knowledge based on current research and recommended practices related to addressing barriers, and (c) designing/implementing individualized approaches to addressing barriers. These systematic and intentional efforts may transform the barriers we encounter today into the successes we celebrate tomorrow.

References

Adams, K., & Galanes, G.G. (2009). *Communicating in groups: Applications and skills* (7th ed.). McGraw-Hill.

Albin, R., Lucyshyn, J., Horner, R., & Flannery, K. (1996). Contextual fit for behavioral support plans: A model for "goodness of fit." In L. Keogel, R. Koegel, & G. Dunlap (Eds.), *Positive behavioral support: Including people with difficult behavior in the community*. Paul H. Brookes.

Al-Samarraie, H. & Hurmuzan, S. (2018). A review of brainstorming techniques in higher education. *Thinking Skills and Creativity, 27*, 78–91.

Beukelman, D., & Light, J. (2020). *Augmentative and alternative communication: Supporting children and adults with complex communication needs* (5th ed.). Paul H. Brookes.

Besant, H. (2016). The journey of brainstorming. *Journal of Transformative Innovation, 2*, 1–7.

Haiba, M. E., Elbassiti, L., & Ajhoun, R. (2017). Idea management: Idea generation stage with a qualitative focus. *Journal of Advanced Management Science, 5*, 271–278.

Horner, R. H., Salentine, S., & Albin, R. W. (2003). *Self-assessment of contextual fit in schools*. The University of Oregon.

Johnston, S., Reichle, J., & Evans, J. (2004). Supporting augmentative and alternative communication use by beginning communicators with severe disabilities. *American Journal of Speech-Language Pathology, 13*(1), 20–30.

Kim, E. (2017). Workshop design for enhancing the appropriateness of idea generation using analogical thinking. *International Journal of Innovation Studies, 1*, 134–143.

Korde, R., & Paulus, P.B. (2017). Alternating individual and group idea generation: Finding the elusive synergy. *Journal of Experimental Social Psychology, 70*, 177–190.

Linabary, J. (2013). *Small-group communication: Forming and sustaining teams. Creative Commons.* https://smallgroup.pressbooks.com/

McLaughlin, T. W., Denney, M. K., Snyder, P. A., & Welsh, J. L. (2012). Behavior support interventions implemented by families of young children: Examination of contextual fit. *Journal of Positive Behavior Interventions, 14*(2), 87–97.

Mildon, R., Wade, C., & Matthews, J. (2008). Considering the contextual fit of an intervention for families headed by parents with an intellectual disability: An exploratory study. *Journal of Applied Research in Intellectual Disabilities, 21*, 377–387.

Monzalve, M., & Horner, R. H. (2021). The impact of the contextual fit enhancement protocol on behavior support plan fidelity and student behavior. *Behavioral Disorders, 46*(4), 267–278.

Raison, B., Lukshin, D., & Bowen-Ellzey, N. (2015). *Group problem solving process*. Ohio State University.

Index

Note: Page numbers in **bold** reference non-text material.

O